To

Turner ...

with

Every good wish

from

Ray Seymour

PLASTICS

for

CORROSION-RESISTANT APPLICATIONS

RAYMOND B. SEYMOUR

President, Corrosion Resistant Plastics Division
Loven Chemical of California
Newhall, Calif.

AND

ROBERT H. STEINER

Naugatuck Chemical Co.
Naugatuck, Conn.

This book was prepared while both authors were
with Atlas Mineral Products Co., Mertztown, Pa.

REINHOLD PUBLISHING CORPORATION
NEW YORK
CHAPMAN & HALL LTD., LONDON
1955

Copyright 1955 by
REINHOLD PUBLISHING CORPORATION

Library of Congress Catalog Card Number 55-9173

REINHOLD PUBLISHING CORPORATION

Publishers of Chemical Engineering Catalog;
Chemical Materials Catalog; "Automatic Control";
"Materials & Methods"; Advertising Management
of the American Chemical Society

PRINTED IN THE USA BY EDWARDS BROTHERS, INC.

DEDICATION

Because of their inherent resistance to most corrosives, the use of properly selected plastics as materials of chemical construction would appear to be obvious. However, this was not always the case. Many years of "patient money" and confidence in technologists was required before plastics were accepted for this end use. This book is dedicated to those men of vision who demonstrated their confidence in plastics by adhering to the Statement of Principles by the Plastics Industry and investing in research and development programs which proved the utility of plastics as engineering materials. The Statement of Principles by the Plastics Industry is given on the next page.

STATEMENT OF PRINCIPLES BY THE
PLASTICS INDUSTRY

Plastic materials challenge industry with new concepts of design, engineering, construction, processibility and usefulness.

The properties of plastic materials, when correctly used, open up great new areas of service to industry and the public.

Improper use can do irreparable damage to the plastics industry, to both manufacturers and processors of the materials.

Therefore, we as manufacturers and processors of plastic materials reaffirm our adherence to the principles upon which the healthy growth of a great industry depends and undertake to:

I. Understand thoroughly the properties and limitations of all plastic materials handled by us;

II. Apply the correct plastic materials to all industrial end uses, designing and engineering them for maximum value, performance and safety;

III. Use great care to select the correct plastic materials for all consumer items, designing and engineering them to insure value, satisfaction, safety and pleasure to all users;

IV. Sell plastic materials, and all industrial and consumer items made therefrom, on the merits of the materials, applications and design, and free of extravagant, insupportable claims.

All to the end that plastic materials already available, and others that may come, will bring to industry and public alike all the benefits, economies and satisfactions inherent in these versatile engineering and construction materials.

PREFACE

Since the beginning of time man has had to cope with corrosion. As manufacturing processes have developed in complexity and size, engineers are obliged to give more and closer attention to plant and equipment disintegration caused by corrosion. The advent, development and application of plastics and resins for corrosion resistance introduced a complete new line of tools for the engineer to employ in dealing with corrosion. Plastics for Corrosion Resistant Applications has been published to answer the demand for a compendium of comprehensive technical data on the corrosion-resistant properties of various plastics and resins. While different plastics and resins of various types have been used for corrosion resistance, those individuals designing or making the installation have had a paucity of information upon which to rely for guidance. This book is constructed to serve the engineer, the chemist and the user. It treats with the various plastics and resins in the form in which they are applied such as coatings, linings, impregnants, adhesives, pipe and structural shapes for numerous industrial applications.

The authors have conducted exhaustive tests to evaluate the relative resistivity of plastics and resins to different reagents. Moreover in this treatise is much down-to-earth information, that hard to find ingredient, "know how," based on the practical experience of the authors. Such information and data the engineer and installer must have for the design and construction of installations to effectively resist the growing ravages of corrosion. If the reader is seeking information on the comparative chemical resistance of cements, coatings, linings, pipe, reinforced or thermoplastic structures, it will be found herein. The tables including these data are one of the most valuable parts of this book.

In addition to treating with plastics and resins the authors have included information on concrete, masonry and steel. While it may be reasoned that these materials do not belong in a book whose title would indicate it is devoted entirely to plastics, since many who will use this book as a reference on corrosion in the interest of completeness and convenience it is appropriate that this information on these materials be included.

Corrosion is induced in many varied and devious ways. In one process it may be due to excessive acidity; in another to excessive alkalinity; or it may be induced by the cumulative effect of mild concentrations of acids or alkalies or by the other agents. In any event, designing to eliminate or minimize the disintegration caused by corrosion involves employing the appropriate material in the correct proportion and the proper manner and in the necessary thickness or concentration to insure optimum results.

Whether the reader is concerned with corrosion in any of these fields: aeronautics, architecture, automotive, chemicals, communications, fire protection, food processing, marine, metallurgy, military, mining, paper, petroleum, refrigeration, textiles, transportation, water supply or others, here he has a source for authoritative data that will serve him in specifying materials for a process, a plant or building to eliminate, offset or at least minimize decomposition due to corrosion.

William T. Cruse
Executive Vice President
Society of the Plastics Industry

SCOPE

Some corrosion engineers who recognize that the corrosion process is, by definition, restricted to metals, may object to the title, "Plastics for Corrosion Resistant Applications." Admittedly, it would be more appropriate to use the term "chemical" rather than "corrosion" resistant but this nomenclature might not be as readily understood by those who will find this book to be most useful.

Throughout the book, the plastics chemist may find generalizations and conclusions which may be questioned from an academic or classical viewpoint. Both the corrosion engineer and the chemist may criticize the lack of depth in treatment of both the corrosion and plastics. However, it is felt that these deficiencies are not significant to the many readers who are seeking reliable information which will permit the proper application of plastic materials of construction.

Raymond B. Seymour
Robert H. Steiner

ACKNOWLEDGMENTS

The authors acknowledge the many contributions of the following experts whose comments and criticisms were invaluable:

Turner Alfrey, The Dow Chemical Co., Midland, Michigan
H. B. Allport, National Carbon Co., Cleveland, Ohio
Rod T. Antrim, Pacific Clay Products Co., Los Angeles, Calif.
George L. Baumgartner, Armstrong Cork Co., Lancaster, Pa.
William E. Brown, The Dow Chemical Co., Midland, Michigan
Walter M. Bruner, E. I. duPont de Nemours & Co., Wilmington, Del.
W. J. Canavan, Bakelite Co., New York, N. Y.
William T. Cruse, The Society of the Plastics Industry, New York, N. Y.
Willard de Camp Crater, Naugatuck Chemical Co., Naugatuck, Conn.
Robert P. Desch, Armstrong Cork Co., Lancaster, Pa.
Earl A. Erich, Tube Turn Plastic Co., Louisville, Ky.
J. O. Everhart, The Ohio State University, Columbus, Ohio
Martin Flentje, American Water Works Service Co., Inc., Philadelphia, Pa.
Robert S. Hallas, Bakelite Co., New York, N. Y.
Richard H. Hardesty, E. I. duPont de Nemours & Co., Wilmington, Del.
Norry Hastings, Rezolin, Inc., Los Angeles, Calif.
George Laaff, The Bolta Co., Lawrence, Mass.
Jean F. Malone, B. F. Goodrich Chemical Co., Cleveland, Ohio
Edward P. Mampe, Haveg Corp., Newark, Del.
James P. McNamee, U. S. Rubber Co., Providence, R. I.
J. Alex Neumann, American Agile Corp., Bedford, Ohio
George Reed, American Hard Rubber Co., New York, N. Y.
Edward A. Reineck, Quaker Oats Co., Chicago, Ill.
Frank W. Reinhart, U. S. Dept. of Commerce, National Bureau of Standards, Washington, D. C.
M. G. Robinson, Bakelite Co., New York, N. Y.
Fred Schneider, Firestone Plastics Co., Pottstown, Pa.
Edward T. Severs, Mellon Institute, Pittsburgh, Pa.
S. W. Shepard, Chemical Construction Corp., Linden, N. J.
Norman Skow, Synthane Corp., Oaks, Pa.
Kenneth Tator, Kenneth Tator Associates, Corapolis, Pa.

Beaumont Thomas, Stebbins Engineering & Manufacturing Co.,
    Watertown, N. Y.
H. E. Waldrip, Gulf Oil Corp., Houston, Texas
J. S. Whitaker, Bakelite Co., New York, N. Y.
Frank L. Whitney, Jr., Monsanto Chemical Co., St. Louis, Mo.
Ivan V. Wilson, Monsanto Chemical Co., Springfield, Mass.
C. L. Wurdeman, Rezolin, Inc., Los Angeles, Calif.

Acknowledgment for Photographs

American Agile Corporation, Bedford, Ohio
American Cyanamid Corporation, New York, N. Y.
Arndt-Preston-Chapin-Lamp & Keen, Inc., Philadelphia, Pa.
Bakelite Company, Div. of Union Carbide & Carbon Corp., New
    York, N. Y.
Dow Chemical Company, Midland, Michigan
E. I. duPont de Nemours & Company, Wilmington, Del.
Eastman Chemical Products, Inc., New York, N. Y.
B. F. Goodrich Chemical Company, Cleveland, Ohio
Goodyear Tire & Rubber Company, Akron, Ohio
H. N. Hartwell & Sons, Boston, Massachusetts
Haveg Corporation, Newark, Del.
Hooker Electrochemical Company, Niagara Falls, N. Y.
Kellogg Company, New York, N. Y.
Koppers, Company, Pittsburgh, Pa.
Monsanto Chemical Company, Springfield, Mass.
Pfaulder Company, Rochester, New York
Resistoflex Corporation, Belleville, N. J.
Rohm & Haas Co., Philadelphia, Pa.
Shell Chemical Co., New York, N. Y.
Synthane Corporation, Oaks, Pa.

The assistance of the following Atlas corrosion engineers is also
appreciated:
    J. Carl Bovan   George P. Gabriel   Walter R. Pascoe
    Donald F. Deakin   Gerald F. Gilbert, Jr.   Frank E. Pegg
        Joseph A. Snook   Willis G. Thomas, Jr.
The assistance of Miss Jean D. Fenstermacher, Mrs. Mary L.
Geist, and Miss Corine S. Reinert of the Atlas Mineral Products
Co., who arranged and typed the manuscript is gratefully appreciated.

Permission to use information previously published by the authors
in the following publications is also acknowledged:

American Dyestuff Reporter
Chemical Engineering
Chemical Engineering Progress
Corrosion

Engineering News-Record
Finishing Publications, Inc.
Food Engineering
Journal American Water Works Association
Journal of the Society of Plastics Engineers
Modern Plastics
Organic Finishing
Paper Trade Journal
Public Works
Sewage & Industrial Wastes
Southern Chemical Industry
Southern Power & Industry
Water & Sewage Works

TABLE OF CONTENTS

TABLE OF CONTENTS

SECTION I
GENERAL INFORMATION
ON PLASTICS

1. INTRODUCTION

To solve corrosion problems properly, an engineer should have a working knowledge of cathodic protection, corrosion inhibitors, ceramics, metals, wood and plastics. Obviously, few can assimilate this wide variety of information, but all engineers should be acquainted in a general way with all the tools that are available for counteracting corrosion.

Because most courses in corrosion prevention are taught by metallurgists, few students learn the fundamentals of other methods of counteracting corrosion. In most instances, knowledge of other materials of construction is accumulated from advertisements in trade journals and interviews with salesmen. Such methods are helpful, providing the student has previously received sufficient fundamental training to permit proper evaluation of sales information of proprietary materials.

It is sincerely hoped that the information presented in this book will help the corrosion engineer not only to solve problems through the use of a wider selection of materials but also aid him in the evaluation of corrosion data obtained. It is assumed that plastics will be used more frequently for service in the presence of corrosives when the type of knowledge presented herein is more widely available. However, it must be emphasized that all corrosion-resistant materials must be selected on the basis of their ability to out-perform all other products when evaluated under identical conditions.

When ample consideration is given to economics, length of service and resistance to attack by specific chemicals, plastics are often found to be superior to many other materials of construction. Plastics should be considered neither as a substitute nor as a panacea. Their potential usefulness should be evaluated and compared with other materials of construction in the solution of every problem in corrosion.

Plastics will not perform miracles but in a large number of instances will prove superior to all other known materials in preventing corrosion. Since it is of utmost importance to know deficiencies as well as advantages of all proposed materials, an attempt has been made to present broad practical knowledge in subsequent chapters. This information should aid in bringing about a sound evaluation of plastics as materials of construction.

Additional Available Information

The information in subsequent chapters is restricted primarily to the application of plastics in corrosive environments. Many excellent textbooks on plastic materials have already been published, and no attempt has been made to supply general information on this subject. It is suggested that those interested in a broader knowledge of plastics consult some of the references listed at the end of Chapter 5.

While an attempt has been made to supply up-to-date knowledge on plastics as materials of construction, the reader should remember that this is a dynamic field in which new information is being recorded almost daily. Those who desire to keep abreast of current developments in this field must refer to several trade journals. Corrosion, a monthly publication of the National Association of Corrosion Engineers, contains considerable useful information on plastics for corrosion-resistant applications in the abstract section of each issue. The biennial Materials of Construction Report published in Chemical Engineering includes a guide to chemical resistance and a directory of trade names and producers. It also provides information on specific applications of corrosion-resistant materials. The annual Materials of Construction Review, which supplements the September issue of Industrial & Engineering Chemistry, Modern Plastics, British Plastics and Materials & Methods are also good sources of current information.

Arrangement of Chapters

It will be noted that the material in the first few chapters is intended primarily to supply background information. All commercially available plastic materials are reviewed in Chapter 5. An attempt has been made to show the effect of structure on chemical resistance in this chapter. High-molecular weight materials, such as rubber and cellulose, which may not be classified as plastics in other publications but are of interest to the corrosion engineer, have been included.

The order in which plastics are presented in Chapter 2 is followed whenever possible in subsequent chapters. In some cases, plastics without commercial value for a specific application are not discussed. In other instances, a brief description of little used plastics is given in order to show their advantages and disadvantages for specific end uses.

While testing techniques are outlined in Chapter 6, it should be observed that as yet few of these tests have been established as standards. The techniques that have been developed for testing the corrosion resistance of metals cannot be used for plastics, but some progress has been made in the development of appropriate modifications of these techniques. In other instances, it has been necessary to develop completely new testing procedures for plastic materials.

In addition to following the order of presentation used in Chapter 2, an attempt has been made to compare the utility of plastics for specific applications at the end of each chapter. Thus, physical properties of coating materials are compared in Table 7-1 (p. 103), and the relative resistance of five typical commercial coatings in many different acids, alkalies, salts, gases, and organic materials are given in 7-2 (p. 104). Typical commercial coatings have been graded from 1 to 10 for ten different properties in Table 7-3 (p. 106). These values have been weighed equally and totaled for each of the coatings.

The chemical list and industrial applications used in Table 7-2 (p. 104) is similar to that which has appeared in the data sheets published by the authors in Chemical Engineering Progress. This same method of comparing physical, chemical and practical properties has been repeated in the chapters on organic linings, chemical-resistant mortar cements and thermoplastic structural materials. In addition, an attempt has been made in Chapter 24 to summarize these data for many applications. It is hoped that these data on the selection of plastics for the solution of corrosion problems will help the engineer to focus his attention on materials having the best possible chance of solving a specific problem.

Casting resins, cellular plastics and industrial adhesives are not used exclusively in corrosive environment, but information on their resistance to chemicals is often required. Likewise, the degree of corrosion in water and sewer mains is usually mild, yet chemical-resistant plastics are often used for these applications. Obviously, this type of knowledge will prove more valuable as improvements in service lines are made.

The use of reinforced plastics, thermoplastic structures and plastic pipe is relatively new. The information available on the chemical resistance of the most important of these materials has been summarized. Impervious graphite discussed in Chapter 12 is an important commercially available chemical-resistant product.

The information on design in Chapters 20 and 21 may not at first seem appropriate for this book. However, the successful application of plastic materials in masonry construction as discussed in Chapter 22 is dependent to a large extent on proper design.

It is of interest to note that brick joined with plastic cement performs a service not possible when either material is used alone. The critical reader will recognize that many of the other problems in construction can also be solved with proper combinations of steel, concrete, brick or plastics.

The successful engineer must visualize proper combinations and utilize the outstanding properties of each specific material in the solution of industrial problems. A knowledge of the subject matter discussed in each of the subsequent chapters, together with information contained in the suggested references, should enable every reader to acquire this important point of view.

Suggested References

"Properties of Plastics in the Chemical Industry," C. Howard Adams and R. A. McCarthy, "Symposium on Plastics as Materials of Construction," American Chemical Society, Division of Paint, Plastics and Printing Ink Chemistry, New York, September, 1954.

"Engineering Plastics into Chemical Plants," H. E. Atkinson, "Symposium on Plastics as Materials of Construction," American Chemical Society, Division of Paint, Plastics and Printing Ink Chemistry, New York, September, 1954.

"University Research on Engineering Properties of Plastics," Frederick J. McGarry, "Symposium on Plastics as Materials of Construction," American Chemical Society, Division of Paint, Plastics and Printing Ink Chemistry, New York, September, 1954.

"References on Plastics for the Corrosion Engineer," Corrosion, 9, No. 6, 197-8 (1953).

2. A SHORT HISTORY OF PLASTIC MATERIALS OF CONSTRUCTION

The history of plastics in general has been discussed in the references cited at the end of this chapter and no attempt will be made to duplicate information published previously. This chapter will be restricted primarily to a discussion of developments which are particularly significant for use of plastics as materials of chemical construction.

It should be noted that while their application has often been unrecognized, plastics have played an important role in many construction developments. The wings of many of the pioneer airplanes were coated with cellulose nitrate or cellulose acetate dope. Waxes of various kinds have been used as molds—indeed they have often been called "man's first plastic."* The development of the phonograph industry was dependent to a large extent on shellac-base records. The modern electronics industry would not be practical without polyethylene insulation and plastic potting compounds.

Many other illustrations could be cited but the above should suffice to show that many materials, formerly abhorred by the classical organic chemist, have been used as materials of construction for centuries. The use of plastics and related materials has been accelerated in recent years with the development of new knowledge of the chemistry and physics of large organic molecules.

Some of the historical background for specific plastics is outlined in this chapter. However, as stated previously, the reader should consult the references cited at the end of the chapter for additional information.

THERMOPLASTIC MATERIALS

Sulfur

Molten sulfur and admixtures have been used for centuries for joining various construction materials. Inscriptions on headstones joined to the bases with sulfur in graveyards of America's first colo-

---

*Knaggs, N., "Adventures in Man's First Plastic," New York, Reinhold Publishing Corp., 1947.

nists indicate that such materials have withstood over two centuries of weathering. One of the first patents for such admixtures was a British patent granted to B. F. Ortet in 1856.

While related products have been used in the U.S. for over fifty years, plasticized sulfur cements were not available until 1934. Much of the early work on plasticization through the use of "Thiokol" was done at the Mellon Institute of Industrial Research. Superior odorless plasticizers have replaced "Thiokol" for this application in recent years. It is of interest to note that over fifty million pounds of plasticized sulfur cement is produced annually in the United States.

Polyethylene

Low molecular weight polyethylene products were produced in the laboratory at least fifty years ago, but solid high molecular weight polythylene was not available until 1934. Its commercial production was the direct result of studies by Fawcett and Gibson.

Polyethylene was introduced commercially in the United States in 1943. It is now available in several different molecular weight ranges. In spite of the difficulties associated with high-pressure techniques, the amount of this plastic produced has increased every year. It has been estimated that over a billion pounds will be produced annually by 1965.

Polyisobutylene

Low molecular weight polyisobutylene products were prepared by treatment of isobutylene with concentrated sulfuric acid by Butlerow and Grianov in Germany in 1873. However, a satisfactory high molecular weight commercial product was not developed until 1937, when a patent was issued to Otto and Mueller-Cunradi.

Polyisobutylene is now available in several grades based on different molecular weights. It is used to improve paraffic wax and natural rubber for applications, such as water-resistant coatings, caulking compositions and adhesives. Considerable quantities of carbon-filled polyisobutylene are used as sheet tank linings on the European continent.

Asphalt

The use of natural asphalt possibly predates the first application of any other resinous products still in commercial use. Noah's Ark was waterproofed by caulking both the inside and outside of the structure with an asphalt-like pitch. It has been reported that asphalt was used by the Sumerians for the manufacture of mastic flooring over 5,000 years ago, and that the Babylonians paved their streets with this same material. Naturally occurring asphalt is still used to some extent but most commercial asphalt is a by-product of the petroleum industry.

Asphalt is used as filled and unfilled melts, as a solution in organic solvents and as an aqueous dispersion. A large amount of asphalt is utilized in road building and waterproofing. A considerable quantity is also used for chemical resistant construction.

Coal-tar Pitch

While the properties of coal-tar pitch are somewhat similar to those of asphalt and wood pitch, this product has been available for less than one hundred years. The process for coking coal was pattented in 1861 by Becker and Serles. The large-scale production of wood pitch was described many years earlier by the eminent chemist, Robert Boyle.

Like asphalt, coal-tar pitch is used as a hot melt solution in organic solvents and aqueous suspension. The main application of coal-tar pitch is in the production of filled caulking compositions and inexpensive coal-tar coatings. The latter find considerable use in the protection of metal pipelines.

Coumarone-Indene Resins

That coumarone and indene could be isolated from coal-tar naphthas and polymerized to solid materials in the presence of sulfuric acid was demonstrated by Kraemer and Spilker in 1890. Commercial production of these resins undertaken in 1920, now exceeds 20,000,000 pounds annually.

Polystyrene

Styrene was first polymerized by Simon in 1839. While crude polystyrene was known in the laboratory for over a century, the commercial product was not available in this country until 1937. Monomeric styrene was produced in the laboratory by Berthelot in 1865 but storage of this product was not practical until the discovery of organic inhibitors in 1922.

The principal use of polystyrene is for the production of molded and extruded products. In spite of its relatively good resistance to chemical attack, it is generally considered too brittle for use as a structural material. However, it has been used to a large extent for the manufacture of refrigerator panels and wall tile.

Styrene Copolymers

Because of their higher softening points, copolymers of styrene with 15 to 30 per cent acrylonitrile have been of interest to the organic chemist for many years. Products of this type have been available commercially in Europe and in the U.S. for approximately fifteen years, but have had limited use. The more recent commercial introduction of acrylonitrile blends has created considerable demand for this product. This blend consists of mixtures of styrene-acrylonitrile and butadiene-acrylonitrile copolymers. When extruded in the form of sheet and pipe this plastic product has been used industrially for chemical resistant piping and exhaust systems.

The so-called "upside-down" butadiene-styrene copolymers, or high styrene-butadiene copolymers, were introduced shortly after World War II. These products were stronger than the well known GR-S synthetic rubber and have greater resistance to impact than polystyrene. They are used as reinforcing resins for rubber and for floor tile, shipping containers, shoe soles, leather goods and protective coatings. They are also blended with polystyrene or GR-S to form high-impact plastic materials.

Acrylates

Commercialization of acrylic resins both in Germany and the United States resulted from the efforts of Otto Rohm, who produced polymers of methyl methacrylate in Germany in 1900. Plastics of this type have been produced commercially in the United States since 1931.

Polymethyl methacrylate may be cast, molded or extruded. Acrylate sheet, structures and pipe are used to some extent in the chemical industry when clarity together with moderate chemical resistance is required. Large quantities of polymethyl methacrylate sheet are also used by the aircraft and automotive industries and for transparent displays and working models.

Vinyl Chloride

Vinyl chloride was first synthesized by V. Regnault in 1835 and studied further by E. Baumann in 1872. However, little interest was shown in this product until 1912 when I. Ostromislensky attempted to utilize polymers of vinyl chloride.

The original polymers lacked stability to light and heat and were hard and insoluble in organic solvents. Commercialization was delayed until plasticizing techniques were developed. Copolymerization also helped to overcome some of the shortcomings of early products. More recently methods have been devised to utilize unplasticized polyvinyl chloride in the form of rigid pipe, sheet and structures.

The best known vinyl copolymer is that produced by the copolymerization of vinyl chloride with a small amount of vinyl acetate. While preliminary experimental work was presumably carried on simultaneously by I. G. Farbenindustrie, E. I. DuPont de Nemours & Co. and Carbide & Carbon Chemicals Co., the latter was successful in obtaining basic patents and introducing the product commercially. This copolymer is used as a coating, lining, and flexible tubing.

Polyvinyl Acetate and Its Derivatives

Polyvinyl acetate was first described by Klatte in 1912, who prepared vinyl acetate by the addition of acetic acid to acetylene in the presence of mercuric oxide. Klatte and Rollette prepared polyvinyl acetate in 1914 by heating the monomer in the presence of benzoyl peroxide. Water dispersions of polyvinyl acetate have been used to a small extent as coatings, but this polymer has been utilized primarily for the manufacture of polyvinyl alcohol and acetals such as polyvinyl butyral.

Polyvinyl alcohol was first produced in 1924 by Herman and Haehnel, who saponified the ester with alcoholic potassium hydroxide. In spite of its poor resistance to water, this product is used to some extent as a solvent resistant gasket and tubing material.

Polyvinyl Butyral

Polyvinyl butyral was first described in 1934 in a patent issued to Skirrow and Morrison. It was first produced commercially in this country in 1937. In addition to being the base of the WP-1 wash priming system, it has been used to a large extent as the inner layer in modern safety glass and as a wire coating.

Vinylidene Chloride Copolymers

Vinylidene chloride was first prepared by Regnault in 1838, but polymers of vinylidene chloride were not produced commercially until almost a century later. The most widely used plastics of this type are actually copolymers of vinylidene chloride based on the original studies by Wiley in 1936. Vinylidene chloride-vinyl chloride copolymers have been extruded to form film, pipe, tubing and fibers. Filled plasticized copolymers of vinylidene chloride and acrylonitrile have been used in the form of sheets for tank linings.

Polyfluorocarbons

Polymers of chlorotrifluoroethylene were first reported by Schloffer and Sherer in 1934. This polymer, first produced commercially in the United States during World War II under the direction of W. T. Miller, has been used for gaskets, valve seats, tubing and atomic energy applications. Ruff and Breitschneider prepared tetrafluoroethylene in 1933 by heating tetrafluoroethane with zinc dust. This monomer is now manufactured by the pyrolysis of chlorodifluoromethane, which is prepared by the fluorination of chloroform.

In 1941, Plunkett described the unexpected polymerization of this monomer in the presence of zinc chloride. Because of its outstanding chemical resistance and anti-adhesive properties, this product has found considerable application as a gasket, film, tubing and coating material in spite of its high cost.

Silicones

The first silicon-containing organic chemical compounds were prepared in the laboratory by Friedel, Crafts and Ladenburg in 1863. This phase of organic chemistry was investigated quite thoroughly by Kipping in 1904. Kipping published over fifty papers on this subject, but commercialization of silicones was delayed until 1943.

Much of the development of this plastic was based on research by J. F. Hyde, W. R. Collings, and S. L. Bass. Silicones have outstanding resistance to elevated temperatures and good water repellent and dielectric properties. They have been used as defoaming agents, high temperature finishes and heat resistant gaskets.

Polyamides

Casein adhesives were patented by Ross in 1876 but casein plastics were not introduced until 1897. Much of the early work was done by Spitteler and Krische, who were successful in producing white slates for school children. They called their product Galalith (from the Greek meaning milkstone). More recently, casein fibers have been produced both in Italy and in the United States.

Synthetic polyamide plastics were first described in 1899 by Gabriel and Manes, who prepared products of this general type by heating aminocaproic acids. This type of reaction was investigated further in 1932 by Carothers. In his classical experiments, he developed nylon by condensing adipic acid with hexamethylene diamine.

Along with the development of phenol formaldehyde resins by Dr. Leo Baekeland, this discovery which was based on an unusual understanding of fundamental concepts is one of the great contributions to modern plastic technology.

Polyurethanes

In 1848, Wurtz observed that ethylisocyanate reacted readily with ethyl alcohol to produce urethane. Reaction of organic diisocyanates with dihydric alcohols was investigated by Bayer in 1937. This basic reaction has been employed to produce a wide variety of polymers which are useful as fibers, adhesives, films, elastomers and cellular plastics.

ELASTOMERS

Natural Rubber

While natural rubber has been known for centuries, its utility was limited until 1839 when Charles Goodyear provided a less tacky product by heating rubber with sulfur and litharge. The term "vulcanization" was coined by Brockedon, a friend of Hancock, another pioneer in the rubber field.

By using larger proportions of sulfur than his older brother, Nelson Goodyear produced hard rubber or ebonite in 1851. Most of the varied uses of soft and hard rubber are well known. Both products have been used for pipe, tubing and tank linings.

RUBBER DERIVATIVES

Isomerized Rubber

Isomerized rubber was first prepared in 1910 by Harries by the reaction of rubber with concentrated sulfuric acid. Other investigations were made subsequently by Kirchhoff in 1920 and Staudinger and Fisher in 1926.

Fisher treated rubber with paratoluene sulfonic acid and obtained a product called thermoprene. Since products of this type proved to have excellent adhesion, they were used to adhere sheet rubber to steel in the lining of tanks. These materials have also been used as coatings and general adhesives.

Rubber Hydrochloride

Rubber hydrochloride was first described by Matthews in 1805 but was not available commercially in the country states until about 1935. It has been used successfully as a plasticized film for packaging perishable products such as citrus fruits.

Chlorinated rubber

Chlorinated rubber was first produced by Roxburgh in 1801, but was not manufactured commercially until 1859 when Englehard and Day and Havemann independently patented processes for making this rubber derivative. It was first used as a protective coating in 1915 and predates most of the other commercial protective coatings.

SYNTHETIC RUBBERS

Butyl Rubber

That some of the deficiencies of the previously cited polyisobutyenes could be overcome by the introduction of unsaturation in the polymer molecule was recognized for many years. However, attempts to produce a similar material with a small amount of unsaturation were unsuccessful until 1937 when Thomas and Sparks polymerized small amounts of isoprene with isobutylene. The resulting product, called "butyl" rubber, can be vulcanized to produce compositions with excellent resistance to chemicals, sunlight and gaseous diffusion. Butyl rubber has been used for gaskets, tank linings and tubing.

Chlorosulfonated Polyethylene

The tendency for polyethylene to cold flow has been overcome by heating the chlorosulfonated derivative with litharge and other curing agents. This product, introduced commercially in 1952, is said to have superior resistance to heat, sunlight and chemicals.

Styrene Rubber

Rubber-like products were produced in Germany during World War I by the sodium-catalyzed polymerization of dimethylbutadiene but their manufacture was discontinued shortly after it. The more successful butadiene rubbers produced in more recent years were called Buna. Their name was derived from the original process ("Bu" for butadiene and "Na" for sodium). However, the use of sodium as a catalyst was discontinued in favor of aqueous emulsion polymerization systems.

Buna S, the copolymer of butadiene and styrene, was described in investigations by Tschunker and Bock. It was first produced commercially in Germany in 1932. Relatively small quantities were produced in the United States just before World War II. The tremendous quantities that were manufactured subsequently made a vital contribution to America's self-sufficiency during the war. Buna S, also called GR-S, can be used almost interchangeably with natural rubber for the production of gasket, hose and rubber linings. Improvements such as low temperature polymerization have made it possible to produce a rubber having properties vastly superior to the original Buna S.

Acrylonitrile Rubber

The oil-sensitivity of Buna S was overcome in 1933 by Konrad and Tschunker by the copolymerization of acrylonitrile and butadiene. This product has been used for the manufacture of oil-resistant gaskets, hose and tank linings.

Neoprene

The commercial production of neoprene in 1931—the first successful United States-produced synthetic rubber—was based on the coordination of independent discoveries by J. A. Nieuwland and W. Carothers. The former prepared vinyl acetylene from acetylene in the presence of cuprous chloride. Carothers converted Nieuwland's vinyl acetylene to chloroprene by the addition of hydrochloric acid and ammonium chloride. Chloroprene was then polymerized in an aqueous emulsion system to produce neoprene rubber. Large quantities of this product are now manufactured for use in mechanical goods, adhesives, coatings and tank linings.

Polysulfide Rubber

So-called thioplasts or polysulfide rubbers were produced in the laboratory in 1840 by Lavig and Weidmann, but were not available commercially until almost a century later. This type of product was rediscovered in the United States in 1920 by J. C. Patrick while attempting to prepare a new anti-freeze from ethylene dichloride and sodium polysulfide. It was called "Thiokol." A similar commercial product was developed simultaneously by J. Baer in Switzerland. Subsequently, a company was organized by Longstreth in Kansas City to make this odoriferous solvent-resistant rubber. Much of the early production of "Thiokol" was consumed in the plasticization of sulfur cements.

At the beginning of World War II, polysulfide rubber was proposed as an elastomer to replace natural rubber in automobile tires. In spite of its odor and tendency to cold flow, considerable quantities are now used for oil-resistant mechanical goods, caulking compositions and coatings.

CELLULOSE DERIVATIVES

Cellulose Nitrate

Cellulose nitrate was first synthesized by Bracannot in 1832 and Pelouze in 1838. The first attempt to utilize it commercially was that of Alexander Parks in 1855. Unfortunately, his process required large volumes of solvents and was not economical.

In 1848, J. P. Maynard and S. L. Bigelow proposed a solution of cellulose nitrate for medical use under the name of collodion. Three years later, Archer produced commercial photographic film from cellulose nitrate.

In 1868, a printer named John Wesley Hyatt added camphor to cellulose nitrate in order to produce a plastic billiard ball. As a result, he was awarded a $10,000 prize by the firm of Phelan and Collender. His product, called "Celluloid," was the basis for much of the plastic progress during the last quarter of the 19th century. Cellulose nitrate is now used for lacquers and plastic sheet.

Cellulose Acetate

Cellulose acetate was first described by Schutzenberger in 1865. The original product was not of commercial interest since it required expensive solvents and was much more expensive than the more flammable cellulose nitrate. One of the major improvements was made by G. W. Miles in 1903, who prepared an ester with fewer acetyl groups. This product was soluble in acetone. Many improvements in cellulose acetate plastics were also made by Camille and Henri Dreyfus. Because of its inherent toughness and fair resistance to flame, cellulose acetate molded and extruded parts have been used industrially. However, their poor resistance to corrosion has limited their use as chemical-resistant materials.

Cellulose acetate butyrate was first described by Clarke and Malm in 1932. Commercial manufacture was started the same year and the material became available as a molding powder in 1938. The mixed ester has a lower water resistance than cellulose acetate. Cellulose acetate butyrate is used as piping and tubing in the chemical and petroleum industries when resistance to acids and alkalies is not required.

Cellulose Ethers

Ethyl cellulose was first produced in 1912 by Leuchs, Lilienfeld and Dreyfus working independently in Germany, Austria and France, respectively. It has been available commercially in the United States since 1935. It is not attacked by corrosive salts and has been used as a hot dip coating for the temporary protection of metal objects.

Methyl cellulose was first prepared in the laboratory by Suida in 1905. It was produced in commercial quantities by Dreyfus several years later. Because of its lack of resistance to water, it is not used in chemical-resistant construction. Most commercial applications of methyl cellulose are based on its solubility in water.

THERMOSETTING RESINS

Polyesters

While simple esters are well known in classical organic chemistry, the so-called polyester resins were not described until 1901. While Watson Smith, the inventor, suggested the application of these new plastics as a cement for use with glass and earthenware, he apparently failed to recognize their potentials based on the reactions of glycerol and phthalic acid.

In 1915, W. C. Arsem proposed that part of the phthalic acid be replaced by a molar equivalent of oleic acid in the manufacture of polyesters. In 1922 Weisburg described the various stages of polyester resin formation. Undoubtedly the most important contribution was made by Kienle, who developed the fatty acid process for modifying alkyd resins in 1927. In the early 1930's, Carothers and co-workers showed the influence of the structure of alcohol and acid molecules on polymerization and laid the foundation for the development of much of the present knowledge of condensation polymerization.

Polyallyl acrylate was described as early as 1873 but polyallyl esters were not available commercially until 1940. In 1941 polyallyl diglycol carbonate was produced using methods described by A. Pechukas and F. Strain.

In 1939, Rust described the copolymerization of vinyl acetate and diethylene glycol maleate. Subsequent improvements and replacement of vinyl acetate by styrene during World War II led to the unsaturated polyester resins which are now widely used with glass fiber reinforcement.

General-purpose unsaturated polyesters have limited chemical resistance but when reinforced with fiberglas mat or fabric they have been used for the fabrication of pipe and industrial exhaust systems. Specialty polyester resins having excellent resistance to chemicals and flame are available commercially.

Urea Resins

Presumably, crude urea resins were used by the early Egyptians but the earliest account of the reaction of urea with formaldehyde was not recorded until 1884. A patent on this plastic was issued to John in 1920. It became available commercially in the early 1930's as a result of research by A. M. Howald. Urea resins are less resistant to corrosives than phenolic resins and since they are much lighter in color, they have been used for the molding of kitchenware and as a binder for plywood.

Melamine Resins

Melamine was described by Liebig in 1834 but melamine formaldehyde resins were not available commercially until 1939. The basic patent was granted to W. F. Talbot in 1941 following a complicated interference action in the U.S. Patent Office. Like urea resins, melamine products are not noted for their resistance to chemicals. However, because of their greater resistance to heat and water, they are often used for kitchenware and plywood adhesives.

Phenolic Resins

Adolph von Bayer attempted to prepare a substitute for shellac from the reaction of phenol and formaldehyde as early as 1872. This work was followed by that of Morgan in 1893, Kleeberg in 1891, Smith in 1899, Floomer in 1902 and Story in 1905. Most of these investigators were at least partly successful in producing a resin through the acid condensation of phenol and formaldehyde but they were not able to control the reaction.

Dr. Leo Baekeland, who may be classed with Hyatt and Carothers as one of the three most important plastics pioneers, patented phenol formaldehyde resins in 1907. One of the reasons for his success was the recognition that temperatures above boiling were required and that reaction rates could be controlled by the presence of small amounts of alkalies.

Raschig, in Germany, and Redman, Conrad and Aylsworth in the United States, were successful in developing commercial processes competitive to the Baekeland process. Separate firms were established here but they were later consolidated as the Bakelite Corporation. In 1913, Albert and Behrend described an oil-modified phenolic resin which made the phenolic coating industry possible.

Phenolic resins possess excellent resistance to acids, salts, and some solvents and hence find many applications in the chemical process industry. They are used principally as castings, moldings, adhesives and coatings.

Epoxy Resins

Epoxy resins which were introduced commercially in Switzerland prior to 1946 are now being manufactured in sizable quantities in the United States. Because of their excellent chemical resistance and good electrical properties, they have been used to considerable extent as coatings, casting resins, potting compounds and adhesives.

Furan Resins

Both furfuryl alcohol and furfural have been available commercially in the United States for many years. It has been well known that these products can be resinified by strong acids but that the reaction is difficult to control. The first patent on furan polymers was issued to Miner and Trickey in 1928.

Considerable quantities of furfural are used in the impregnation of graphite. Polymers of furfuryl alcohol are used as chemical resistant cements. Both impregnated graphite and the cements have excellent resistance to acids, alkalies, salts and solvents.

Because of the newness of many of the foregoing discoveries, the full utility of plastics has been far from realized. Additional new plastics will be developed, of course. However, some of the major improvements in plastics technology to date have been made by practical men who saw the possibility of using specific products to solve specific problems.

It is hoped that the information in subsequent chapters will help lay the groundwork for proper utilization of plastics as materials of construction. Knowledge of this type will make additional improvements possible. Some of the information required will be found in Chapter 3 on Plastic Fundamentals.

Suggested References

A. J. Buck, British Plastics, 9, 16 (1937).

"Plastics and Coal," N. J. Megson and K. W. Peiffer, Chemistry & Industry, 59, 247 (1940).

"Chemistry of Synthetic Resins," Carlton Ellis, Reinhold Publishing Corp., New York, 1935.

"The Chemistry of Commercial Plastics," R. L. Wakeman, Reinhold Publishing Corp., New York, 1947.

"The Chemistry and Technology of Plastics," R. Nauth, Reinhold Publishing Corp., New York, 1947.

"The Technology of Adhesives," J. Delmonte, Reinhold Publishing Corp., New York, 1947.

"Synthetic Resins and Rubbers," P. O. Powers, John Wiley & Sons, Inc., New York, 1943.

3. PLASTICS FUNDAMENTALS

An attempt will be made in this chapter to outline the basic concepts of high molecular weight structural materials. A brief survey of the structure of plastics, methods of plastic production and fabrication of plastics and rubbers will be presented. The references cited at the end of the chapter are recommended to any one desiring additional information.

The Society of the Plastics Industry has defined a plastic as "any one of a large and varied group of materials which contains as an essential ingredient, an organic substance of large molecular weight and which, while solid in the finished state, at some stage in its manufacture has been or can be formed into various shapes by flow, usually through application singly or together of heat and pressure." While this definition is technically correct, it may be a bit too cumbersome for many engineers. In this book, plastics will be considered simply as high molecular weight organic materials which can be utilized advantageously by forming into useful shapes.

Classification of Plastics

Basic plastics materials may be classified in several different ways. One of the oldest methods was on the basis of origin into "natural," "artificial" and "synthetic" plastics. Natural plastics are naturally occurring high-molecular weight materials such as rubber, cellulose, casein, waxes and asphalts. Their derivatives such as chlorinated rubber and cellulose acetate are sometimes referred to as artificial plastics. On the other hand, synthetic plastics are based on low molecular weight compounds which are built up or "polymerized" into long chains or highly complex networks by controlled chemical reactions. A classification which is more significant to the practicing engineer is based on molecular structure. These two classes are thermoplastic and thermosetting plastics.

Thermoplastics consist primarily of long chains of atoms with regularly reoccurring groups attached to the backbone of the molecule. These chains are highly kinked or coiled about each other like the contents of a plate of spaghetti, but are not attached by chemical bonds. As indicated by the name, thermoplastics are softened at elevated temperatures. In this state, the plastics can be formed by molding, calendering, extrusion, or casting and will retain their new form when cooled below the forming temperature. This change in physical form is reversible and can be repeated indefinitely provided no chemical decomposition takes place. Some typical thermoplastics are polystyrene, polyvinyl chloride and nylon.

Thermosetting plastics, on the other hand, contain highly complex, cross-linked structures which cannot be softened with heat. These are usually formed from low molecular weight materials or "prepolymers" by heat and/or the chemical action of catalysts or curing agents as discussed later in this chapter. Phenolic, furan, epoxy, urea and melamine resins are some of the more important thermosetting plastics.

A third method of classification, based on relative flexibility, consists of plastics and elastomers or rubbers. Plastics are not readily deformed by low stresses and any deformation incurred is permanent or comparatively slowly reversible. In contrast, elastomers are more or less elastic, easily deformed by low stresses and recover their original shape readily. Many elastomers are thermosetting and contain many cross-linkages per molecule.

POLYMERIZATION REACTIONS

Addition Polymerization

Most synthetic thermoplastics are produced by the addition of small unsaturated molecules to a growing chain under the influence of heat and/or catalysts. The most common polymerization catalysts are peroxygen compounds such as benzoyl peroxide or potassium persulfate.

In the addition polymerization process, the unsaturated molecules or monomers add on to an activated molecule to form a chain with an active end capable of adding additional monomer groups. This addition takes place in very rapid sequence without the elimination of any compounds. This reaction leads to the formation of very long chains with molecular weights ranging from 10,000 to over 200,000. The polymerization of ethylene may be depicted as follows:

$$CH_2 = CH_2 \xrightarrow{\text{heat}} \text{---} CH_2 - CH_2 - CH_2 - CH_2 - CH_2 - CH_2 \longrightarrow$$

ethylene   a short segment of the polyethylene molecule

Two or more different unsaturated monomers may be polymerized together to produce copolymers whose properties usually differ from those of either of the products formed when the monomers are polymerized separately. Many of the most important thermoplastics such as vinyl chloride-vinyl acetate resins and styrene-butadiene plastics are copolymers.

When molecules containing two unsaturated groups such as butadiene $(CH_2 = CH - CH = CH_2)$ or divinylbenzene $(CH_2 = CH \mathbin{<\!\!\!>} CH = CH_2)$ are polymerized, cross-linked infusible polymers can be produced as illustrated below:

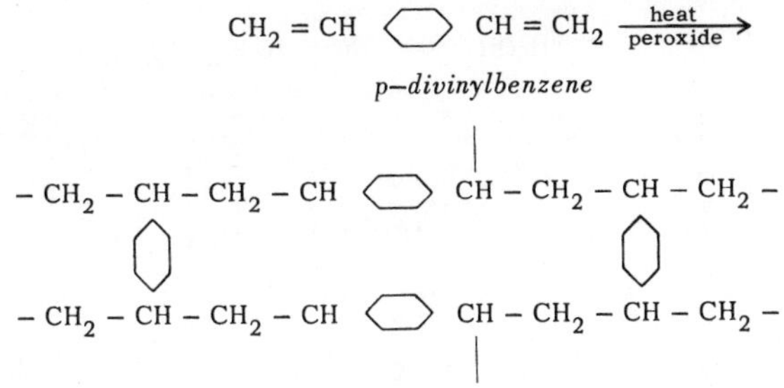

$$CH_2 = CH \diagdown \diagup CH = CH_2 \xrightarrow[\text{peroxide}]{\text{heat}}$$

p—divinylbenzene

$$- CH_2 - CH - CH_2 - CH \diagdown \diagup CH - CH_2 - CH - CH_2 -$$

$$- CH_2 - CH - CH_2 - CH \diagdown \diagup CH - CH_2 - CH - CH_2 -$$

a segment of the polydivinylbenzene molecule

Condensation Polymerization

Condensation reactions take place when molecules containing two or more reactive groups are reacted together with the elimination of simple molecules such as water. If each reactant contains only two reactive groups, linear thermoplastics such as nylon are produced. This type condensation is illustrated below:

$$NH_2 - (CH_2)_6 - NH_2 + HOOC\ (CH_2)_4\ COOH \longrightarrow$$

hexamethylene diamine   adipic acid

$$NH_2 - (CH_2)_6\ NH \left[- OC\ (CH_2)_4 - CONH\ (CH_2)_6 - NH \right]_x OC(CH_2)_4COOH + H_2O$$

nylon   *water*

Similarly, thermoplastic polyesters may be formed by the reaction of a dihydric alcohol such as ethylene glycol and a dicarboxylic acid such as adipic acid. This reaction is illustrated below:

$$HO\ (CH_2)_2\ OH + HOOC\ (C_6H_4)\ COOH \longrightarrow$$

ethylene glycol   phthalic acid

$$HO\ (CH_2)_2O \left[- OC\ (C_6H_4)\ COO\ (CH_2)_2 - O \right]_x OC\ (C_6H_4)\ COOH + H_2O$$

thermoplastic polyester plastic   *water*

However, if either reactant contains more than two active groups, a thermosetting plastic is obtained. Since urea, melamine and phenolic plastics are all produced from intermediates having more than two reactive groups, the final products are thermosetting plastics. However, the chemistry of formation of these products is too complicated to serve as an example. Hence, a more simple polyester reaction will be used for this illustration.

If glycerol is substituted for ethylene glycol in the previous example a three-dimensional or thermosetting plastic will be obtained because of the presence of three active groups in one of the reactants. This type condensation is illustrated below:

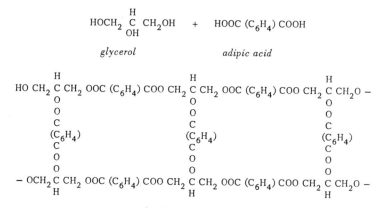

a segment of a thermosetting polyester plastic

Plastics Production Methods

Condensation polymers such as polyesters, urea, melamine, phenolic, epoxy and furan resins are usually produced in conventional heated reaction vessels equipped with agitators and condensers. The rate of the reaction is observed through change in viscosity, index of refraction and acid number or the amount of water evolved.

In almost every case, it is essential to stop the reaction at a predetermined point as measured by one or more of the previously cited constants. In addition to cooling the partial resin, it is often necessary to add an inhibitor to prevent further reaction at ordinary temperatures.

Addition polymers can be produced in similar equipment. Polymerization reactions are exothermic and the heat of polymerization may vary from 250 to 350 Btu per pound of monomer. Nevertheless, heat and/or catalyst are required to activate the monomer molecules which will continue to grow until termination. The chain length or molecular weight is an inverse function of the temperature and catalyst concentration. With this type of polymerization, the ultimate molecular weight is achieved in the reactor.

Polymers of vinyl monomers may be produced by (1) bulk, (2) solution, (3) suspension, and (4) emulsion polymerization.

In bulk polymerization, the solvent-free monomer is heated in the presence or absence of a catalyst until practically all the monomer is converted to polymer. Since the reaction is exothermic, it is essential that provisions be made to dissipate the heat of reaction. This is usually accomplished by polymerization in sheets not thicker than 2 inches. If this precaution is not taken, it is impossible to control the molecular weight and sometimes impractical to produce the polymer at all without risking damage to equipment and personnel. Many laboratory accidents have resulted from a lack of understanding of this basic concept. Polystyrene has been produced on a large scale by this method. The bulk polymer is usually granulated, but may also be extruded and chopped to produce uniform rod-shaped particles.

Monomers may be dissolved in solvents and the resulting solution may be heated in the presence of catalysts to produce polymers. Better temperature control is achieved with this technique because of the dilution effect. Some polymers may precipitate from the solutions during the reaction, but others must be separated by evaporation or precipitation with a nonsolvent. Acrylonitrile and vinyl chloride may be polymerized in solution but this technique is used primarily for the manufacture of copolymers of vinyl chloride and vinyl acetate.

The requirement for good heat transfer may be accomplished by suspending the monomer in the form of droplets in water. Providing heat and/or catalysts are present, continuous stirring in the presence of suspension agents such as polymethacrylic acid or gelatin will produce polymers in the form of minute beads with fairly uniform molecular weight. The polymer is easily filtered to remove the water and water-soluble impurities. The product is dried with conventional equipment. Polystyrene, polyvinyl chloride and polyvinyl acetate have been manufactured by the suspension technique.

The ultimate in heat transfer is brought about by use of the so-called "emulsion technique." In contrast to the suspension polymerization technique, which employs moderate agitation usually in the presence of organic peroxide catalysts, emulsion polymerization requires the use of efficient agitation and surface active agents such as alkyl aryl sulfonates plus water-soluble catalysts such as potassium persulfate. In most cases, it is necessary to replace the oxygen in the air space in the reactor with an inert gas such as nitrogen. Modern emulsion processes often employ a "redox" catalyst system consisting of both an oxidizing and a reducing agent. The polymer is obtained in the form of a finely divided dispersion or latex.

Unless emulsion polymers are to be used in this form, it is necessary to coagulate and wash the polymer as free as practical from the emulsifier before drying. Polystyrene, polyvinyl acetate and most types of synthetic rubber are produced by emulsion process.

Machine Fabrication of Plastics

Almost all available plastic materials may be shaped by one or more standard molding techniques. Compression molding in which the plastic particles are placed in a heated die and formed under pressure is possibly the simplest method. Unless curing takes place during the molding process, the die must be cooled before removal of pressure. Compression molding is used most advantageously with thermosetting plastics and rubbers.

Thermosetting plastics may be molded much more rapidly by a two-stage process called "transfer molding." In this process, the plastic is softened under pressure in a heated chamber and then forced into the heated mold cavity.

Many common molded thermoplastic parts are produced by injection molding in which the plastic granules are fed into a heated chamber equipped with a plunger which injects a measured amount of semifluid plastic into the cold mold. In this automatic process, the molded part is ejected as the plunger returns, prior to repeating the injection of more heat-softened material into the cavity. Objects weighing as much as 15 pounds can be injection molded by modern molding machines.

Extrusion resembles injection molding except that the softened thermoplastic is forced continuously by a screw mechanism through a carefully designed die. The material is then cooled in a water bath to prevent deformation. Rigid or flexible pipe, rod, strips, or filaments with a wide variety of cross-sections are produced continuously by this technique.   The extrusion of unplasticized polyvinyl chloride pipe using a twin-screw extruder is shown in Figure 3-1.

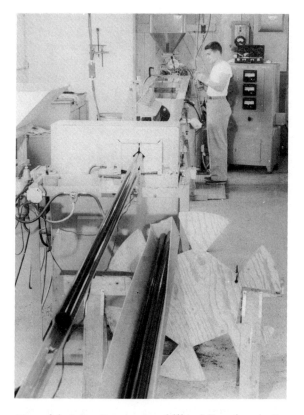

Figure 3-1. Automatic extrusion of 1½-inch Type 1 unplasticized polyvinyl chloride pipe with a twin-screw extruder.

Both reinforced and nonreinforced thick plastic sheets can be manufactured by pressing the materials between hot platens in large flatbed presses. The thermoplastic sheets discussed in Chapter 16 are usually formed by laminating several thin calendered sheets together in a large press.

Plastic laminates, of the type discussed in Chapter 14, may be reinforced by paper or fabric. The fabric may be cotton, glass cloth or glass mat. In most instances, thermosetting resins are used and they are cured during the heating and pressing process.

Low pressure or contact laminates are formed with very little pressure. It is often possible to use the so-called "bag molding process" in which the sheet is placed against the mold surface and the assembly is enclosed in a flexible impervious bag. The air is then exhausted so that the plastic is forced against the mold surface.

Natural rubber and other polymers may be compounded on a rubber mill consisting of two heavy heated metal rolls rotating in opposite directions. Large batches may be compounded in heavy-duty equipment, such as a Banbury mixer. The compounded material may be molded, extruded or sheeted on a calender. A calender which consists of three or more heated rolls forms a fairly uniform thin sheet having controlled thickness from .001 to over .050 inch. The thin calendered sheet may be plied up to form a heavier sheet, using the same equipment or by employing the previously described lamination process. Sheet linings such as those described in Chapter 8 are usually produced by these techniques.

Many coatings, chemical-resistant mortar cements, casting resins, adhesives, caulking compounds and plastic water and sewer jointing materials are produced by blending the solid and liquid components in closed or open vessels equipped with suitable agitators.

Field Fabrication Methods

Modern materials of construction must be supplied on the job in a form that requires minimum equipment and skill for further assembly. Plastic materials of construction must not only meet this requirement but must also be available in a form that can be applied by tradesmen who are usually unskilled in the plastics know-how.

Hot Melts

Plasticized sulfur, polyisobutylene, asphalt, coal-tar pitch, coumarone-indene and ethyl cellulose compositions are supplied as solid materials which may be applied by melting techniques. This simple method of application usually produces a structure which may be used as soon as the molten mass has solidified.

Most directions suggest melting a small quantity of lumps of the material at the start and adding additional product slowly to the molten material. The use of this technique, temperature control and good agitation on the job will minimize decomposition of molten plastic products during application.

Coatings

Most plastic materials can also be applied as solution in organic solvents. Styrene-butadiene copolymers, polymethyl methacrylate, vinyl chloride-vinyl acetate copolymers, polyvinyl acetate, polyvinyl butyral, vinyl chloride-acrylonitrile copolymers, silicones, alkyds, isomerized rubber, rubber hydrochloride, chlorinated rubber, neoprene, cellulose esters and ethers, phenolic, epoxy and furan resins have been supplied commercially in the form of solutions in organic solvents.

Most protective coatings consist of solutions of a plastic compounded with pigments, fillers, stabilizers and other ingredients. The solvent must be selected so that it will deposit a continuous solvent-free film shortly after application. The solvent may be released at ordinary or elevated temperatures depending on whether or not oven-baking is used.

Small amounts of solvents may also be present in casting resins, impregnants, industrial adhesives and caulking compositions. Heavy films of solvent-type coatings described in Chapter 8 are sometimes classified as organic linings.

Most plastics can also be supplied as water dispersions. Such products, sometimes called "latices," are less hazardous since they are free from toxic or flammable solvents. In some instances, the material deposited from aqueous dispersions must be heated to produce a continuous film.

Aqueous dispersions of products such as asphalt, coal tar, coumarone-indene resins, polyvinyl butyral, alkyds, and cellulose derivatives are usually produced by mechanical dispersion of a solution or molten polymer in water in the presence of an efficient emulsifying agent. However, many polymeric materials are readily available as aqueous dispersions since emulsion polymerization techniques are used in their manufacture.

Natural rubber is a latex tapped from the rubber tree. The latex contains about 35 to 40 per cent solids and is usually concentrated further by centrifuging or heating. Polymers and copolymers of styrene including butadiene-styrene rubber (GR-S), copolymers of acrylonitrile and styrene, polyfluorocarbons and some types of polysulfide rubbers are also produced as aqueous dispersions.

Polymers and copolymers of vinyl chloride are also available as low viscosity, high solids dispersions in organic liquids called "organosols." They do not become soluble in the selected liquid until heated. As in the case of many aqueous dispersions, the deposited material must be heated to secure a continuous void-free film.

If the organic liquid is a comparatively nonvolatile liquid (plasticizer) the dispersion is called a "plastisol." Most plastisols consist of discrete particles of polymers or copolymers of vinyl chloride suspended in esters of phthalic acid such as dioctyl phthalate. The deposited film must be heated at a temperature of 325 to $375°F$ in order to fuse the plasticizer and the resin to form a continuous, tough, flexible product. Plastisols may be cast or molded to form a wide variety of useful products. If a gelling agent is added to the plastisol, it may be applied as a paste, and is called a "plastigel."

Curing of Plastics

As mentioned earlier in this chapter, most thermoplastic materials attain their maximum molecular weight during the manufacturing process. Further compounding and application techniques such as melting, dissolving and heat forming are strictly physical in nature and no chemical changes occur.

However, thermosetting and elastomeric materials are usually supplied as comparatively low molecular products. The final cross-linked or vulcanized products are too insoluble in solvents to be applied as hot melts or heat-formed by any process such as molding, extrusion, or lamination. The conversion from the fusible, soluble form to the cross-linked infusible form must take place after the material has been applied in the form of coatings, linings, or cements.

The transformation may result in additional polymerization under the influence of heat and pressure (phenolic, urea, and melamine resins) or by the effect of catalyst or curing agents (phenolic, furan, epoxy and polyester resins, neoprene and natural rubber). This type of reaction is usually referred to as curing, vulcanization or setting.

The classical definition of a catalyst is a material which influences the reaction of chemical substances without itself being used up in the reaction. This definition applies to surface catalysis but is not broad enough to describe catalysts used in plastic or rubber technology.

The types of materials used as curing agents vary widely in their composition and depend upon the chemical nature of the plastic or rubber. For example, liquid phenolic and furan resins can be cured by the addition of strong acids, unsaturated polyesters by peroxy compounds, epoxy resins by polyamines, natural rubber by sulfur, neoprene by inorganic oxides, and liquid polysulfide rubbers by lead peroxide. In many cases, the curing action will take place at ordinary temperatures but the application of heat is required in some instances.

Some readers may find that the information in this chapter is too fragmentary. Others may feel that such knowledge is irrelevant to corrosion engineering. Those in the first group can secure additional information from the references at the end of the chapter. The information discussed in Chapter 4, however, is essential to all engineers interested in the use of plastics as materials of construction.

Suggested References

"Engineering Materials Manual," T. C. Du Mond, Reinhold Publishing Corp., New York, 1951.

"The Chemistry of Large Molecules," R. E. Burk and O. Grummitt, Interscience Publishers, Inc., New York, 1943.

"Meet the Plastics," C. N. Robinson, Macmillan Co., New York, 1949.

"Vinyl and Related Polymers," C. E. Schildknecht, John Wiley & Sons, Inc., New York, 1952.

"The Chemistry and Technology of Plastics," R. Nauth, Reinhold Publishing Corp., 1947.

"Synthetic Resins and Rubbers," P. O. Powers, John Wiley & Sons, Inc., New York, 1943.

"A Manual of Plastics and Resins," W. Schack, Chemical Publishing Co., New York, 1950.

"Elastomers and Plastomers," Vols. I and II, R. Houwink, Elsevier Publishing Co., New York, 1949.

"Fundamentals of Synthetic Polymer Technology," R. Houwink, Elsevier Publishing Co., New York, 1949.

"High Polymer Reactions," H. Mark and R. Raff, Interscience Publishers, Inc., New York, 1941.

"Chemistry of Synthetic Resins," C. Ellis, Reinhold Publishing Corp., New York, 1935.

"Fundamental Principles of Polymerization," G. D'Alelio, John Wiley & Sons, Inc., New York, 1952.

"Principles of Polymer Chemistry," P. J. Flory, Cornell University Press, Ithaca, New York, 1953.

4. PHYSICAL PROPERTIES OF PLASTICS

Most engineers know that it is dangerous to generalize when considering the use of various products as materials of construction. They recognize that different points of view must be considered when using wood, glass, brick, portland cement, nonferrous metals and other well known construction materials. Design engineers who have worked with plastics realize that many of the accepted concepts are not applicable in this field and that the same design principles do not apply for all plastic materials.

Certain generalizations can be made about thermoplastic and thermosetting plastics, but it must be remembered that many physical properties are specific for each material. Several physical properties for uncompounded and unfilled plastics are given in Table 4-1 and Figure 4-1, but it must be remembered that many of these properties can be modified considerably by compounding procedures.

A review of these values will show that the specific gravity of plastics is considerably less than that for metallic materials of construction. It will also show that the tensile strength varies from 1,300 to 12,000 psi at room temperature and that these values decrease rapidly as the temperature is increased above 150°F. The tensile strength of highly oriented crystalline polymers, such as nylon and saran, which exceed 50,000 psi at room temperature, compare favorably with most metals. These values become more impressive when compared with metals on a weight rather than a volume basis. However, it must be remembered that direct comparison of physical properties of plastics and other materials should be avoided in order to prevent inaccurate conclusions. Data, such as those given in Table 4-1, may be used to differentiate plastic materials but comparison with values for other materials may lead to erroneous conclusions.

The maximum allowable working stress should be determined before plastic structures are designed. This requires a knowledge of stress-strain characteristics under the anticipated service conditions. At the present time some data are incomplete but it must be remembered that limited test data are better than none at all.

Most published strength data for plastics have been secured at room temperature and since they are based on short term tests, do not make allowances for creep. This factor, called "dauerstandsfestigkeit" by German engineers, has been the stumbling block for many design engineers unfamiliar with the characteristic properties of plastic materials. This same property is associated with metals

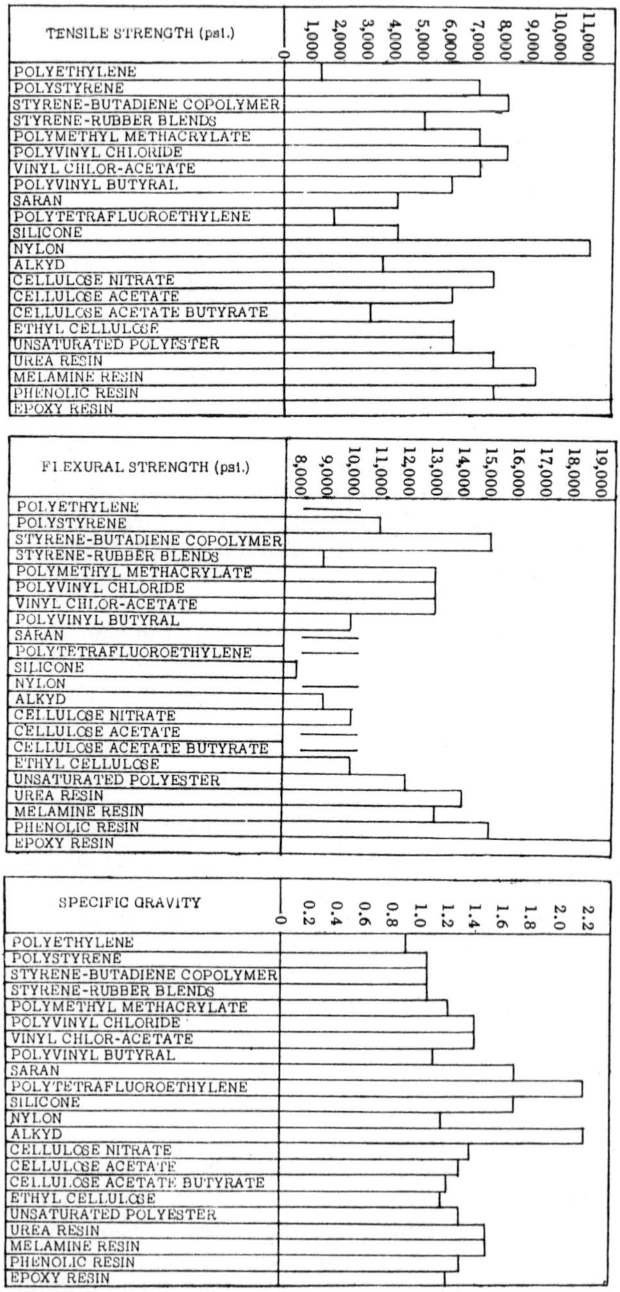

TENSILE STRENGTH (psi.)	0	1,000	2,000	3,000	4,000	5,000	6,000	7,000	8,000	9,000	10,000	11,000
POLYETHYLENE												
POLYSTYRENE												
STYRENE-BUTADIENE COPOLYMER												
STYRENE-RUBBER BLENDS												
POLYMETHYL METHACRYLATE												
POLYVINYL CHLORIDE												
VINYL CHLOR-ACETATE												
POLYVINYL BUTYRAL												
SARAN												
POLYTETRAFLUOROETHYLENE												
SILICONE												
NYLON												
ALKYD												
CELLULOSE NITRATE												
CELLULOSE ACETATE												
CELLULOSE ACETATE BUTYRATE												
ETHYL CELLULOSE												
UNSATURATED POLYESTER												
UREA RESIN												
MELAMINE RESIN												
PHENOLIC RESIN												
EPOXY RESIN												

FLEXURAL STRENGTH (psi.)	8,000	9,000	10,000	11,000	12,000	13,000	14,000	15,000	16,000	17,000	18,000	19,000
POLYETHYLENE												
POLYSTYRENE												
STYRENE-BUTADIENE COPOLYMER												
STYRENE-RUBBER BLENDS												
POLYMETHYL METHACRYLATE												
POLYVINYL CHLORIDE												
VINYL CHLOR-ACETATE												
POLYVINYL BUTYRAL												
SARAN												
POLYTETRAFLUOROETHYLENE												
SILICONE												
NYLON												
ALKYD												
CELLULOSE NITRATE												
CELLULOSE ACETATE												
CELLULOSE ACETATE BUTYRATE												
ETHYL CELLULOSE												
UNSATURATED POLYESTER												
UREA RESIN												
MELAMINE RESIN												
PHENOLIC RESIN												
EPOXY RESIN												

SPECIFIC GRAVITY	0	0.2	0.4	0.6	0.8	1.0	1.2	1.4	1.6	1.8	2.0	2.2
POLYETHYLENE												
POLYSTYRENE												
STYRENE-BUTADIENE COPOLYMER												
STYRENE-RUBBER BLENDS												
POLYMETHYL METHACRYLATE												
POLYVINYL CHLORIDE												
VINYL CHLOR-ACETATE												
POLYVINYL BUTYRAL												
SARAN												
POLYTETRAFLUOROETHYLENE												
SILICONE												
NYLON												
ALKYD												
CELLULOSE NITRATE												
CELLULOSE ACETATE												
CELLULOSE ACETATE BUTYRATE												
ETHYL CELLULOSE												
UNSATURATED POLYESTER												
UREA RESIN												
MELAMINE RESIN												
PHENOLIC RESIN												
EPOXY RESIN												

Figure 4-1. Physical properties of typical uncompounded plastic material.

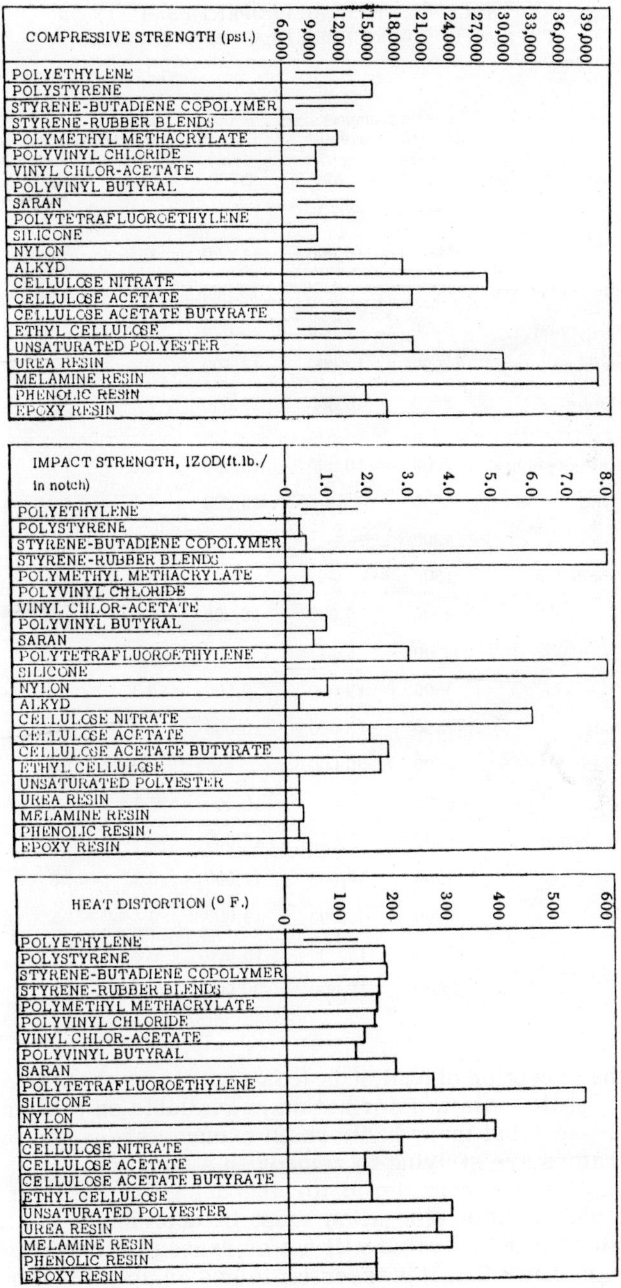

COMPRESSIVE STRENGTH (psi.)

Scale: 6,000 9,000 12,000 15,000 18,000 21,000 24,000 27,000 30,000 33,000 36,000 39,000

POLYETHYLENE
POLYSTYRENE
STYRENE-BUTADIENE COPOLYMER
STYRENE-RUBBER BLENDS
POLYMETHYL METHACRYLATE
POLYVINYL CHLORIDE
VINYL CHLOR-ACETATE
POLYVINYL BUTYRAL
SARAN
POLYTETRAFLUOROETHYLENE
SILICONE
NYLON
ALKYD
CELLULOSE NITRATE
CELLULOSE ACETATE
CELLULOSE ACETATE BUTYRATE
ETHYL CELLULOSE
UNSATURATED POLYESTER
UREA RESIN
MELAMINE RESIN
PHENOLIC RESIN
EPOXY RESIN

IMPACT STRENGTH, IZOD (ft.lb./ in notch)

Scale: 0 1.0 2.0 3.0 4.0 5.0 6.0 7.0 8.0

POLYETHYLENE
POLYSTYRENE
STYRENE-BUTADIENE COPOLYMER
STYRENE-RUBBER BLENDS
POLYMETHYL METHACRYLATE
POLYVINYL CHLORIDE
VINYL CHLOR-ACETATE
POLYVINYL BUTYRAL
SARAN
POLYTETRAFLUOROETHYLENE
SILICONE
NYLON
ALKYD
CELLULOSE NITRATE
CELLULOSE ACETATE
CELLULOSE ACETATE BUTYRATE
ETHYL CELLULOSE
UNSATURATED POLYESTER
UREA RESIN
MELAMINE RESIN
PHENOLIC RESIN
EPOXY RESIN

HEAT DISTORTION ($^{\circ}$F.)

Scale: 0 100 200 300 400 500 600

POLYETHYLENE
POLYSTYRENE
STYRENE-BUTADIENE COPOLYMER
STYRENE-RUBBER BLENDS
POLYMETHYL METHACRYLATE
POLYVINYL CHLORIDE
VINYL CHLOR-ACETATE
POLYVINYL BUTYRAL
SARAN
POLYTETRAFLUOROETHYLENE
SILICONE
NYLON
ALKYD
CELLULOSE NITRATE
CELLULOSE ACETATE
CELLULOSE ACETATE BUTYRATE
ETHYL CELLULOSE
UNSATURATED POLYESTER
UREA RESIN
MELAMINE RESIN
PHENOLIC RESIN
EPOXY RESIN

Figure 4-1. (Continued).

TABLE 4-1. PHYSICAL PROPERTIES OF
TYPICAL UNCOMPOUNDED PLASTIC MATERIALS

ASTM Method	Tensile Strength (psi) D638	Compressive Strength (psi) D695	Flexural Strength (psi) D790	Impact Strength Izod (ft lbs/in. notch) D256	Specific Gravity D792	Heat Distortion (264 psi)(°F) D648
Polyethylene	1300	–	–	–	0.9	–
Polystyrene	7000	16,000,	11,000	0.35	1.05	185
Styrene butadiene copolymer	8000	–	15,000	0.5	1.05	190
Styrene-rubber blends	5000	7,000	9,000	8	1.05	175
Polymethyl methacrylate	7000	12,000	13,000	0.5	1.2	170
Polyvinyl chloride	8000	10,000	13,000	0.7	1.4	165
Vinyl chloride – vinyl acetate copolymer	7000	10,000	13,000	0.6	1.4	145
Polyvinyl butyral	6000	–	10,000	1.0	1.1	125
Saran	4000	–	–	0.7	1.7	200
Polytetrafluoroethylene	1800	–	–	3.0	2.2	270
Silicone	4000	9,000	8,000	8	1.7	550
Nylon	11,000	–	–	1.0	1.14	360
Alkyd	3500	19,000	9,000	0.3	2.2	375
Cellulose nitrate	7500	28,000	10,000	6.0	1.38	210
Cellulose acetate	6000	20,000	–	2.0	1.3	145
Ethyl cellulose	6000	–	10,000	2.3	1.14	152
Unsaturated polyester	6000	20,000	12,000	0.3	1.3	300
Urea resin	7500	30,000	14,000	0.3	1.5	275
Melamine resin	9000	40,000	13,000	0.4	1.5	298
Phenolic resin	7500	15,000	15,000	0.3	1.3	160
Epoxy resin	12,000	17,000	20,000	0.5	1.2	160

but, with the exception of lead, it is less significant at ordinary temperatures. Little definite information is available on this important factor at present, but many basic resin manufacturers and progressive fabricators are striving to remedy this situation.

When plastics are considered for the design of structures, the maximum permissible elongation must be determined and it must be ascertained that this value will not be exceeded in service. Experience has shown that it is essential to design above the maximum stress at which no additional elongation will occur after three or four weeks under anticipated service conditions.

Deformation under load (creep or cold flow) is less for filled than unfilled plastics. It is also less for thermosetting than for thermoplastics and is least for reinforced thermosetting plastics.

A review of the data in Table 4-1 will show that the heat distortion temperature of unfilled, uncompounded plastic varies from 125 to 550°F. Most of the heat distortion points are below 200°F. Fortunately, most structures operate at temperatures below the lowest heat distortion point listed. It is also of interest to note that the temperature coefficients of plastic materials are negative. Thus, the strength increases as the temperature decreases and vice versa.

In addition to knowing the maximum anticipated working stress, information on "stress concentration" must also be available. Whenever possible the design engineer must attempt to eliminate stress concentration by: (1) avoiding sharp inside corners, (2) minimizing the occurrence of abrupt changes in thickness, (3) keeping holes to a minimum and locating them properly, and (4) avoiding unnecessary notches. Actually, all four precautions are associated with the same phenomenon notch sensitivity. This property is most important in unfilled thermoplastics. It is almost negligible with most reinforced thermosetting plastics.

Notch sensitivity is defined as the tendency for a product to be weakened unduly as a result of surface or edge indentations. The reduction in tear resistance of plastic films or paper which occurs when the edge is cut is a practical illustration of this phenomenon.

Actually, glass and ceramic materials are more notch sensitive than plastics. The glass blower takes advantage of this property when cutting glass rod or tubing. He simply makes an indentation with a file and then readily breaks the glass. Obviously, it would be foolhardy to design glass columns or pipelines with avoidable notches or other types of stress concentration. Though plastics are somewhat less notch sensitive, the same general precautions must be listed as with glass, otherwise extremely large factors of safety must be used.

Many other physical properties, such as impact resistance, tensile strength, modulus of elasticity and deformation under load are correlated with creep, and the effect of temperature on these properties must always be taken into consideration. With the exception of polytetrafluoroethylene and silicones, few plastics can be used continuously at temperatures above 350°F. Such properties as coefficient of expansion, thermal conductivity, dielectric strength and weathering properties are characteristic for specific plastics. Plastics are not affected as adversely as metals at low temperatures and are superior as heat and electrical insulators.

Additional information on this subject can be obtained by referring to the references at the end of this chapter. However, there is still much to be learned, and most available data are inadequate. It is hoped that this brief discussion will help the reader to understand some of the physical limitations of plastics. Some pertinent information on chemical structure can be obtained from the following chapter.

Suggested References

"Fundamentals of Plastics," H. M. Richardson and J. W. Wilson, McGraw-Hill Publishing Co., New York, 1946.

"Technical Data on Plastics," Plastic Materials Manufacturers Association, Washington, D. C., 1954.

"Effect of Environmental Conditions on Mechanical Properties of Organic Plastics," T. S. Carswell and H. K. Nason, Modern Plastics, 21, No. 10, 121 (1944).

"Mechanical Properties of Plastics at Normal and Sub-Normal Temperatures," T. P. Obery, T. R. Schwartz and D. A. Shim, Modern Plastics, 20, No. 8, 87 (1943).

"Plastics in Structural Design," V. E. Meharg and L. E. Welch, Modern Plastics, 22, No. 1, 117 (1944).

"Properties and Permanence of Plastic Bearing Materials," L. M. Tichvinsky, Modern Plastics, 17, No. 9, 54 (1940).

"The Behavior of Plastics Under Repeated Stress," B. J. Lazan and A. Yorgiades, Symposium on Plastics, ASTM, 66 (1944).

"Structural Plastics," H. C. Engel, C. B. Hemming and H. R. Merriman, McGraw-Hill Publishing Co., New York, 1950.

"Cold Flow of Thermoplastic Materials," C. H. Penning and L. W. A. Meyer, Modern Plastics, 17, No. 3, 90 (1939).

"Transition Temperature and Cubical Expansion of Plastic Materials," F. E. Wiley, Ind. Eng. Chem., 34, 1052 (1942).

"Engineering Properties of Plastics," F. B. Fuller, Modern Plastics, 20, No. 10, 95 (1943).

"Creep and Cold Flow of Plastics," J. Delmonte and W. Dewar, Modern Plastics, 19, No. 2, 73 (1941).

"Long Time Tension and Creep Tests of Plastics," C. E. Staff, H. M. Quackenbos, Jr., and J. M. Hill, Modern Plastics, 27, No. 6, 93 (1950).

"Creep and Time—Fracture Strength of Plastics Under Tensile Stresses," B. Chasman, Modern Plastics, 21, 145 (1944).

"The Mechanical Properties of Polyethylene," R. H. Carey, SPE Journal, 10, No. 3, 16 (1954).

5. RELATION OF CHEMICAL RESISTANCE TO MOLECULAR STRUCTURE

Practical tests are required to ascertain the chemical resistance of applied plastics but considerable knowledge of the chemical resistance of the base plastic may be determined from an examination of the chemical structure. In general, corrosives and plastics may be divided on the basis of polarity into polar and nonpolar materials.

Like materials attract; unlike materials repel. This is a general rule which may be used as a guide to predict the effect of specific corrosives on plastics. Obviously, however, a knowledge of the nature of both the chemical environment and the plastic structure is required in order to apply this rule.

Plastics having polar groups, such as hydroxyl (OH), carboxyl (COOH) and methoxyl (OCH$_3$) are usually swollen or even dissolved by polar liquids such as water and ethyl alcohol. In contrast, polar plastics are resistant to nonpolar organic solvents such as gasoline, benzene or carbon tetrachloride.

As might be assumed from the above, plastics having a large number of nonpolar groups such as hydrogen (H), methyl (CH$_3$) and phenyl (C$_6$H$_5$), attached to the backbone of the plastic molecule are resistant to polar solvents such as water and ethyl alcohol but are usually swollen or dissolved by nonpolar solvents such as gasoline, benzene or carbon tetrachloride.

Acids, alkalies and salts are polar, whereas most common solvents, except water, alcohol, glycols and glycerol, are nonpolar. In general, plastics used for corrosion-resistant applications contain a plurality of nonpolar groups.

Gelatin, casein, starch, methyl cellulose, carboxy methyl cellulose, hydroxyethyl cellulose, polyethylene glycols and polyvinyl alcohol are all high molecular weight plastics but are seldom considered for corrosion-resistant applications. As shown by the structural formulas for chain segments in Table 5-1, these materials contain a large number of polar groups. Structural formulas for other plastics are shown to illustrate the effect of specific reoccurring groups. An explanation of specific structural formulas, however, is beyond the scope of this discussion.

In contrast to the more polar polymers, polyethylene, polyisobutylene, asphalt, coal-tar pitch, coumarone-indene resins, polystyrene, polymers or copolymers of vinyl chloride or vinylidene chloride, polychlorotrifluoroethylene, polytetrafluoroethylene, nat-

TABLE 5-1. MOLECULAR STRUCTURE AND CHEMICAL RESISTANCE OF PLASTICS

PRODUCT	FORMULA	RESISTANCE					
		Water	Nonpolar Organic Solvents	Salts	Alkalies	Non-Oxidizing Acids	Oxidizing Acids
Thermoplastics:							
Plasticized sulfur	S	+	–	+	–	+	–
Polyethylene		+	–	+	+	+	+
Polyethylene glycol		–	+	–	–	–	–
Polyisobutylene		+	–	+	+	+	+
Asphalt	Polycyclohydrocarbons	+	–	+	±!	+	–
Coal-tar pitch	Aromatic hydrocarbons	+	–	+	+	+	–
Coumarone-indene resins		+	–	+	+	+	–
Polystyrene		+	–	+	+	+	–
Styrene butadiene copolymer		+	–	+	+	+	–

Polymer						
−	−	−	−	+	+I	−
+	−	+I	+	+	+	−
−	−	−	+	+	+	−
+	+I	+	+	+	+	+
−	+	+I	+I	+I	+I	−
+	−	+	+	+	+	+I

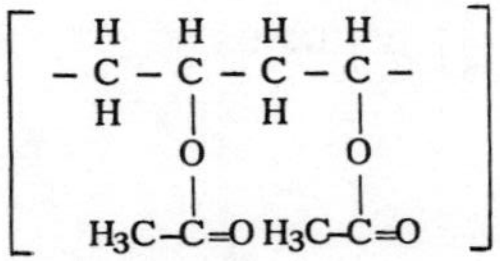

+ essentially no effect at temperatures below 100°F
± some effect
− attacked

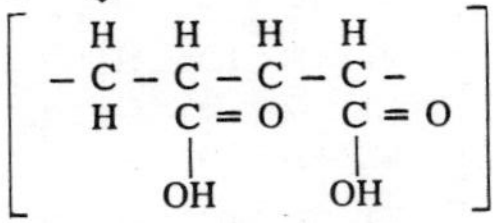

Styrene acrylonitrile copolymer

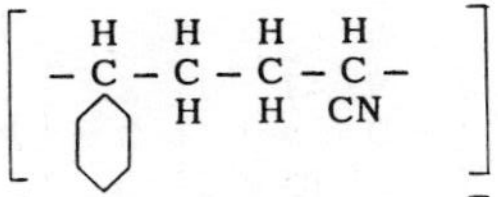

$$\left[-\overset{\underset{|}{H}}{C} - \overset{\underset{|}{H}}{C} - \overset{\underset{|}{H}}{C} - \overset{\underset{|}{H}}{C} - \right]$$
H H H H
⬡ H CN

Polyacrylic acid

$$\left[-\overset{\underset{|}{H}}{C} - \overset{\underset{|}{H}}{C} - \overset{\underset{|}{H}}{C} - \overset{\underset{|}{H}}{C} - \right]$$
H C=O H C=O
   OH   OH

Polymethyl acrylate

OCH₃

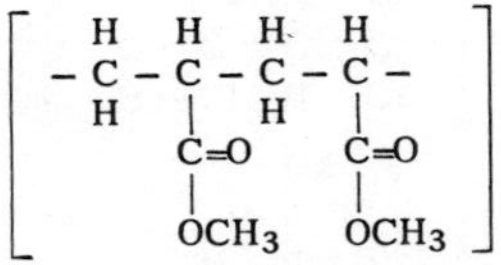

Polymethyl methacrylate

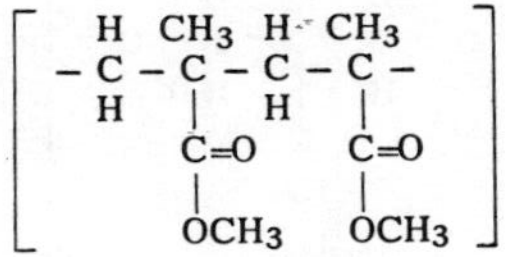

CH₃   CH₃
OCH₃   OCH₃

Polyvinyl chloride

H Cl H Cl
H H   H H

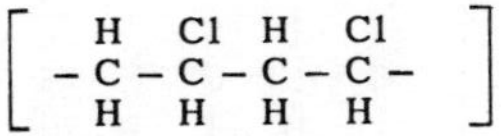

Vinyl chloride – vinyl acetate copolymer

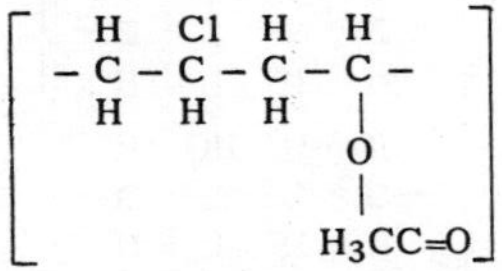

Cl H
H   H   O H₃CC=O

Polyvinyl acetate

H₃C—C=O H₃C—C=O

TABLE 5-1 (Continued).

PRODUCT	FORMULA	Water	Nonpolar Organic Solvents	Salts	Alkalies	Non-Oxidizing Acids	Oxidizing Acids
				RESISTANCE			
Polyvinyl alcohol	$\begin{array}{cccc} H & H & H & H \\ -C{-}C{-}C{-}C{-} \\ H & OH & H & OH \end{array}$	–	+	–	–	–	–
Polyvinyl butyral	$\begin{array}{cccc} H & H & H & H \\ -C{-}C{-}C{-}C{-} \\ H & H & | & H \\ & & O{-}CH{-}O \\ & & | \\ & & C_3H_7 \end{array}$	+	–	+	+	+	+
Chlorinated Polyether	$\begin{array}{c} Cl \\ | \\ H\ C\ H \\ |\ \ |\ \ | \\ -O{-}C{-}C{-}C{-}O{-} \\ |\ \ |\ \ | \\ H\ C\ H \\ | \\ Cl \end{array}$	+	+	+	+	+	+
Polyvinylidene chloride	$\begin{array}{cccc} H & Cl & H & Cl \\ -C{-}C{-}C{-}C{-} \\ H & Cl & H & Cl \end{array}$	+	±	+	+	+	+
Vinylidene chloride – acrylonitrile copolymer	$\begin{array}{cccc} H & Cl & H & CN \\ -C{-}C{-}C{-}C{-} \\ H & Cl & H & H \end{array}$	+	±	+	–	+	+
Polychlorotrifluoroethylene	$\begin{array}{cccc} Cl & F & Cl & F \\ -C{-}C{-}C{-}C{-} \\ F & F & F & F \end{array}$	+	+	+	+	+	+

Polytetrafluoroethylene

$$\left[\begin{array}{cccc} F & F & F & F \\ -C & -C & -C & -C- \\ F & F & F & F \end{array}\right]$$

Silicone

$$\left[\begin{array}{c} CH_3 \\ -Si-O- \\ CH_3 \end{array}\right]$$

Nylon

$$\left[\begin{array}{c} H \quad\quad H \quad O \quad\quad\quad O \quad H \\ -N-(CH_2)_6 \; N-C(CH_2)_4 \; C-N(CH_2)_6 \; N- \end{array}\right]$$

Polyurethanes

$$\left[\begin{array}{c} H \quad O \quad\quad\quad\quad O \\ -N-C-O-(CH_2)_6-O-C- \end{array}\right]$$

Saturated polyester

$$\left[\begin{array}{c} O \quad\quad\quad\quad\quad O \\ -(CH_2)_9-CO-(CH_2)_9-C-O-(CH_2)_9-C-O- \end{array}\right]$$

Natural and synthetic Rubbers and Derivatives:

Natural rubber

$$\left[\begin{array}{c} H \quad CH_3 \; H \quad\quad H \quad CH_3 \; H \quad H \\ -C-C=C-C-C-C=C-C- \\ H \quad\quad\quad\quad H \quad H \quad\quad\quad\quad H \end{array}\right]$$

Isomerized rubber (Thermoprene)

$$\left[\begin{array}{c} CH_3 \\ C-CH_2 \quad\diagdown \; CH_3 \\ -C \quad\quad C-C \quad C- \\ \diagup \quad\quad\quad\quad | \quad | \\ H \quad\quad\quad\quad H \quad H \end{array}\right]$$

Butyl rubber

$$\left[\begin{array}{c} H \quad CH_3 \; H \quad CH_3 \; H \quad H \\ -C-C-C-C-C=C-C- \\ H \quad CH_3 \; H \quad\quad\quad\quad CH_3 \; H \end{array}\right]$$

+ essentially no effect at temperatures below 100°F
± some effect
− attacked

TABLE 5-1 (Continued).

PRODUCT	FORMULA	RESISTANCE					
		Water	Nonpolar Organic Solvents	Salts	Alkalies	Non-Oxidizing Acids	Oxidizing Acids
Chlorosulfonated polyethylene		+	−	+	+	+	+
Rubber hydrochloride		+	−	+	+	+	−
Chlorinated rubber		+	−	+	+	+	−
Styrene rubber		+	−	+	+	+	−
Acrylonitrile rubber		+	±	+	−	+	−
Neoprene		+	−	+	+	+	−
Polysulfide rubber		+	±	+	±	+	−

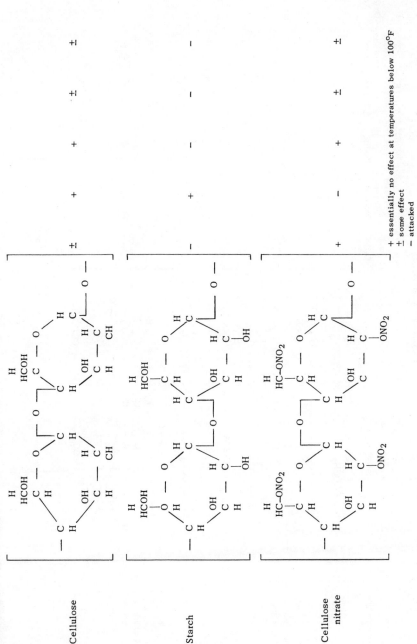

TABLE 5-1 (Continued).

PRODUCT	FORMULA	Water	Nonpolar Organic Solvents	RESISTANCE Salts	RESISTANCE Alkalies	Non-Oxidizing Acids	Oxidizing Acids
Cellulose acetate		+	–	+	–	+–	–
Cellulose acetate butyrate		+	–	+	–	+–	–

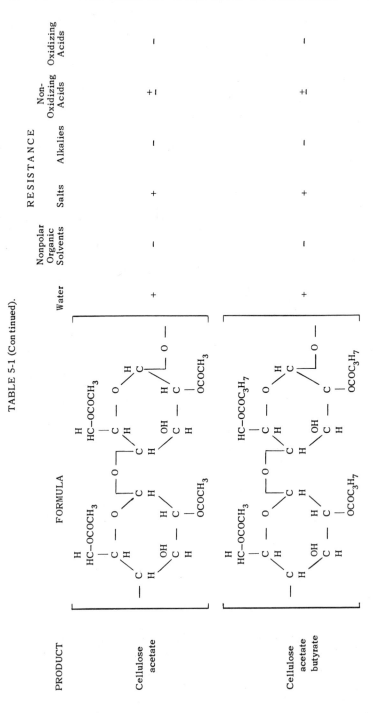

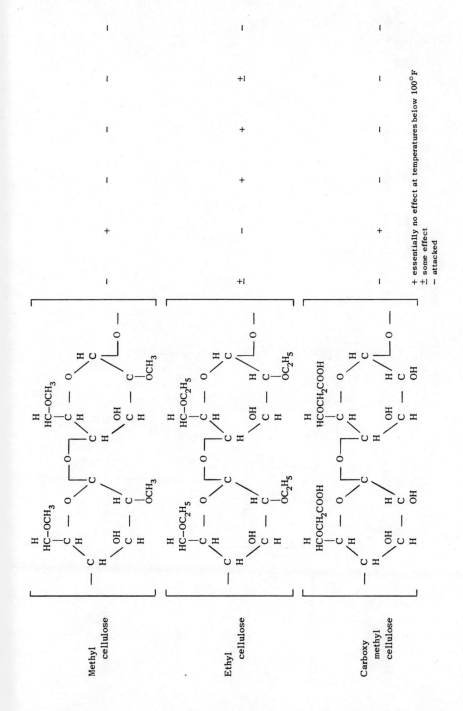

+ essentially no effect at temperatures below 100°F
± some effect
– attacked

TABLE 5-1 (Continued).

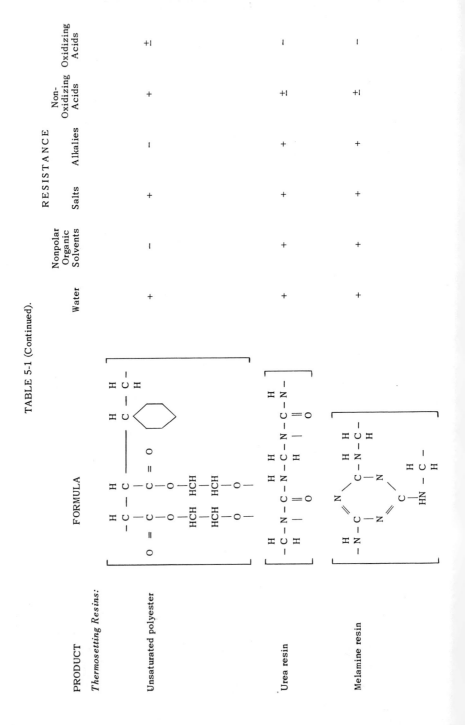

PRODUCT	FORMULA	Water	Nonpolar Organic Solvents	RESISTANCE Salts	Alkalies	Non-Oxidizing Acids	Oxidizing Acids
Thermosetting Resins:							
Unsaturated polyester		+	−	+	−	+	±
Urea resin		+	+	+	+	±	−
Melamine resin		+	+	+	+	±	−

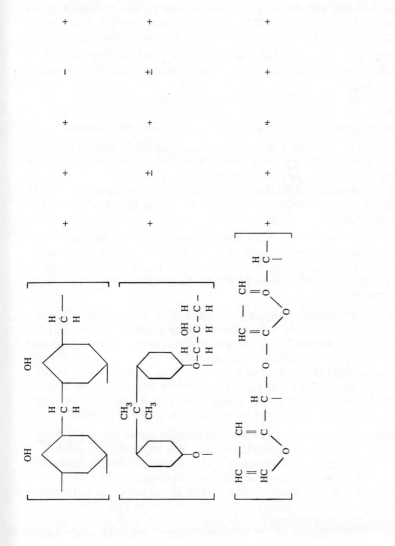

Phenolic resin

Epoxy resin

Furan resin

+ essentially no effect at temperatures below 100°F
± some effect
− attacked

ural rubber, butyl rubber, neoprene, phenolic resins and furan resins are generally resistant to non-oxidizing acids, salts and alkalies but are less resistant to organic solvents. As might be concluded by an examination of their chemical formulas, nylon, saturated polyesters, cellulose acetate and ethyl cellulose occupy an intermediate position. They are less resistant to corrosive chemicals but are more resistant to solvents due to their somewhat polar nature.

In addition to polarity, the resistance of reactive groups to specific chemicals must also be considered. Water, alcohol, benzene and other organic solvents may dissolve a plastic but in general neither these nor neutral salts react chemically with the plastic molecule. However, more active chemicals, such as sodium hydroxide, hydrochloric acid and nitric acid may attack specific groups.

For example, alkaline materials such as aqueous sodium hydroxide may saponify ester groups present in cellulose acetate, cellulose acetatebutyrate, oil-base paints, polyvinyl acetate, polymethyl acrylate and polyesters. Alkalies may also hydrolyze cyano groups in polymers of acrylonitrile and react with acidic hydroxyl groups in phenolic resins.

Non-oxidizing acids such as hydrochloric and phosphoric acids may hydrolyze these materials in much the same manner. In addition, hydrochloric acid may react with unsaturated plastics such as natural rubber to form products whose properties will differ from the original material.

Oxidizing chemicals such as concentrated sulfuric acid, chromic acid and chlorine dioxide may oxidize many groups. These corrosives attack the double bonds in phenolic resins, furan resins and natural rubber. Strong nitric acid and chlorine may actually nitrate or chlorinate polystyrene, coumarone-indene resins and phenolic resins. Concentrations and temperatures of the chemicals, of course, should be considered, but these factors are secondary in importance to the ability of the corrosives to react with specific groups.

In addition to considering the chemical make-up of the plastic material itself, it is also essential to know the chemical resistance of all fillers, stabilizers, plasticizers and other additives present. Cellulosics, such as wood flour, and mineral carbonates such as ground limestone, are not recommended as fillers for plastics in corrosion-resistant applications. Silica, glass and asbestos are often used as fillers or reinforcing agents but are not recommended when the product is used in the presence of strong alkalies, hydrofluoric acid or hydrofluosilicic acid.

While a final evaluation of chemical resistance cannot be made until specific materials are tested under actual service conditions, considerable useful information can be secured by determining the resistance of a plastic structure to the following typical chemicals.

Polar:

Water
Salt: 10% sodium chloride
Alkalies: 10% sodium hydroxide
Non-oxidizing acids: 25% sulfuric acid
Oxidizing acids: 50% nitric acid

Nonpolar:

Aliphatic solvent: kerosene
Aromatic solvent: toluene
Vegetable oil: cotton seed oil

THERMOPLASTICS

Plasticized Sulfur

While sulfur is not usually considered as a plastic material, plasticized sulfur meets most of the requirements. It is ductile and can be formed by heat. Commercial products, which have been available for at least twenty-five years, have the chemical resistance of sulfur but are much stronger, more ductile and more useful.

Most commercial sulfur cements contain from 50 to 60 per cent sulfur, the remainder consisting primarily of graded silica or carbon aggregate plus suspending agents and plasticizers. Carbon black is usually added to minimize settling of the filler while the cement is in the molten state.

Plasticizers such as polyolefin sulfides have been used to produce ductility. Since the latter property is based primarily on the plasticizer content, it can be varied by increasing or decreasing the amount of plasticizer.

Since sulfur changes from a rhombic to a monoclinic crystalline form at 96°C (205°F) and these two forms have different specific gravities, sulfur cements must not be used above this critical temperature. Likewise, since sulfur is soluble in many organic solvents and attacked by alkaline solutions, it should not be used in the presence of most solvents nor at a pH greater than 10. It can be oxidized to sulfur dioxide and should not be used in highly oxidizing media. However, plasticized sulfur cements are completely resistant to all non-oxidizing acids and salts.

Polyethylene

Polyethylene is one of the most chemically resistant materials at ordinary temperatures. Its simplicity of manufacture and high chemical resistivity make it one of the most important industrial plastics. In general, polyethylene may be considered as a very high molecular weight paraffin. It has a low water absorption, low specific gravity, good electrical properties and good resistance to most acids, salts and alkalies. It is swollen but not completely dissolved by many organic solvents.

Polymers of ethylene oxide differ from polyethylene primarily because of the presence of ether linkages and terminal hydroxyl groups. These products, sometimes called polyethylene glycols, are actually water-soluble and are not suitable for chemical-resistant construction.

Polyisobutylene

As is evidenced from its formula, polyisobutylene is similar in structure to polyethylene. However, the methyl groups present on the polymer chain produce greater flexibility and decrease the chemical resistance somewhat. It is considerably less resistant to heat and is tackier than polyethylene. Its use in the United States has been principally for adhesives and chewing gum. However, carbon-filled polyisobutylene is used widely in Europe as a tank lining.

Asphalt

Many asphalts are natural occurring materials and have been used for centuries. There is some controversy over definition because of attempts to differentiate between the natural occurring asphalts such as gilsonite, grahamite and glance pitch, and the petroleum asphalts. For simplicity, all asphalts may be defined as colloidal systems consisting of polycyclic compounds and minor amounts of carbon. Many asphalts contain some acidic constituents. They are sometimes attacked by sodium hydroxide but are resistant to most non-oxidizing acids and corrosive salts.

As might be predicted from a consideration of their chemical composition, they are destroyed by concentrated sulfuric acid and dilute nitric acid. Their structure is too complicated to permit accurate representation by simple formulas.

The most widely used asphalts are based on petroleum residues, the specific constitution of which depends upon the source of the crude oil. One of the oldest natural occurring asphalts found at Lake Trinidad contained as much as 40 per cent clay. Other natural occurring asphalts are gilsonite, glance pitch, rafaelite and grahamite.

Elaterite and wurzilite are similar in chemical properties to the other asphalts but are much less soluble in organic solvents. Contrary to general opinion, there is no great difference in the usefulness of comparable by-product and natural asphalts. The physical and chemical constants of any specific asphalt are much more important than data on its origin.

Coal-Tar Pitch

Coal-tar pitch is a product of indefinite composition whose chemical and physical properties are dependent to a large extent upon the distillation techniques used in its production. Since it is essentially an aromatic hydrocarbon in nature, its chemical constitution differs from asphalt which is composed primarily of cycloparaffins. However, the physical properties of the two materials are somewhat similar. Coal-tar pitch is slightly soluble in aromatic solvents and less heat stable than asphalt.

Coumarone-Indene Resins

Coumarone and indene which are present in coal-tar naphthas can be polymerized to solid materials in the presence of sulfuric acid. The structural formulas for polycoumarone and polyindene are not given separately in Table 5-1 since most commercial products are copolymers and mixtures of both materials.

Coumarone-indene resins are softened readily by heat and are soluble in many different organic solvents. They are widely used in the compounding of rubber and in the manufacture of varnishes, floor tile and printing inks. Coumarone-indene resins are resistant to most non-oxidizing acids, salts and alkalies but are not used extensively in chemical-resistant construction. These and related products are sometimes called mineral rubbers.

Polystyrene

As might be concluded from its structure, polystyrene is soluble in most nonpolar organic solvents such as benzene and ethylene dichloride. It is completely resistant to non-oxidizing acids, salts and alkalies but is attacked by chlorine, chlorine dioxide, chromic acid, nitric acid and concentrated sulfuric acid. It has a low specific gravity, low water absorption and excellent dielectric properties. It is somewhat brittle and this shortcoming limits its usefulness in chemical-resistant construction. As will be evident from subsequent discussion, this deficiency has been overcome by copolymerization and compounding with synthetic rubbers.

Styrene Copolymers

The most widely used styrene copolymers are those produced from styrene and small amounts of butadiene or acrylonitrile. As might be concluded from its structural formula, the chemical resistance of the butadiene copolymer is similar to that of polystyrene. The butadiene units promote some flexibility in the molecule. These copolymers are less brittle than polystyrene. Styrene-butadiene copolymers are widely used as aqueous suspensions in water-type paints. Some protective coatings are based on solutions of this copolymer in aromatic solvents.

Copolymers of styrene and acrylonitrile have better impact resistance than polystyrene, although their resistance to acids and alkalies is slightly inferior. Copolymers of styrene and acrylonitrile are sometimes blended with acrylonitrile rubber to improve their impact resistance. The chemical resistant of this blend is essentially the same as the copolymer. This so-called acrylonitrile copolymer blend is extensively used for the production of plastic pipe, sheet and fittings.

Acrylates

The acrylates are usually flexible and are seldom used in chemical-resistant construction. They have good resistance to salts and fair resistance to acids but are readily saponified by alkaline solutions. Polyacrylic and polymethacrylic acids are water-soluble and are not used in chemical-resistant construction.

The methacrylates are more rigid, and presumably because of steric hindrance, are not readily saponified. Methacrylates such as polymethyl methacrylate are available as clear sheets and are used occasionally in chemical-resistant construction when transparency is required. Solutions of methacrylates have been used to a limited extent as protective coatings. Clear sheets of polymethyl methacrylate have been solvent or heat-welded to form equipment used in the plating industry.

Polyvinyl Chloride and Copolymers

Polyvinyl chloride is available commercially both in plasticized and unplasticized forms. The differences between rigid unplasticized polyvinyl chloride and ordinary polyvinyl chloride before plasticization are primarily in molecular weight and molecular weight distribution. The two products have essentially the same structural formula and chemical resistance. However, the chemical resistance of polyvinyl chloride is usually reduced by the addition of plasticizers.

Most commercial formulations for chemical-resistant rigid unplasticized polyvinyl chloride and plasticized polyvinyl chloride are resistant to attack by non-oxidizing acids, salts and alkalies. The main difference between the two types of products is the varying degree of resistance to temperature, oxidizing materials and hot alkalies.

In addition to plasticization, considerable improvement in processing characteristics has also been attained by copolymerizing vinyl chloride with other monomers. The most widely used material of this type is produced by the copolymerization of vinyl chloride with minor amounts of vinyl acetate. While the presence of the acetate group lowers the chemical resistance of the product, copolymers produced from small amounts of vinyl acetate have sufficient chemical resistance to justify their use in many industrial applications.

Unplasticized rigid polyvinyl chloride is classified as Type I normal impact and optimum chemical resistant and Type II optimum impact and normal chemical resistant. These are used primarily for extruded pipe, molded parts, and heat-welded thermoplastic structures.

Plasticized polyvinyl chloride is used for mechanical goods and sheet linings. It is too insoluble to be used as a coating without the adaptation of special techniques, such as organosols or plastisols. The vinyl chloride-vinyl acetate copolymer is used primarily in the form of solutions in organic solvents. Most vinyl coatings are based on this copolymer.

Chlorinated Polyethers

One of the newest plastics available as a material for chemical construction is a chlorinated polyether derived from pentaerythritol. This product, which is crystalline in nature, has outstanding resistance to heat and chemicals. Chlorinated polyethers may be readily extruded, calendered and molded. They have a specific gravity of 1.4 and tensile strengths above 3,000 psi, at the boiling point of water.

This type of plastic has a heat distortion point of 185°F and excellent electrical properties. It may be predicted that the product will find considerable use for chemical-resistant applications at temperatures in the range of 150 to 260°F.

Polyvinyl Acetals

Since it is hydrolyzed quite readily by acids and alkalies and has high moisture absorption, polyvinyl acetate is not used to any great extent in corrosion-resistant construction. Mixtures of aqueous dispersions of polyvinyl acetate and hydraulic cements have been proposed as monolithic floor coatings. Decorative coatings are also produced by compounding aqueous dispersions of this polymer.

Saponification of polyvinyl acetate produces polyvinyl alcohol which is water-soluble. This product is used occasionally for solvent-resistant tubing and gaskets. The water resistance of these products is usually improved through a surface reaction with formaldehyde.

The reaction of polyvinyl alcohol with higher molecular weight aldehydes such as butyraldehyde yields polymeric acetals such as polyvinyl butyral which are not soluble in water and have fair chemical resistance. Polyvinyl butyral is the plastic component of standard wash primer systems as well as the interlayer for automobile windshield safety glass.

Vinylidene Chloride Polymers

Vinylidene chloride and its copolymers with vinyl chloride and acrylonitrile are available under the generic name of saran. As indicated by its structural formula, it resembles vinyl chloride but has twice as many chlorine atoms per molecule. Polymers of vinylidene chloride and many of its copolymers are resistant to most nonoxidizing acids and salts.

Copolymers of vinylidene chloride and acrylonitrile form flexible sheets when plasticized and filled with carbon. This product is less chemically resistant than the hard polymers and is not recommended for use with warm alkaline or hot acid solutions. Plasticized copolymers of vinylidene chloride are also used for the production of pipes, tubing, and valves. Saran has also been used to a small extent in the form of aqueous dispersions and solutions for protective coatings.

Polyfluorocarbons

Polymonochlorotrifluoroethylene and polytetrafluoroethylene are more expensive than polyvinyl chloride but have superior resistance to oxidizing agents, solvents and high temperature. Polytetrafluoroethylene is somewhat more chemically resistant than polymonochlorotrifluoroethylene but both are used widely as gaskets, diaphragms, valve seats and mechanical goods where outstanding chemical resistance is required.

Both products have been used successfully at temperatures as high as 400°F, even in the presence of concentrated nitric acid. Polytetrafluoroethylene is resistant to almost all chemicals except molten alkali metals and hot flourine. These products, sometimes called polyfluorocarbons, are available as molded or extruded parts and as aqueous dispersions. Aqueous dispersions have been applied to various metal surfaces with subsequent baking to fuse the resin particles and form smooth resistant coatings. Compositions based on polyfluorocarbons are also used as chemical resistant non-galling pipe dopes for plastic and metal alloy pipe.

Silicones

The silicone plastics differ from all other commercially available plastics in that they contain silicon rather than carbon atoms in the basic molecular chain. As might be expected, such plastics have outstanding heat resistance. Some silicones have been reported to have been used continuously at temperatures in excess of 400°F. Many commercial silicone products have poor resistance to alkalies and solvents but have fair resistance to non-oxidizing acids. Their principal use in chemical-resistant construction is as gasket materials, water repellents, and high temperature resistant coatings.

Polyamides

Nylon is insoluble in most organic solvents except hot formic and acetic acids and phenol. It is resistant to corrosive salts but is hydrolyzed by hot acids and alkalies. Its use as an oriented fiber is well known and beyond the scope of this book. Polyamides have not been used to any great extent as corrosion-resistant materials in the chemical industry.

Polyurethanes

Polyurethanes can be obtained by the reaction of polyisocyanates and polyhydric alcohols. The basic urethane reaction has been known for over fifty years but the industrial application of polymers of this type is a fairly recent development.

Polyurethane fibers, waterproofing agents, coatings and adhesives have been widely used in Germany for over fifteen years. Adaptations of some of this technology have been made in the United States in recent years. The products have good resistance to water and petroleum solvents but are not as suitable as the more chemical resistant plastics for continuous contact with corrosives. They have been used as adhesives, abrasion-resistant rubbers, coatings and cellular products. These products although too new to merit detailed discussion, are described briefly in subsequent chapters.

ELASTOMERS AND DERIVATIVES

Natural Rubber

As one might expect from a study of its structural formula, natural rubber is not attacked by alkalies, corrosive salts or most non-oxidizing acids. However, hydrochloric acid adds to the double bond present in the molecular structure to form rubber hydrochloride.

Natural rubber is not satisfactory for use in the presence of non-polar solvents such as vegetable and mineral oils, gasoline, benzene and carbontetrachloride. It is not recommended for exposure to oxidizing substances such as nitric acid, concentrated sulfuric acid, chromic acid, sodium hypochlorite and chlorine dioxide.

Unvulcanized rubber flows excessively at ordinary temperatures but vulcanized soft rubber may be used satisfactorily at temperatures up to 150°F. Hard rubber or ebonite produced by the reaction of relatively large amounts of sulfur with natural rubber contains fewer oxidizable double bonds. It is more resistant to heat and chemicals.

Natural rubber and other elastomers are not true plastics. However, they are high molecular weight polymers and are used widely as materials of construction. Hard rubber and many rubber derivatives are true plastics.

The inherent chemical resistance of vulcanized natural rubber has been known for many years. However, natural rubber was not used to any great extent for chemical-resistant construction prior to 1925 since no satisfactory method of bonding rubber to steel was known before that time. The first practical adhesive for this purpose was prepared by Fisher by heating natural rubber in the presence of organic sulfonic acids. The resulting products, sometimes called polycyclo rubbers, are plastics and contain few unsaturated groups.

As indicated by a typical structural formula, chemical properties of this type product are similar to natural rubber. However, they are not vulcanizable and tend to cold flow. They do not possess rubbery properties and are more like shellac than natural rubber.

Rubber has been used as a latex, mixtures of rubber latex and hydraulic cement, as a solution in organic solvents and as soft and hard vulcanized rubber. The last two constitute the major applications of natural rubber in chemical process equipment. Vulcanized soft rubber is utilized as a tank lining, gasket, hose, tubing and to form expansion joints in brick sheathings.

Butyl Rubber

One of the principal deficiencies of polyisobutylene is its lack of resistance to heat. This deficiency has been overcome in part by copolymerizing isobutylene with small amounts of isoprene to produce butyl rubber. When considering the structural formula for butyl rubber, it should be remembered that the vulcanizable isoprene groups in the molecule constitute only 1 or 2 per cent of the entire structure, the remainder being polyisobutylene groups. With the exception of its greater resistance to flow, vulcanized butyl rubber has essentially the same chemical resistance as polyisobutylene.

Chlorosulfonated Polyethylene

As indicated by its formula, chlorosulfonated polyethylene is obtained by reacting polyethylene with chlorine and sulfur dioxide. This derivative resembles polyethylene somewhat but is considerably more polar. Thus, it will adhere more readily to metallic surfaces and has superior heat resistance.

Because of the presence of the active groups, the product can be heat cured with basic compounds such as litharge to produce a rubber-like material that is resistant to most solvents, salts, acids, alkalies and oxidizing agents at temperatures up to $212°F$. This product is new and little background data based on experience are available. However, indications are that chlorosulfonated polyethylene will have specialized use in the construction field.

Rubber Hydrochloride

Rubber hydrochloride may be represented best by the structural formula shown in Table 5-1. It is seldom used as a chemical-resistant material except inadvertently in rubber-lined equipment exposed to hydrochloric acid. As might be expected from its formula, rubber hydrochloride is more soluble in organic solvents and is much less elastic than natural rubber. Its principal use is for packaging.

Chlorinated Rubber

Chlorinated rubber is nonelastic and is soluble in a wide variety of organic solvents. As indicated by its structural formula, the resistance of chlorinated rubber to non-oxidizing salts, alkalies and acids is similar to natural rubber. Because it contains fewer double bonds, chlorinated rubber is more resistant to oxidizing agents than natural or synthetic rubber.

The principal use of chlorinated rubber is for the production of protective coatings and adhesives. Attempts to use chlorinated rubber for extruded pipe or molded plastics have not been promising because of its inherent poor heat stability.

Isomerized or cyclized rubber has been used as an adhesive and as a protective coating. It is being replaced somewhat by styrene-butadiene copolymers.

Styrene Rubber

Styrene rubber, sometimes called Buna S or GR-S, is the most widely used synthetic rubber. However, its application in chemical-resistant construction is less than that of natural rubber, primarily because of industry's greater familiarity with the latter.

An examination of its structural formula shows that styrene rubber is similar to natural rubber in its resistance to alkalies, acids, salts and solvents. Its physical properties, however, are somewhat inferior but this deficiency is being overcome through improved manufacturing and compounding techniques.

Acrylonitrile Rubber

Acrylonitrile rubber, sometimes called Buna N or GR-A, is used occasionally in chemical-resistant construction when oil resistance is an essential requirement. It is being used to some extent as a blending agent to increase the impact resistance of polyvinyl chloride and styrene-acrylonitrile copolymers. Since it contains cyano groups, GR-A is less resistant to alkalies than natural and synthetic rubber. It has good resistance to acids, salts and aliphatic hydrocarbon solvents.

Neoprene

As indicated by its structural formula, neoprene or polychloroprene is related chemically to natural rubber. The substitution of chlorine for a methyl group produces superior resistance to vegetable and mineral oils, aging and high temperatures.

Hydrochloric acid and related compounds which react with natural rubber surfaces actually permeate neoprene. Hence, neoprene linings are not recommended for use in the presence of concentrated hydrochloric or hydrofluoric acids. When cured with litharge and similar curing agents, neoprene is resistant to all other non-oxidizing acids, salts and alkalies.

Neoprene is available in the form of tubing, sheet linings, putty-like cements, protective coatings and aqueous dispersions. Sheet neoprene is not as widely used in chemical-resistant construction as natural rubber but is recommended for specialized uses when oil resistance is required. Because neoprene yields solutions with high solids content, it is used as a quality protective coating in the chemical industry. Neoprene coatings can be cured at ordinary temperature to produce elastic films that do not flow even at the temperature of boiling water.

Some types of neoprene are less soluble and more adhesive than the product used for heavy-duty coatings. Solutions of the more adhesive type are often used as maintenance coatings.

Polysulfide Rubber

These products are somewhat rubbery and have excellent resistance to solvents. While somewhat odoriferous, they have good resistance to salts and non-oxidizing acids and fair resistance to alkalies.

Polysulfide rubbers are available as liquids which may be converted to flexible solids at room temperature. These liquid polymers are used as solvent-resistant caulking compositions. A newly developed use for liquid polysulfide rubbers is in combination with epoxy resins in flexible coatings and adhesives. The solid has also been used as a plasticizer for sulfur cements, for solvent-resistant mechanical goods and as a flame-sprayed coating for some marine equipment. Aqueous dispersions have been used to produce solvent-resistant tank linings.

CELLULOSE DERIVATIVES

Cellulose Esters and Ethers

As is apparent from its structural formula, cellulose is a polyglucoside; the dimer, cellobiose, being the simplest unit. Starch is also a polymer of glucose but its simplest dimer unit is maltose, an isomer of cellobiose. Cellulose in its natural form of wood has been used for chemical-resistant construction for many years.

Modern economics have made the use of wood impractical in many applications in the chemical process field. Wood is resistant to most salts and solvents but is swollen by water and slowly attacked by acids and alkalies, the rate of attack being governed to a large extent by the type of wood used.

Cellulose nitrate is resistant to salts and some acids but is attacked by alkalies. Cellulose nitrate is soluble in many solvents and is highly inflammable. It is widely used for rapid drying coatings but does not find much use in corrosion-resistant construction.

Because of its inherent toughness and fair resistance to flame, molded and extruded parts of cellulose acetate have been used industrially but not extensively as chemical-resistant materials.

Since cellulose acetate butyrate and other mixed esters can be more readily plasticized and have better water resistance than cellulose acetate, they have been used in the chemical industry as pipe and tubing where mild service is required. Like cellulose acetate, it is resistant to salt and petroleum solvents but is not recommended for use in acid and alkaline service. Extruded cellulose acetate butyrate pipe has been used quite extensively in the petroleum industry and to some extent for transporting water and gas.

Because of its lack of resistance to water, methyl cellulose is not used in chemical-resistant construction. Most commercial applications are based on its solubility in water.

Ethyl cellulose is more water resistant than methyl cellulose. It is not attacked by corrosive salts and finds some use as a hot-dip coating for temporary protection of metal objects. Carboxymethyl cellulose is too water soluble to merit consideration as a chemical-resistant plastic.

THERMOSETTING PLASTICS

Polyesters

Unsaturated polyester plastics, sometimes called unsaturated styrene alkyds, are now widely used when reinforced with glass fibers. These products have good resistance to non-oxidizing acids and corrosive salts at moderate temperatures but are not suitable for use with alkaline solutions or strong oxidizing agents.

Properly selected polyesters reinforced with chemical grade glass fibers have been suggested for use as pipe, ductwork and small self-supporting tanks. Polyesters differ from most of the plastics discussed previously since they are thermosetting and thus, when cured, cannot be softened by heat and pressure.

Urea and Melamine Resins

Both urea and melamine resins are resistant to heat, some solvents and most salts. They are not used extensively as chemical resistant materials.

Phenolic Resins

Phenolic resins are essentially alkaline or acidic condensation products of phenol and formaldehyde. A dihydric phenol such as resorcinol, or a substituted phenol such as cashew nut oil may be used in place of phenol to form faster setting, more adhesive and more flexible products. Furfural may also be used in place of formaldehyde.

Phenolic resins contain free hydroxyl groups which are attacked by alkalies. They have excellent resistance to salts, many solvents and non-oxidizing acids. They are used as heat-cured coatings, molding powders, casting resins and cements.

Epoxy Resins

Reaction products of bisphenol A and epichlorohydrin called epoxy or ethoxyline resins do not contain free phenolic groups and, hence, have good alkaline resistance at moderate temperatures. They are excellent adhesives and are resistant to salts, some solvents and non-oxidizing acids. Epoxy resins are used as room temperature catalyzed coatings, cements, castings and heat-cured coatings.

Furans

Furfural and furfuryl alcohol can be polymerized by acids to produce infusible products which have excellent resistance to most chemicals. Proprietary cements, pipe and chemical-resistant structures based on filled resins from furfuryl alcohol and furfural have been available commercially for several years.

Unfortunately, these products, as well as those prepared from acetone and furfural, are all grouped under the general term of furans. Thus, in the absence of additional classification data, only the experienced chemist can differentiate between these products. Fortunately, for the corrosion engineer, most furans are resistant to heat, alkalies, salts, solvents and non-oxidizing acids. So-called furan cements are attacked by chlorine, sodium hypochlorite, nitric acid, chromic acid, concentrated sulfuric acid and other oxidizing agents.

Summary

While there is no substitute for past experience and on-stream plant testing programs, an understanding of the molecular structure of plastics should aid immeasurably in the selection of nonmetallic materials of construction. The proper use of basic plastics knowledge should prevent misinterpretation of test results.

If actual tests on a specific product are completely contrary to predictions, application methods and the possible presence of non-resistant fillers, etc., should be investigated. Obviously, the information in this chapter cannot be used intelligently unless the generic nature of the plastic material under consideration is known. Methods for testing plastic materials are discussed in the next chapter.

Suggested References

"Protective and Decorative Coatings," Joseph J. Mattiello, Vol. 1, John Wiley & Sons, Inc., New York, 1941.

"The Chemistry of Synthetic Resins," Carlton Ellis, Reinhold Publishing Corp., New York, 1935.

"Chemistry of Commercial Plastics," R. L. Wakeman, Reinhold Publishing Corp., New York, 1947.

"Handbook of Plastics," H. R. Simonds, D. Van Nostrand Co., Inc., New York, 1943.

"An Introduction to Engineering Plastics," D. W. Brown and W. T. Harris, Murray Hill Book Co., Inc., 1947.

"Modern Plastics Encyclopedia and Engineers Handbook," issued annually by Plastics Catalog Corp.

"Synthetic Resins and Rubbers," P. O. Powers, John Wiley & Sons, Inc., New York, 1943.

"Corrosion Handbook," Uhlig, John Wiley & Sons, Inc., New York, (1948) (supplement 1954).

"Basic Criteria for Evaluating Some Plastic Materials of Construction," Raymond B. Seymour, Corrosion, 10, No. 1, 37-47 (1954).

"Synthetic Resins and Polymers," Raymond B. Seymour in "Organic Finishing Handbook," p. 36, 1954.

"Plastics Meet the Acid Test," Raymond B. Seymour, Modern Plastics, Aug. 1950.

"Plastic Materials of Construction," Raymond B. Seymour, Corrosion, 9, No. 5, 152-9 (1953).

"Industrial Plastics," W. M. Bruner and P. J. Wayne, Chem. Eng., 60, No. 7, 193 (1953).

"Resistance of Plastics to Chemical Reagents," J. Delmonte, Plastics, (Chicago), 3, 36, Nov. 1945.

"Effects of Solvents Upon Organic Plastics," J. Delmonte, Ind. Eng. Chem., 34, 764 (1942).

"Resistance of Plastics to Chemical Reagents," G. M. Kline, R. C. Rinker and H. Meindl, A.S.T.M. Proc., 41, 1246 (1941).

"Vulcanizable Elastomers as Materials of Construction," B. M. G. Zwicker, Symposium on Polymeric Materials of Construction, American Institute of Chemical Engineers, Springfield, Mass., May 18, 1954.

"Thermosetting Resins Reviewed for the Chemical Engineer," R. J. Schatz and S. H. Rider, Symposium on Polymeric Materials of Construction, American Institute of Chemical Engineers, Springfield, Mass., May 18, 1954.

"Vinyl Plastics as Materials of Construction," Raymond B. Seymour, Symposium on Polymeric Materials of Construction, American Institute of Chemical Engineers, Springfield, Mass., May 18, 1954.

"Properties of Polyethylene, Polytetrafluoroethylene, Polymonochlorotrifluoroethylene, Acrylic Resins, and Cellulosics," J. J. Ondrejcin, Symposium on Polymeric Materials of Construction, American Institute of Chemical Engineers, Springfield, Mass., May 18, 1954.

"Plastics," Raymond B. Seymour, Ind. Eng. Chem., Oct. 1954.

"16th Biennial Materials of Construction Report," Chem. Eng., 172-234, Nov. 1954.

6. TESTING OF PLASTICS

No product should be considered as a material of construction in the absence of adequate information on its significant physical properties. As might be anticipated, the lack of adequate information has resulted in innumerable misapplications of plastics as evidenced by premature failures.

Many design engineers are cognizant of the physical data available and the test methods used for metallic materials. Too few are familiar with this type of information in the plastic field. It is the purpose of this chapter to present a listing of standard test methods for the determination of physical, thermal and electrical properties with references to the detailed procedures. A more thorough discussion of chemical resistance studies is included because of the sparseness of the available literature on this subject.

MECHANICAL PROPERTIES

As a result of cooperative work by industry and government scientists, the American Society for Testing Materials (ASTM) has developed standard test methods for plastic materials of construction. The methods are published triennially with annual revisions. As might be expected, ASTM Committees are continually developing new test methods which are required by new applications of old materials or routine applications of newer materials of construction. Both points of view apply in the plastics field since new applications are continually being investigated and new plastics are being introduced at an unprecedented rate.

Many of the tests that are applicable to other materials may be applied with modification to plastics. In other instances, new concepts must be developed. For example, while engineers are conscious of the creep properties of metals at elevated temperatures, they sometimes fail to recognize the importance of this property when designing plastics.

All materials exhibit some degree of creep under load and hence, realistic factors of safety must be used. Creep properties exhibited by some unfilled thermoplastics are comparable to those observed for structural metals at 2000°F. Hence, instantaneous or short term physical tests on such plastics are seldom sufficient. It is recommended that most tests be conducted over a long period of time in order to measure the degree of creep or cold flow.

Tensile Strength, Elongation and Modulus of Elasticity

The measurement of tensile strength and many other mechanical properties of plastics are affected by the rate of testing speed. Obviously, tensile tests for plastics must be made at established standard rates of speed.

In ASTM Test D638, a molded dumbbell-like rigid plastic specimen measuring 8.5 inches in length and having a width of 0.5 inches at its narrowest section is pulled until it breaks. Stress-strain curves are plotted and the modulus of elasticity is determined from straight line sections of the curve. The section beyond the straight line where the strain begins to increase without increasing the load is the yield strength. Obviously, service loads for rigid plastics should be considerably less than the yield strength.

This limitation does not necessarily hold for elastomers which are often usable beyond this point. Different dumbbell-like specimens are used for testing elastomers by ASTM Method D412. Much heavier specimens are employed for testing plastic cements according to ASTM Method C307.

Compressive Strength

Compressive strength tests are essentially the reverse of those previously described for tensile strength. Mostly cylindrical and cubical specimens have been used. The standard compressive strength test methods for rigid plastics and plastic cements are ASTM D695 and C306, respectively.

Flexural Strength

Flexural strength, or the resistance of the plastic to bending, is measured by exerting a force on the center of a span of a test bar when supported near its ends. The standard test method for rigid plastics is D790.

Impact Test

The impact test is one of the most controversial, yet most widely used test for plastic materials. It is extremely useful for laboratory comparison of materials tested under identical conditions. However, comparative impact data between different types of plastics and between plastics and other materials of construction often lead to erroneous conclusions.

Destructive impact tests made under practical service conditions have some commercial value. However, this type of test is costly and somewhat unscientific. Modifications of such tests using a falling ball have shown promise but are possibly too simple to be widely accepted.

In the Charpy Test which is used extensively in Europe, the plastic specimen is mounted as a simple beam and broken by a sharp blow by a pendulum striking the center point between supports. The Izod Test in which the specimen is held at one end only is most widely used in America.

Better reproducibility with impact tests has been obtained using notched specimens. Obviously such tests may supply misinformation when notch sensitive plastics are compared with materials which are not as sensitive to this phenomenon. The most widely used test method for impact resistance is ASTM D256.

Hardness

Hardness is a composite property which may be determined using a Shore Durometer for elastomers or a Rockwell Hardness Tester for rigid plastics and plastic cements. Plastics and plastic cements are tested by ASTM Method D85. Elastomers are tested by ASTM Method D656.

Creep

While creep has been measured by ASTM Method D674, better test methods are now under investigation. Fortunately, its importance on design is now recognized, and it can be predicted that considerable progress will be made in the development of more satisfactory methods for the measurement of this important property.

THERMAL PROPERTIES

Many of the thermal properties of plastics are comparable to those observed for metals and other commonly used materials of construction. Thus, plastics undergo reversible changes with temperature and are deformed under load and with heat. In addition to these well understood phenomena, there are also changes which take place with variations in humidity and others which depend upon the methods of manufacture and fabrication as well as variables in the composition of the plastics used.

Thermal Expansion

The coefficient of linear expansion of most plastics is higher than that of metals. The value for the coefficient of linear expansion for plastics is usually in the order of $1 \times 10^{-4}/°C$. The method used to measure the coefficient of expansion of both plastics and plastic cements is described in ASTM Method D696. The apparatus consists of two quartz tubes with the inner tube being placed between the plastic materials and a dilatometer. The outer tube is immersed in a heated bath. Thus, any increase in length of the plastic moves the inner tube and this movement is measured by the dilatometer.

The coefficient of expansion of soft materials such as elastomers cannot be measured by this method. Instead, a more simple volume dilatometer is used as described in ASTM Method D864. It is beyond the scope of this chapter to discuss thermal expansion in greater detail. However, it should be pointed out that the coefficient of expansion for the entire useful range of any plastic should be known before the engineer attempts to design equipment.

Softening Points

Methods of measurements of softening points depend to a large extent upon the properties of the materials measured. Thus, the softening point of asphalts, coal tars and petroleum hydrocarbons are often measured by the ring and ball technique in accordance with ASTM Method D36. This is a simple method in which a molten plastic is placed within a brass ring and then immersed in a heated liquid. A metal ball of given weight is placed in the center of the plastic. The liquid is heated at a definite rate and the temperature at which the ball drops through the ring is noted.

Another method used to determine a related property is the penetrometer as described by ASTM Method D5-25. In this test, the depth of penetration of a needle at a specific temperature is measured.

In a comparable method by Vicat, a force of 11 lbs is exerted on a needle with a 1 mm square cross-section and the temperature at which the needle sinks 1 mm is termed the Vicat temperature resistance.

Heat Distortion

In ASTM Method D648, which is used for both plastics and plastic cements, a plastic bar supported as a simple beam is subjected to a fiber stress of 264 psi at its center. It is heated at a rate of $2°C$ per minute and the temperature at which it has deflected 0.010 inch at the center is termed as the heat distortion temperature.

In a variation of this method, a maximum fiber stress of 66 psi is used and the distortion temperature is recorded. It must be remembered that while both methods will show variations in degree of resistance to heat of similar plastic materials, the heat distortion measurement cannot be used as an absolute value. Information on deformation of plastic under load may be obtained from ASTM Method D621.

Flammability

Rubber, plastics, many elastomers and some other common materials of construction, like wood, will burn when ignited by an intense flame. However, with the exception of cellulose nitrate, which is seldom recommended as a material of construction, few are more easily ignited than wood. Also, it should be remembered that some plastics such as polyfluorocarbons and saran do not support combustion even in the presence of an intense flame. The flammability of plastics and elastomers may be measured by ASTM Methods D568, D635, and D757.

Thermal Conductivity

The thermal conductivity of plastics is low when compared to metals. This conductivity is higher for mineral or carbon-filled plastics than for unfilled products or those with nonconductive fillers. For example, while the thermal conductivity of copper is 0.72 Btu/sq ft/sec/°F/in., the thermal conductivity of most plastics is in the range of 0.00024 to 0.0010 Btu/sq ft/sec/°F/in. The thermal conductivity of both plastics and plastic cements is measured by ASTM Method D325.

ELECTRICAL PROPERTIES

Most standard methods for the determination of electrical properties can be used with plastic materials.

Dielectric Strengths

The dielectric strengths for the molded specimen necessary to cause a breakdown of a plastic is usually measured by ASTM Method D149. In this method, a disc having a diameter of 10 cm and a thickness of 3.2 mm is mounted between cylindrical electrodes and the voltage is increased step by step or held at a specific voltage reading for a period of time.

Volume Resistivity

The volume resistivity of plastics or mortar cements is usually measured by ASTM Method D257. Because of the effect of water in reducing resistivity, the specimens are usually conditioned for 96 hours at 90 per cent relative humidity and 35°C.

Dielectric Constant and Power Factor

The dielectric constant and power factors may be measured through the use of an alternating current bridge using the Wheatstone bridge principle. The techniques used, which are beyond the scope of this chapter, are described in ASTM Method D150.

Arc Resistance

Because the surfaces of some plastics carbonize when an electric discharge is cast over the surface, they become conductors rather than insulators. This property is measured by ASTM Method D495 in which two electrodes are placed at a certain distance from the surface of the plastic and the effect of the electrical discharge is evaluated.

TESTING FOR CHEMICAL RESISTANCE

Because of the relative newness of chemical-resistant materials and the impracticability of adapting standard tests used for corrosion-resistance studies with metals, very little background is available to guide the engineer in testing the chemical resistance of plastic materials of construction. Corrosion of metals, which is predominantly electrochemical in nature, usually progresses at a fairly uniform rate and can be expressed quantitatively as IPY (inches per year) values.

While it is not within the scope of this discussion to describe specific reaction mechanisms, it should be emphasized that unlike metals, plastics are not subject to corrosion. They are usually either attacked fairly rapidly by chemicals or are resistant to these materials in specific solutions.

The chemical resistance or organic coatings has been considered briefly by Champion but no specific reference is made to resin cements or plastic structures. Several organizations are attempting to develop methods for determining chemical-resistance tests for plastics.

ASTM Committee C-3 has developed tentative standard testing methods for chemical-resistant mortars. The Thermoplastic Structures Division of the Society of the Plastics Industry has devised standard methods of test for rigid polyvinyl chloride and related plastics.

Protective Coatings

Because protective coatings were one of the first industrial applications of plastics, chemical-resistance tests for plastics are actually techniques for measuring the effectiveness of protective coatings. As discussed in Chapter 7, protective coatings are used primarily for the protection of tank, pipe and structural steel exteriors against attack by chemical fumes, gases, spray and occasional spillage.   It is well known that the limiting factor in the effectiveness of an applied coating is determined to a large extent by the skill and conscientiousness of the painter. An inferior application job can discredit the finest coating. Reputable corrosion engineers do not recommend the use of thin organic coatings for protection of metals under conditions of continuous immersion with corrosives.

Spot tests are frequently used as preliminary checks for the resistance of coatings to liquid or solid corrosives. In the usual technique, a small drop of the reagent to be tested is placed on a coated steel panel and covered with a watch glass to prevent evaporation. After 24 to 48 hours, the drop is washed off and the coating examined for discoloration, softening, blistering or other signs of attack. This is a satisfactory method for rapid screening of many commercial coatings.

In the simplest quantitative test, a film of the coating material is immersed in specific chemicals and the change in volume and weight are determined. Data from such tests exclude permeability and application technique but are invaluable in determining the basic chemical resistance of the coating material and can be used advantageously in preliminary screening surveys. Certain products, such as baked phenolics, are usually considered too brittle to be investigated by this testing technique.

In the most widely used tests, coated steel panels are exposed to the corrosive environment under conditions which are anticipated under practical conditions. In this test (ASTM D-870-46T), the steel panels may vary from 1 x 2 to 3 x 6 inches and the coating may be applied by spraying, brushing or dipping. Difficulties involved in using commercial paint application methods, particularly in coating sharp edges and corners of small samples, are so obvious that failures occurring with 1/2 inch of the edges are disregarded, even though such attack may often affect the entire panel through under-film corrosion. A steel plummet approximately 1/2 inch in diameter and 2 to 4 inches long with a "Teflon" strip cemented in a depression in one end is sometimes preferred as a test specimen. Sharp edges are eliminated in this test but the difficulties associated with attempts to duplicate commercial application techniques cannot be eliminated. Typical test plummets are illustrated in Figure 6-1.

(Courtesy of Goodyear Tire & Rubber Company)

Figure 6-1. Immersion tests on coated steel plummets.

Panels which simulate surface conditions actually encountered in plant practice by including imperfections such as sharp edges, crevices, gouges, weld spatter, etc., have been developed and have shown promise as test specimens under practical exposure conditions. Admittedly, it is impossible to duplicate actual plant application practices and the correlation between results for these test panels and actual plant conditions are, at best, qualitative. One of the inherent difficulties in tests of this nature is the tendency for the applicator to be more careful in coating test panels than can be anticipated in customary plant painting procedures.

Testing for pinholes or holidays in coated coupons is a difficult problem. While high-voltage spark testers are valuable when used by experienced technicians, the inexperienced operator may allow the spark to remain too long at one spot or use too high voltage. Improper testing will actually burn holes through the coating.

Conductivity testing procedures for detecting surface discontinuities are practical for lined tanks but since they require at least one bare metal spot for grounding an electrode, they are not as practical for testing small completely coated samples.

A so-called nondestructive tester having an applied potential of less than 70 volts is now available. The inspection electrode provided with this equipment consists of a damp cellulose sponge which is brushed over the coated surface. A ground wire is clamped to the bare metal surface and an alarm is actuated whenever a flow of current occurs as a result of contacts with imperfections or pinholes.

Unfortunately, corrosive atmospheric conditions are far from constant even in a specific plant location. Thus, in spite of elaborate methods which have been proposed to provide synthetic atmospheres, it is impossible to reproduce actual service conditions in the laboratory.

In spite of preliminary screening and laboratory exposure tests, no protective coating can be considered satisfactory until a small test area has been investigated under actual plant conditions. It is desirable that the test section be selected so as to include the most difficult coating conditions. Obviously, the application of a protective coating on a test area by plant maintenance men under the supervision of a corrosion engineer is costly and time consuming but this test is many times more reliable and at least as economical as laboratory testing programs.

Organic Linings

As discussed in Chapter 8, a lining may be described as a protective coating with a thickness greater than 60 mils. With the exception of vinyl plastisols and plastigels, which may be sprayed or troweled in layers varying from 25 to 125 mils, linings are usually applied as sheets rather than solutions or dispersions.

The evaluation of linings is less difficult than coatings for the following reasons:

1. Linings are usually described generically rather than by trade names.
2. Linings are usually applied by trained applicators using approved methods.
3. Since linings are usually 3/32 to 1/4 inch thick, the occurrence of pinholes in the body of the material is virtually eliminated.
4. It is almost impossible to burn holes through thick linings by spark-testing procedures. Therefore, imperfections in welds and overlaps can be readily determined by high-voltage spark testing procedures.

Preliminary tests on small samples of sheet lining materials usually eliminate products that are attacked chemically as evidenced by swelling, softening or disintegration. It is important to conduct tests under actual conditions of use. Therefore, materials, such as saran rubber, neoprene or natural rubber should be cured before testing. Conclusions on chemical resistance should be based on changes in weight, volume and physical properties.

Most tank lining applicators furnish completely covered steel test panels for immersion tests under actual operating conditions. Such samples should include welds or overlaps where the sheet is joined so that these vulnerable spots may be tested adequately. Since specialized techniques are required for the successful application of plastic or rubber sheet linings, corrosion engineers should not attempt to prepare their own test samples. Typical lining test samples are shown in Figure 6-2.

Chemical-Resistant Mortar Cements

The method for testing chemical resistant cements tentatively approved by ASTM Committee C-3 requires a determination of the weight and volume changes of 1/4 inch thick discs having a diameter of 1 inch. These are completely immersed in 60-ml test solutions, at different test temperatures under static conditions. This type of sample was chosen because the large ratio of surface to volume presents greatest opportunity for chemical attack. Since some chemical-resistant cements show an initial weight loss resulting from the extraction of catalyst residues and low molecular weight resins, emphasis is placed on rate of change in weight or volume over a period of time rather than on initial changes after immersion.

In spite of initial gain or loss in weight, satisfactory chemical-resistant cements are not progressively attacked by the test solutions. Observations must also be made on the appearance of the corrosion media and the test sample, as well as on volume and weight change, before acceptance or rejection of a specific chemical-resistant cement.

Resistance data for a commercial carbon-filled phenolic cement exposed to sulfuric and nitric acids are given in Table 6-1. Cements of this type have been immersed in boiling 50 per cent sulfuric acid continuously for periods in excess of ten years without failure. However, as shown by the data for 10 per cent nitric acid, they are not satisfactory for nitric acid service except for occasional exposure at moderate temperatures.

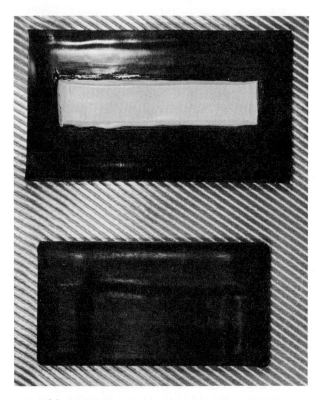

Figure 6-2. Steel test samples protected by sheet linings using joining strip (left) and lap construction.

The following conclusions may be drawn from the data given in Table 6-1.

1. No significant physical change was noted at any temperature with 50 per cent sulfuric acid.

2. While tests were not continued until no further loss in weight occurred, the weight change data obtained with 50 per cent sulfuric acid show that the rate of change in weight decreases with time.

3. Significant physical changes in both the test solution and the cement were noted in 10 per cent nitric in practically every test.

4. With the exception of tests made at room temperature, the cement was attacked too rapidly to recommend its use in the presence of 10 per cent nitric acid. The initial increase in weight is probably

TABLE 6-1. EFFECT OF TIME AND TEMPERATURE ON CHEMICAL RESISTANCE
OF A TYPICAL CARBON-FILLED PHENOLIC CEMENT

Temp. (°F)	Time (days)	50% Sulfuric Acid			10% Nitric Acid		
		Cumulative Wt./Change (%)	Sample Appearance	Solution Appearance	Cumulative Wt./Change (%)	Sample Appearance	Solution Appearance
77	1	−0.1	A	A	+0.8	A	A
	7	−0.3	A	A	+1.0	B	F
	14	−0.8	A	A	+0.7	B	F
	28	−1.2	A	A	+1.2	B	F
	56	−1.8	A	A	−0.3	B	G
122	1	−0.3	A	A	+0.7	A	F
	7	−1.5	A	A	+1.5	B	F
	14	−2.5	A	A	+1.4	B	F
	28	−3.4	A	A	+0.1	C	G
	56	−4.2	A	A	−8.2	D	G
194	1	−1.1	A	A	+0.2	B	F
	7	−4.2	A	A	−40	D	H
	14	−6.0	A	A	−65	D	H
	28	−7.2	A	A	−100	E	H
	56	−8.1	A	A	−	−	−

The data were obtained from an average of three values.

Code: *Sample Appearance*   *Solution Appearance*

A no change   A no change
B slight etching; grayish tinge   F slightly yellow
C moderate etching; gray color   G deep yellow, little sediment
D badly attacked   H deep yellow, black sediment
E completely disintegrated

due to the formation of oxidation products which are dissolved or washed off after long term immersion.

Compressive and tensile strength data have been considered as a means of determining chemical resistance. These values decrease when cement specimens are chemically attacked. However, all data obtained to date indicate that such changes can be correlated with simple weight and volume changes. Qualitative breaking tests on exposed discs after weighing are possibly as useful as quantitative tensile strength data.

The chemical resistance of silica-filled and carbon-filled phenolic cements are compared in Table 6-2. For this test, standard ASTM discs were exposed for ten days to various chemical reagents and the per cent change in weight has been tabulated.

The effect of time on the chemical resistance of silica-filled and carbon-filled phenolic cements tested at room temperature is shown in Table 6-3.

TABLE 6-2. EFFECT OF CORROSIVES ON PHENOLIC CEMENTS
AT VARIOUS TEMPERATURES

(10 Days' Exposure)

Reagents	Silica-Filled (°F)			Carbon-Filled (°F)		
	70	150	194	70	150	194
Saturated aqueous sodium chloride	0.4	0.5	−0.2	0.8	0.6	−0.5
Mineral oil	−2.2	−7.2	0	−0.9	−3.4	−4.0
Vegetable oil	0	0	0	−2.9	−2.6	−8.3
10% Sodium carbonate	−0.1	0.9*	−0.3*	−0.2	−0.1	−2.3
20% Sodium hydroxide	0*	0.1*	−1.5*	−21.2*	−100*	−100*
5% Sodium hypochlorite	−8.1**	–	–	−1.9**	–	–
10% Chromic acid–10% sulfuric acid	−1.1	−3.1	−3.3	−1.5	−9.1	−10.3

*Samples lost most of original strength.
**Samples slightly etched.

TABLE 6-3. EFFECT OF TIME ON THE CHEMICAL RESISTANCE
OF PHENOLIC CEMENTS AT ROOM TEMPERATURE

Reagents	Silica-Filled (Days)			Carbon-Filled (Days)		
	10	20	30	10	20	30
Saturated aqueous sodium chloride	0.4	0.1	1.2	0.8	0.4	−1.7
Mineral oil	2.2	0	0	0.9	3.5	3.9
Vegetable oil	0	0	0	2.9	5.1	5.5
10% Sodium carbonate	−0.1	1.1	0.5	−0.2	0.5	−0.8
5% Sodium hypochlorite	−8.1	−3.1**	−10.9**	−1.9	−1.6**	−1.6**
10% Chromic acid–10% sulfuric acid	−1.1	−1.7*	−2.4*	−1.5**	−2.6**	−3.6**

*Physical properties adversely affected.
**Slightly etched.

The effect of time on the chemical resistance of phenolic cements at 150 and 194° F., respectively, is shown in Tables 6-4 and 6-5.

TABLE 6-4. EFFECT OF TIME ON CHEMICAL RESISTANCE
OF PHENOLIC CEMENTS AT 150°F

Reagents	Silica-Filled (Days)			Carbon-Filled (Days)		
	10	20	30	10	20	30
Saturated aqueous sodium chloride	0.7	−0.4	0.1	0.6	−1.1	1.0
Mineral oil	−7.2	0	0	−3.4	−5.4	−6.2
Vegetable oil	0	0	0	−2.6	−4.6	−5.1
10% Sodium carbonate	0.9*	0.1*	0.9*	−0.1	−1.6	0.8
10% Chromic acid–10% sulfuric acid	−3.1	−5.2*	−5.0*	−9.1	−12.1**	−9.0**

*Physical properties adversely affected.
**Slightly etched.

TABLE 6-5. EFFECT OF TIME ON CHEMICAL RESISTANCE
OF PHENOLIC CEMENTS AT 194°F

Reagents	Silica-Filled (Days) 10	20	30	Carbon-Filled (Days) 10	20	30
Saturated aqueous sodium chloride	−0.2	0.3	0	−0.5	−0.8	−2.9
Mineral oil	0	0	0	4.0	18.6	7.1
Vegetable oil	0	0	0	8.3	0	7.5
10% Sodium carbonate	−0.3*	−2.5*	−2.2*	−2.3	−0.8	−2.4
10% Chromic acid–10% sulfuric acid	−3.3*	−5.0*	−4.7*	−10.3**	−4.4**	−34.9**

*Physical properties adversely affected.
**Slightly etched.

Sodium Hydroxide

Concentrated sodium hydroxide has less effect on silica-filled phenolic resin cements than dilute solutions. As might be expected, the effect increases with time and temperature.

TABLE 6-6. EFFECT OF TIME AND TEMPERATURE ON THE
RESISTANCE OF SILICA-FILLED PHENOLIC CEMENTS TO
AQUEOUS SOLUTIONS OF SODIUM HYDROXIDE

Temp.(°F)	Time (Days)	Concentration of Sodium Hydroxide (%) 10	25	40
70	10	5.5	0.1	1.9
150	20	12.2	3.3	2.0
	30	17.4	0.6	1.2
150	3	2.5	2.3	1.1
	7	5.9	5.4	4.4
	14	27.4	11.4	8.4
	(hrs)			
190	6	2.2	6.4	8.4
	13	5.1	31.4	17.4
	19	19.6	38.4	21.4
	25	61.6	−	25.4

As pointed out in Chapter 9 on chemical-resistant cements, poly-furfuryl alcohol cements which are sometimes called furan cements are resistant to alkalies in all concentrations even at elevated temperatures. This observation is substantiated by the data given in Table 6-7.

Reinforced Plastics

Because of their heterogeneous structure, "Fiberglas"-reinforced plastics are much more difficult to test than homogenous plastic materials. Some progress has been made by testing the cast plastic and

TABLE 6-7. EFFECT OF TIME AND TEMPERATURE ON THE
RESISTANCE OF POLYFURFURYL ALCOHOL CEMENT
IN 20% SODIUM HYDROXIDE

Time	Temperature (°F)		
(Days)	70	150	194
10	0	−1.4	−3.9
20	−0.1	−2.7	−1.5
30	−0.8	−3.0	−1.0

the reinforcing member separately using an adaptation of the techniques described for the chemical-resistant cement. Unfortunately, the tests on separate components can be used only to eliminate nonresistant resins and reinforcing agents. Exposures on coupons cut from reinforced plastic sheet are usually more severe than those encountered under actual service conditions because of the fiber exposure.

Some progress in testing plastics of this type has been made by using reinforced plastic discs as closures for inverted screw cap bottles. Since the chemical resistance of reinforced plastics is a function of the resistance of both plastic and reinforcing components as well as fabrication techniques, on-stream testing is usually recommended.

Comparative chemical-resistance data for commercial reinforced polyester laminates given in Table 6-8 demonstrate the type of results that can be anticipated from chemical-resistance tests. However, as stated in Chapter 14 on reinforced plastics, the properties of properly selected chemical-resistant polyester laminates are much superior to typical commercial polyester laminates.

Thermoplastic Structural Materials

Long time testing in the presence of standard and additional specific corrosives under procedures described for ASTM D-543-52T is being investigated for test procedures for thermoplastic structural materials by the Thermoplastic Structures Division of the Society of the Plastics Industry. Correlation of changes in physical properties with time in the presence of specific chemical reagents is also being investigated.

The data showing the effect of nitric acid on unplasticized polyvinyl chloride and styrene-rubber blends in Table 6-9 indicate the importance of determining whether or not change in weight is progressive, as discussed under tests for chemical-resistant cements. Tests of this type may be used to classify various structural plastics.

Since the effect of a chemical on polyvinyl chloride or polyethylene welds may be much greater than for the entire sample, it is important that physical observation of surface effects, as well as weight measurements be made. As in the case of coatings, linings and mortar cements, the use of practical tests on promising materials is

TABLE 6-8. COMPARATIVE CHEMICAL RESISTANCE DATA
FOR COMMERCIAL REINFORCED POLYESTER LAMINATES
(8 Weeks Exposure)

Reagent	Temp. (°C)	Hand Lay-up 2 Layers #261 Glass Cloth 2 Layers Surface Mat			Hand Lay-up 2 Layers 1½-oz. Glass Mat 2 Layers Surface Mat			Pressed Sheet		
		%Wt. Change	% Tensile Retained	Remarks	%Wt. Change	% Tensile Retained	Remarks	%Wt. Change	% Tensile Retained	Remarks
Water	25	+1.6	75.8	A	+1.1	97.6	A	+1.0	76.6	A
	60	+0.7	71.6	B	+0.9	82.8	C	+0.1	60.3	A
	90	−8.0	28.5	C,D	−8.8	85.0	C,E	−0.8	46.6	A
30% Sulfuric	25	+0.8	72.1	D	+0.6	120.1	A	+0.5	84.9	C
acid	60	+2.5	47.5	B,C	+2.3	80.8	B,C,D	+4.2	24.7	C
	90	−5.0	14.0	B,C,D	−0.8	34.2	B,C,D	+2.5	11.0	C,D
50% Sulfuric	25	+0.3	86.1	D	+0.2	117.7	A	+0.4	84.9	C
acid	60	+0.8	58.4	B,C,D	+0.7	92.1	B,C,D	+2.3	54.7	C
	90	−0.3	44.9	B,C,D	+0.8	59.3	B,C,D	+3.8	11.0	C,D
70% Sulfuric	25	−0.1	76.6	D	−0.2	116.7	C	+0.3	82.2	C
acid	60	−0.8	62.5	B,C,E	−1.1	101.4	B,C,D	+1.9	46.6	B,C
	90	−0.9	54.6	B,C,E	−1.1	108.9	B,C,E	+1.6	27.4	C,D
5% Sodium	25	−0.6	39.6	B,C	+0.1	57.8	B,C	+0.4	21.4	B,C
hydroxide	60	+22.2	2.4	B,E	+4.6	11.0	B,C	+15.5	4.1	B,E
10% Nitric	25	+0.9	87.0	B	+1.1	117.9	A	−0.7	73.8	A
acid	60	−1.5	53.6	B,C	−0.1	71.4	B,C,D	−3.4	38.3	A
	90	−21.8	16.5	B,C	−18.5	35.3	B,C,D	−13.8	11.0	C
25% Nitric	25	+0.4	93.5	B	+0.8	92.8	B	−2.3	93.1	C
acid	60	−4.3	43.9	B,C,D	−3.1	72.6	B,C,D	−9.7	19.2	B,C
10% Sodium	25	+1.2	75.3	A	+1.0	111.8	A	+0.7	76.6	C
chloride	60	+1.0	66.1	B,C	+1.1	79.7	A	−0.5	76.6	C
	90	−7.1	34.4	B,C	−5.3	75.9	A	−1.5	76.6	C,D
10% Sodium	25	+1.1	75.5	B,C	+0.8	84.5	C	+1.0	82.2	C
carbonate	60	−0.1	50.3	B,C	−0.2	67.9	C	−0.9	32.8	C
	90	−9.9	32.3	B,C	−6.5	38.1	C	−3.6	13.7	C
10% Alum	25	+1.3	93.5	B	+1.1	107.1	A	+0.9	115.0	A
	60	+1.4	50.3	B,C	+1.3	73.9	A	+0.7	79.5	C
	90	−6.1	20.0	B,D	−5.1	81.4	C	+4.1	57.5	C
10% Acetic	25	+1.2	86.5	B	+1.0	118.5	A	+0.7	87.6	C
acid	60	+0.3	63.1	B,C,D	+1.2	89.6	C,E	+0.9	60.3	C
	90	−8.6	32.1	B,D	−7.8	58.5	C,E	−4.3	52.1	C
95% Ethanol	25	+5.9	94.6	B,C	+3.8	123.4	C	+2.6	115.0	C
5% Sodium	25	+0.3	66.0	B,C	+0.2	99.2	B,C	+1.6	54.7	C
hypochlorite	60	−3.8	54.0	B,C,D	−1.0	83.1	B,C,D	+0,4	46.6	C

Ratings: A — No obvious effect
B — Pinholing, darkening or yellowing of the edge, slight blistering or slight
C — Fibers raised or exposed   surface change
D — Obvious darkening or entire sample
E — Cracked formation, warping of sample and/or black discoloration of entire sample

TABLE 6-9. EFFECT OF NITRIC ACID ON TYPICAL
THERMOPLASTIC STRUCTURAL MATERIALS

Time (days)	Conc. (%)	Temp. (°F)	Type I Polyvinyl Chloride % Wt. Change	Type II Polyvinyl Chloride % Wt. Change	Styrene-Rubber Blend % Wt. Change
1	25	140	0.1	0.4	1.8
7			0.1	0.4	3.3
14			0.15	0.8	4.7
28			0.1	2.0	10.3
1	50	140	0.1	1.6	A
7			0.2	4.0	–
14			0.2	10.6	–
28			0.2	A	–
1	70	77	0.2	4.1	A
7			0.3	10.8	–
14			0.4	A	–
28			0.4	–	–

A – badly swollen

recommended. Testing of small tanks under simulated use conditions is time-consuming and expensive but will give fairly reliable
information to permit selection of the proper material to be used for
all plastic structures.

The presently accepted method for testing rigid plastic structural
materials is an adaptation of the techniques described in ASTM Method
D543-52T. While improvements in testing procedures will be made,
the present data as outlined in Table 6-9 are sufficient to differentiate
between Type I and Type II unplasticized polyvinyl chloride and styrene rubber resin blends.

The test data in Table 6-9 show that while Type I unplasticized
polyvinyl chloride is satisfactory for service with nitric acid in a
wide range of concentrations, Type II unplasticized polyvinyl chloride
can only be used for dilute concentrations. Styrene-rubber resin
blends should not be used in oxidizing acid environment.

Plastic Pipe

Tests used for plastic structures can also be used for testing plastic pipe. In addition, field tests can be made quite readily by inserting
a small section of pipe in an existing line, where it may be examined
periodically.

Summary

Laboratory test methods must be used to eliminate completely
unsatisfactory materials but ultimate recommendations must be

based on practical tests. Obviously, such factors as application techniques, agitation, aeration, changes in liquid level, presence of trace materials and rapid changes in temperature and pressure can be studied best under actual plant practice. The following procedure is recommended:

1. Reliable information on chemical resistance should be secured from reputable manufacturers, trade journals, manufacturer's literature and engineers with practical experience.

2. Laboratory tests should be conducted under conditions which simulate plant environment insofar as possible.

3. Properly prepared samples or preferably test sections or areas should be exposed under actual conditions anticipated in service.

It is the corrosion engineer's function to consider all data available. Sometimes the solution requires considerable judgment. The most economical solution is not always the best, yet there are instances where economics will rule in favor of a product that is satisfactory on a temporary basis yet much less resistant than a more expensive material.

Suggested References

"The Chemical Resistance of Phenolic Resins," Raymond B. Seymour, Corrosion, 7, No. 5, 151-5 (1951).

"The Chemical Resistance of Phenolic and Furfuryl Alcohol Type Coatings," Raymond B. Seymour and Robert H. Steiner, Corrosion, 8, No. 2, 65-8 (1952).

"Resins for Reinforced Chemical Resistant Construction," Raymond B. Seymour and Robert H. Steiner, Proceedings of the Ninth Annual Conference Reinforced Plastics Division, Society of the Plastics Industry, Chicago, Ill. Feb. 3-5, 1954.

"Resistance of Representative Plastic Materials to Hydrofluoric Acid," J. W. Reinhart and H. C. Williams, ASTM Bull. 167, pp. 60-62, (1950).

"Intermittent Immersion Type of Corrosion Testing Apparatus," A. Indelli, Pitture e vernici, 8, No. 1, 29-31 (1952).

"Accelerated Testing," H. Hesse, Farbe u. Lack., 57, No. 2, 68-99 (1951).

"A Time-Temperature Dependent Modulus Concept for Engineering Plastics," C. H. Weber, E. N. Robertson, and W. F. Bartoe, Symposium on Plastics as Materials of Construction, American Chemical Society, Division of Paint, Plastics and Printing Ink Chemistry, New York, Sept. 1954.

"Calculation of Deformation of Plastics Under Complex Stresses," A. A. MacLeod, Symposium on Plastics as Materials of Construction, American Chemical Society, Division of Paint, Plastics and Printing Ink Chemistry, New York, Sept. 1954.

"Creep and Relaxation of Polyvinyl Chloride Rigid Resins," M. L. Dannis, Symposium on Plastics as Materials of Construction, American Chemical Society, Division of Paint, Plastics and Printing Ink Chemistry, New York, Sept. 1954.

"Elastomers and Plastomers, Vol. III—Testing and Analysis," R. Houwink, Elsevier Publishing Company, New York, 1948.

"Handbook of Plastics," H. R. Simonds and C. Ellis, D. Van Nostrand Co. Inc., New York, 1943.

"Corrosion Testing Procedures," F. A. Champion, Chapman Hall, London, 1952.

SECTION II
PLASTIC MATERIALS OF CONSTRUCTION

7. PROTECTIVE COATINGS

Plastics are largely used as protective coatings but unfortunately, misunderstandings of this application have caused considerable confusion among corrosion engineers. While many manufacturers and engineers now recognize many of the essential concepts required for successful coatings applications, there is still a great need for education in this phase of the plastics industry. Adherence to the following basic concepts can help minimize the number of misapplications of protective coatings both in the shop and in the field.

1. Chemical resistance is a function of the chemical structure of the base polymer used and the corrosive environment encountered.

2. While chemical resistance of the base resin is a prerequisite, the compounded coating film must also be resistant to all corrosives anticipated under normal service conditions. Hence, low moisture permeability of the base resin and adequate chemical resistance of pigments, plasticizers and other additives is essential.

3. The chemical resistance of a properly selected coating after application is dependent upon the nature of the material to be protected, surface preparation and application techniques.

4. Structures protected by coatings are not recommended for continuous immersion in corrosives even at ordinary temperatures. However, it should be pointed out that continuous exposure of holiday-free coatings to fresh and salt water environment is acceptable.

5. Performance predictions based on panel tests must be verified using actual service conditions.

The reader should be familiar with the relationship of structure to chemical resistance as discussed in Chapter 5. It is also important to remember that the base resin may account for less than 50 per cent of the total solids content of a proprietary protective coating.

Obviously, the resistance of an applied protective coating is essentially the sum-total of the resistance of all its constituents. In some instances, the presence of less than 5 per cent of a compounding ingredient with low resistance may be tolerated. However, larger amounts should be avoided whenever possible.

Many pigments lack chemical resistance and while films with a low pigment content may not fail completely, the color of the coating may be destroyed by chemical attack. The chemical resistance of a pigment or filler is often affected by its physical form. For example, coatings containing leafing pigments such as flake aluminum behave to a large extent like aluminum. In contrast, those based on atomized aluminum possess many of the properties of the base resin even when large amounts of the pigment are present. In the latter case, the spherical particles are presumably completely coated by the resin.

The main points that should be considered in the selection of appropriate coatings are relative resistance to the environment, ease of application, experience under similar conditions of exposure, cost per year of the applied coating and choice of colors.

Most coatings can be applied by brush, spray or roller coaters. Some mastics and heavy coatings are applied best with high-pressure spray equipment. Presumably the degree of success secured in such cases is the result of heavy, dense films associated with high-pressure application techniques.

Most engineers and maintenance men know the cost of paint cannot be determined by the cost of a gallon of a proprietary coating. Fortunately, many enlightened purchasing agents recognize also that the materials cost is but a small fraction of the total coating insulation cost. Hence, they are interested in economy performance, i.e., cost per year.

When color dynamics are important, neither asphalt nor liquid neoprene should be considered unless they are overcoated with properly pigmented coatings based on lighter colored resins. It is usually more expedient to use one material throughout but it is always advantageous to use a two-color system in coatings application in order to insure proper coverage.

While top quality coatings should be compared generically, it must be remembered that identification by the generic name is no guarantee of quality. Coatings should be purchased on specifications from reliable coatings manufacturers. It is false economy to purchase a protective coating without knowing its solids content and the resin content of the solids.

Both the base resins and pigments should be selected on the basis of their ability to provide low moisture permeability. This property and resistance to ionic diffusion are functions of both specific pigment volume and the compounded coating. Much information can be obtained from data on related systems but there is no substitute for permeability tests on specific coatings.

The chemical resistance of plasticizers is extremely important. Liquid plasticizers may exude or bleed and open up vulnerable paths for attack. Residual solvents may be subject to the same objection as liquid plasticizers. If the deposited films become insoluble in the solvent, any residual solvent may contribute to film permeability. The most chemical resistant film will fail unless it has sufficient inherent adhesiveness to the surface to be protected. It must also be applied properly. If the adhesion is adequate and the structure to be protected is not attacked rapidly by the atmosphere, film imperfections may not be apparent. Thus, a coating on steel may fail rapidly while a comparable coating on wood, aluminum, brick or concrete may last for several years. Obviously the production of vulnerable surfaces such as steel and concrete requires the greatest care in surface preparation and coating application.

Regardless of the high cost of sandblasting and unfilled hopes for miracle surface preparation procedures, all metal surfaces should be properly and meticulously prepared. In spite of many investigations into the simpler methods, all reliable authorities insist that sandblast cleaning be used whenever possible. A No. 2 commercial finish should be provided but a No. 3 finish is sometimes acceptable for maintenance work.

Most nonmetallic surfaces require a minimum of surface preparation. If loose surface contamination is removed and the surface remains dry, there is little chance for improper coatings application. However, osmosis may occur in films with high moisture permeability. This effect may be accentuated by the presence of soluble salts on the protected surface. Even a residual fingerpaint may aggravate this phenomenon. Permeability of moisture through the wood, brick or concrete from the opposite side will also accelerate failure. The nascent hydrogen resulting from corrosion of unprotected steel often penetrates the structures and causes coating failure on the protected side.

Steel surfaces require adequate preparation in order to remove mill scale, rust and contamination. Whenever possible, an NACE Condition 2 surface should be obtained. This can be accomplished by sandblasting or pickling but compromises must be made occasionally for practical reasons. Unfortunately, there is a tendency to pay too little attention to proper surface preparation at the risk of almost certain failure.

The various types of surface preparation have been defined by the National Association of Corrosion Engineers Technical Practice Committee 6-G as follows:

Condition 1—The complete removal of all corrosion products, mill scale, and gray mill scale binder.

Condition 2—Removal of all corrosion products as well as tight and loose mill scale.

Condition 3—Removal of rust and loose mill scale. It is important to note that in addition to pickling, sandblasting, flame-conditioning and cleaning, it is also essential to wipe the surface clean with rags and solvents to remove all grease and other residues.

Unfortunately, it is sometimes difficult to secure a No. 3 finish with used equipment. However, regardless of advertising claims to the contrary, the recommendations of NACE Committee TP 6-G must be followed. All loose scale, rust, grease and superficial dirt must be removed.

Every possible effort should be exerted to secure the best possible surface, and compromises in surface preparation must be held to a minimum. Since weld spatter, protrusions and sharp corners will result in the failure of even the highest quality coatings, it is essential that these objectionable features be avoided.

Most equipment can be protected most readily and economically when first installed. As mentioned previously, it is sometimes impossible to sandblast used equipment in the field. However, when the surface is properly prepared and an adequate thickness of a good protective coating applied, one sandblasting operation may be sufficient for the entire useful life of the equipment. Subsequent coats of a similar coating may be applied from time to time providing the old surface is cleaned and no bare metal is exposed.

Regardless of the method of surface preparation, it is important to remove all dust and grease before applying the first coat of any protective coating. Wherever possible, the first coat should be brush-applied to minimize bridging and to help compensate for the unavoidable presence of incidental surface contamination. Experience has shown that it is advantageous to use a wash primer before applying any protective coating on metal.

The possibility of surface contamination between coats should be recognized and all possible attempts made to prevent moisture or dirt from coming in contact with the coated surface until the job is complete. Many a coating has failed prematurely because of an invisible layer of contaminants between the coats.

Many of the difficulties can be minimized by application of the coating at temperatures above 65°F in a dust-free dry atmosphere. The time between coats should be kept as short as practical but a sufficient time interval must be allowed for complete solvent evaporation.

For best results, industrial coatings should be applied by painters who have had previous experience. A typical spray application of a protective coating is shown in Figure 7-1.

At least three coats of protective coatings must be applied to yield a minimum thickness of 5 mils. This thickness can readily be determined by a thickness meter. Such coatings should be subjected to splash and fume service only. There are cases on record where some degree of service has been secured under conditions of immersion in corrosives but these examples should be considered as exceptions and not as standard case histories.

The absence of pinholes can be ascertained through the use of a high-voltage spark tester as shown in Figure 7-2. However, since these tests may burn through thin spots, the technique is not recommended except for heavy coatings and when used by experienced personnel.

A so-called nondestructive tester having an applied potential less than 70 volts is now available. The inspection electrode provided with this equipment consists of a damp cellulose sponge which is brushed over the coated surface. A ground wire is clamped to the bare metal surface and an alarm is actuated whenever a flow of current occurs as a result of contacts with imperfections or pinholes.

Most protective coatings consist of solutions or dispersions of film-forming resins in organic solvents. Most of the solvents used

(Courtesy of Shell Chemical Company)

Figure 7-1. Spray application of an epoxy resin-based coating on the interior of a storage tank.

are toxic and flammable. Hence, exposure to flames or sparks must be avoided and the coating should not be applied in confined areas unless the applicator is properly protected from inhaling the fumes.

While there is no substitute for practical experience, considerable knowledge of protective coatings can be secured from the evaluation on a generic basis. The remaining discussion follows the order of presentation given in Chapter 5. This same order is also used in other chapters describing specific applications of plastics.

Protective coatings are usually satisfactory for continuous contact with mild corrosives such as fresh and salt water, some solvents and alkalies. Nevertheless, as stated previously, they should be used only for exposure to splash and fumes in the presence of corrosive liquids.

While it must be admitted that it is impossible to evaluate a so-called miracle coating without plant tests, modern protective coat-

Figure 7-2. High-voltage spark tester for detecting "holidays" or pinholes in protective coatings or linings.

ings can be selected scientifically. This selection should be based on a knowledge of the chemical structure of the base resin and compounding ingredients.

Coatings are generally supplied in 1 gallon cans, 5 gallon pails, and 50 gallon drums as compounded solutions in organic solvents or as aqueous dispersions. Most industrial coatings are grey, white or black, but any standard color may be supplied except when the base resin is dark in color.

THERMOPLASTIC COATINGS

Plasticized Sulfur

Attempts have been made to apply molten plasticized sulfur as a coatings material. However, while it has been used successfully as an interlayer between asphalt, it has not been utilized to any great extent as a protective coating by itself.

Polyethylene — Polyisobutylene

Since Polyethylene is not soluble in organic solvents, it cannot be used as a solution coating. It is possible to apply coatings of this plastic using the flame-spraying techniques. Such coatings are rough and are apt to contain pinholes and other discontinuities. However, they are used in specific applications and in atomic energy and chemical plants in the United States.

While, as explained in Chapter 6, carbon-filled polyisobutylene has been extensively used as a lining material in Europe it has found little use as a protective coating in the United States. In some instances, it is blended with polyethylene in order to secure a more readily flame-sprayable product.

Asphalts and Coal-Tar Pitch

Because the base resinous materials are inexpensive, coal-tar pitch, coumarone-indene resins and asphalt cutbacks have been used in large volume in the coatings industry. Coal-tar pitch and asphalt are often used as aqueous dispersions but such products have high water absorption values and are recommended only for light-duty services. In spite of their limited chemical resistance, they are usually considered to be superior to oil-base paints for protection against corrosives.

Coal-tar pitch dissolved in organic solvents is often applied on the exterior of pipes and for the protection of gas, water and sewer plant equipment. In spite of the characteristic black color, it is used in considerable volume where color is not an important consideration. Coal-tar pitch is often applied in the form of a hot melt. It has been used successfully as an interior coating for municipal water mains and for the protection of the exterior of pipelines and off-shore drilling equipment.

When dissolved in organic solvents coumarone-indene resins are sometimes employed as coatings, but they are used more widely as blends with other coating resins. These products are supplied as dark-colored coatings and are much less limited in their application than the coal-tar pitch compositions.

Asphalts are also applied as hot melts for the protection of pipe exteriors and for waterproofing. They are used in large volumes as solutions, commonly called cutbacks. One of the most widely publicized uses of asphaltic coatings has been that of the so-called gilsonite mastics. These products are usually blends of asphalt and gilsonite with mica and other fillers. They are applied under high-pressure to yield heavy black coatings for the protection of industrial equipment.

Mastics are used to considerable extent in the paper, petroleum and chemical industries as coatings for tank exteriors. In some instances, they are compounded with cork to produce an insulating coating. The application of this type of coating to a large cylindrical tank is shown in Figure 7-3.

A typical specification for a gilsonite-asphalt mastic is: solids, 65 to 75 per cent (of which the gilsonite-asphalt materials constitute the major portion); viscosity @ $77°F$, 300,000 to 450,000 cps.

(Courtesy of Emjay Equipment Co.)

Figure 7-3. Application of an insulating mastic coating to a large rubber-lined storage tank.

Styrene Copolymers

High styrene-butadiene copolymers are soluble in aromatic hydrocarbon solvents and are much less brittle than polystyrene. They tolerate considerable amounts of inert fillers and exhibit outstanding adhesive characteristics. As indicated in Chapter 5, these plastics are similar in structure to GR-S rubber except that the proportion of styrene in the copolymer is much higher.

Styrene-butadiene copolymers do not weather as well as saturated hydrocarbon polymers but this deficiency has been overcome to a large extent by proper compounding. These products, which are sometimes called "rubber base" coatings, may be pigmented to produce almost any color. A specification for a typical styrene-butadiene solvent-type coating is as follows: solids content, 35 to 45 per cent (of which at least 60 per cent should be the resin); specific gravity, .95 to .98; viscosity, 300 to 800 cps.

A gallon of the above should cover a minimum of 250 sq ft of surface when applied as a film 2.5 mils thick. Aqueous dispersions of styrene copolymers have not found extensive use industrially because of the high water absorption of the film. However, these products are extensively used as domestic water paints and are available in a wide variety of colors.

(Courtesy of Bakelite Company)

Figure 7-4. Fume duct work coated with a vinyl plastisol.

Acrylates

Organic solutions of polymethyl methacrylate have been used to a limited extent as protective coatings. Aqueous dispersions of these products are also used for painting masonry surfaces.

Vinyl Resins

Technically, "vinyl" is a broad term which includes all products having an ethylenic structure. However, from a practical viewpoint, the term "vinyl" has been accepted in the coatings field to describe low-molecular weight copolymers of vinyl chloride and vinyl acetate. Other vinyl chloride polymers are as resistant and of as much potential commercial interest. However, at present, most vinyl coatings are based on this specific vinyl resin.

The most important vinyl coating resins consist of a copolymer containing approximately seven times as many vinyl chloride as vinyl acetate groups. Another vinyl resin of higher molecular weight containing only one vinyl acetate to twenty vinyl chloride groups has been used to a large extent as a webbing-type and a strippable coating. Because of its lower solubility in organic solvents, it is used much less frequently than the more soluble copolymers.

The more popular vinyl copolymer may be dissolved in mixed ketone-toluene solvent systems to obtain solutions with resin solids content greater than 20 per cent. When suitable pigments, fillers, stabilizers and plasticizers are added, the deposited film will be approximately one-third the total weight applied.

Vinyl resins will not adhere directly to metals or to concrete, but this is usually overcome by the use of a primer system. One standard primer system is based on a chlorinated rubber-resin blend. As a result, a coating with an outstanding performance record in the chemical process industry has been developed consisting of alternate costs of chlorinated rubber and vinyl protective coatings over a wash primer system.

A more direct approach has been accomplished by appropriate modification of the polymeric structure with incorporation of an occasional maleic acid group. Through the use of modern compounding techniques, it is now possible to eliminate the primer system and to apply a vinyl resin coating directly on properly prepared steel, preferably over a wash primer.

A typical specification for an all-purpose vinyl protective coating is as follows: solids content, 27 to 35 per cent; specific gravity, 0.875 to 0.975; viscosity, 200 to 500 cps. The pigments must be ground so that they are completely dispersed and the resin must be compounded so that it has adequate resistance to heat and sunlight. One gallon of a vinyl protective coating should cover a minimum of 200 sq ft of surface to yield a film having a thickness of 1.5 mils.

Vinyl coatings should be compounded to produce maximum resistance to alkalies, corrosive salts, aliphatic solvents and acids. The flexibility and tensile strength of a vinyl film should change less than 25 per cent when immersed for six months at room temperature in 20 per cent sodium hydroxide, 190-proof ethyl alcohol, 50 per cent sulfuric acid, 35 per cent hydrochloric acid, 40 per cent phosphoric acid, aqueous hydrogen sulfide or sea water.

The properties of vinyl coatings have been outlined by the National Association of Corrosion Engineers Unit Committee T-6A. This report includes recommendations for the use of vinyl coatings for the protection of structures in specific corrosive environments.

Vinyl coatings are widely used for protection of metal against splash and fumes of corrosive chemicals and for coating objects which are to be continuously immersed in fresh or salt water. These coatings have been applied successfully in chemical, metal, electroplating and food industries, as well as for the protection of equipment in water and sewage plants.

One of the recently developed vinyl formulations is a very high solids aluminum coating which is sometimes called "liquid metal."

This product has excellent adhesion to many metals and has been used for lining storage tanks containing vegetable oils and other materials that do not attack aluminum.

Properly compounded aqueous vinyl resin dispersions will deposit pinhole-free resinous films but because of the presence of nonvolatile dispersing agents, these films exhibit high permeability to aqueous solutions. Organosols, which are dispersions of vinyl resins in organic solvents, are useful when the resultant coating can be heated in an oven, but obviously such techniques are not applicable for large equipment.

The modification of greatest interest is the so-called vinyl plastisol, which consists of a dispersion of the vinyl resin in a liquid plasticizer. Plastisols, which are liquids with 100 per cent convertible solids, may be applied to a wide variety of surfaces. After the object has been coated or dipped, it is heated to 325 to 375°F, at which temperatures, an irreversible fusion of the plasticizer and resin takes place.

Plastisols have been extensively used for rack coatings and castings. They may be modified to yield very heavy coatings by the addition of gelling agents to form the so-called plastigels. Sections of large duct work and an acid drum coated with a vinyl plastisol are shown in Figures 7-4 and 7-5.

(Courtesy of B. F. Goodrich Chemical Co.)

Figure 7-5. Acid drum coated with a vinyl resin plastisol.

On type of modified vinyl resin makes use of a partially hydrolyzed product. Because of the availability of free hydroxyl groups, the resin is soluble in more polar solvents and is applicable in many instances in which vinyl resin could not be used. Obviously, the hydrolyzed copolymer is not as chemical resistant as the standard vinyl coating but it has a definite place in chemical-resistant coating systems.

A typical coating based on this type of vinyl chloride-vinyl acetate-alcohol resin might contain 15 per cent resin, 3 per cent plasticizer, 22 per cent pigment and 60 per cent solvent. It is often used as a body-coat over the so-called wash primer (WP-1) metal conditioner, followed by a top-coat of a conventional vinyl coating.

Polyvinyl Acetate

Polyvinyl acetate has been proposed for corrosion-resistant application but is too vulnerable to saponification to permit its use except under very mild corrosive conditions. Polyvinyl alcohol, the product obtained by complete saponification, is often used as a solvent-resistant gasket material. It is essential to react the surface of polyvinyl alcohol with aldehydes to prevent swelling by atmospheric moisture.

Polyvinyl butyral, which is obtained by reacting butyraldehyde with polyvinyl alcohol, has been used as the interliner in safety glass. Since it is soluble in alcohol, it has also been applied as a general-purpose coating. Because of its solubility in polar solvents, it was chosen for the WP-1 wash primer system which was developed empirically during World War II.

The standard wash primer system consists of polyvinyl butyral, zinc chromate, phosphoric acid and alcohol. It is applied as a very thin coating and has excellent adhesion to steel, aluminum, zinc, cadmium, tin, and stainless steel. This system can be applied under conditions of high humidity and has given excellent service when further protected by other coatings and immersed in fresh or salt water.

The chemistry of this system is far from simple. Actually, a reaction takes place after application to insolubilize the polyvinyl butyral. Attempts have been made to develop a one-package system but most wash primers are compounded on the job by mixing the phosphoric acid solution with the solution of polyvinyl butyral resin and basic zinc chromate.

Saran

Saran, the generic term for copolymers of vinylidene chloride, is at least as resistant chemically as vinyl chloride copolymers. These products are generally less soluble and are not as widely used as the vinyls. Attempts have been made to supply aqueous dispersions of vinylidene chloride resins as protective coatings.

As in the case of the previously discussed vinyl dispersion coatings, the presence of nonvolatile dispersing agents cause deposited films to be somewhat permeable to aqueous solutions. Excellent results have been reported when coatings deposited from solutions of vinylidene chloride copolymers in methyl ethyl ketone have been tested in sea water and gasoline service.

Polyfluorocarbons

Polytrifluoromonochloroethylene and polytetrafluoroethylene films exhibit excellent resistance to almost all chemicals but are not usually satisfactory as protective coatings. Coatings which are far from pinhole-free can be applied from aqueous dispersions and baked to produce nonadhesive surfaces.

Silicone Coatings

Silicone coatings are seldom considered satisfactory for use in highly corrosive atmospheres. However, silicones are usually recommended for stack coatings and for the protection of other equipment where heat resistance is of prime importance.

Most other organic coatings decompose when exposed to temperatures above $350°F$ but silicone coatings have withstood exposure at $500°F$ for over 1,000 hours without decomposition. Because silicones are expensive, they are sometimes blended with alkyds in order to improve the heat resistance of the latter. They are also added in very small amounts to other coatings and polishes to secure improved workability.

Polyurethanes

Reaction products of toluene diisocyanate and hydroxy-containing polymers have been used in Europe as adhesives and coatings. Some progress has been made in this country using the reaction products of polyesters and organic diisocyanates for these applications. Their properties are sufficiently different from other coatings to justify their consideration for future applications.

Saturated Polyesters

While oil-base paints and alkyds contain some unsaturated groups, coatings of this type will be discussed under the heading saturated polyesters used in its broadest sense.

Oil-Base Paints

Oil-base paints, like alkyds, are used to a large extent for decorative purposes, but in spite of their resistance to sunlight and weather, they are not sufficiently resistant to chemicals to warrant consideration for general use in chemical process plants. High solids oil-base mastics have been used where decorative effects are more important than chemical resistance.

These products are available in a wide variety of colors but are generally used to form a white waterproof seal on cement and cinder block structures. Like asphaltic type mastics, they are also applied under high pressure to produce very heavy coatings.

Alkyds are probably the most widely used synthetic resins in the protective coatings industry. Because of the lack of good chemical resistance characteristics of ester groups, alkyds are not recommended for service in highly corrosive environments. However, they have often proved to be satisfactory in areas where oil-base paints fail. Hence, they should be considered when a general use, decorative coating is required.

Alkyds are characterized by excellent durability and good adhesion to a wide variety of surfaces. While alkyds have fair chemical resistance, they are not, as previously stated, recommended for exposure to strong solvents, acids or alkalies.

NATURAL AND SYNTHETIC RUBBER AND DERIVATIVES

Chlorinated Rubber

In spite of the present popularity of the vinyl coating system, it should be noted that the pioneer synthetic protective coating was based on chlorinated rubber. As indicated previously, chlorine will react with natural rubber to form a plastic material. This product, which is approximately two-thirds chlorine by weight, has excellent adhesion to a wide variety of surfaces and is resistant to many corrosives. Its brittleness is overcome by incorporating large quantities of resins or plasticizers such as chlorinated paraffins.

The main objection to chlorinated rubber is its lack of resistance to heat and sunlight. This deficiency has been overcome to a large extent by adding small amounts of an epoxy resin as a stabilizer. As in the case of the vinyls, chlorinated rubber coatings are available in a wide variety of colors.

The specifications for a typical protective coating based on chlorinated rubber is as follows: solids content, 37.5 to 45 per cent (of which at least 60 per cent of the solids should be chlorinated rubber); specific gravity, 1.05 to 1.2; viscosity, 250 to 600 cps. One gallon of chlorinated rubber coating should yield a film 2 mils thick on a 250 sq ft area.

Chlorinated rubber coatings are not resistant to chlorinated or aromatic hydrocarbon solvents but are resistant to more polar solvents such as alcohol. The flexibility and tensile strength of chlorinated rubber films should change less than 25 per cent when immersed for six months at room temperature in 20 per cent sodium hydroxide, 190-proof ethyl alcohol, 50 per cent sulfuric acid, 3 per cent hydrochloric acid, 40 per cent phosphoric acid, aqueous hydrogen sulfide or sea water.

That natural rubber has characteristic resistance to chemicals has been known for many years. However, rubber is not sufficiently soluble in organic solvents to warrant extensive use as a protective coating. The use of rubber latex as a coating or lining has been limited due to the high water absorption of the deposited film.

Some of the objectionable features of natural rubber have been overcome by cyclization through the use of agents such as chlorostannic acid and by chlorination. Prior to World War II, cyclized rubber was used in sizable volume as a protective coating but has been replaced to a large extent by the copolymer of styrene and butadiene.

Chlorosulfonated Polyethylene

As previously stated, polyethylene is too insoluble in organic solvents to permit its use as a solution coating. As stated in Chapter 5, improved solubility can be secured by reacting this polymer with chlorine and sulfur dioxide. In addition to increased solubility, it also exhibits excellent adhesion to many different surfaces. It is compatible with many different resins and can be heat-cured when compounded with litharge. It has excellent chemical resistance and can be pigmented to produce a wide variety of colors.

Neoprene

The primary reason for the addition of plasticizers to thermoplastic coatings is to obtain a certain amount of flexibility in the film. In contrast to natural rubber, a modified neoprene, viz, Neoprene KNR, is quite soluble in aromatic hydrocarbon solvents and has outstanding elasticity. This combination of properties makes it ideal for use as a heavy-duty protective coating.

High solids neoprene coatings yield heavy films which adhere well to chlorinated rubber-primed surfaces. As previously indicated, the coatings do not require the addition of plasticizers and are usually compounded on the job so that they cure in situ to form coatings which will not flow even when exposed to steam. They may be spray or brush-applied.

A typical specification for a liquid neoprene coating is as follows: solids content, 54 to 58 per cent (of which at least 50 per cent would be neoprene); specific gravity, 1.1 to 1.2; viscosity @ 77°F 1,750 to 2,500 cps.

One gallon of compounded liquid neoprene should yield a coating of at least 5 mils thickness when applied to 140 sq ft of surface.

Military Specification MIL-15058A for neoprene coating for propeller shafts and other marine applications requires a tensile strength of 1,200 psi and an elongation of 250 per cent. It is required that the tensile strength does not vary more than 20 per cent from the initial value after aging for 96 hours at 158 $\pm$ 2°F. This specification also requires a minimum 15 lbs friction‾pull adhesion test, a hardness of 60 to 80 on the Shore A durometer scale, and a water absorption on boiling four days in water of less than 15 per cent.

Most specifications for neoprene coatings require that the cured coating be essentially unaffected by 20 per cent sulfuric acid, all concentrations of sodium hydroxide, ammonium nitrate, and trisodium phosphate, 10 per cent formic acid, aqueous formaldehyde, kerosene, glycerol and coconut oil at temperatures up to 85°F. Neoprene may be applied as a much heavier film than most other coating materials and it is often used in thicknesses as high as 120 mils. The rapid build-up required for such applications can be accomplished through the use of high solids neoprene coating.

The high solids neoprene coating must be compounded on the job and brush-applied. Approximately 30 minutes after mixing it acquires considerable body. This product may be applied over primed surfaces with coats varying in thickness from 15 to 20 mils each. It does not have as much extensibility as standard neoprene coatings but has greater elasticity and flexibility than most other coating materials and has proved to be adequate for many applications.

The following is a typical specification for this modified liquid neoprene coating: a solids content of not less than 57.5 and not more than 65 per cent and a density of not less than 1.1 and not more than 1.15. The deposited film should have a minimum elongation of 200 per cent, a tensile strength of not less than 500 psi and a Shore hardness of not less than 60. A large off-shore condenser barge coated with liquid neoprene is shown in Figure 7-6.

An impeller-type pump coated with neoprene is shown in Figure 7-7.

High solids neoprene trowel cement or putty is available for filling crevices in steel before the application of the coating and for the repair of damaged rubber rolls. Products of this type are compounded before use in the usual manner, but, of course, must be applied with a trowel or high-pressure spraying equipment rather than by brush or standard spraying equipment.

A typical liquid neoprene trowel cement should have a solids content of not less than 80 per cent, of which at least 40 per cent should be sulfur-modified neoprene. It should have a specific gravity of 1.1 to 1.4 and a viscosity of 800,000 to 1,200,000 cps at 77°F.

In spite of the fact that on-the-job compounded liquid neoprene coatings so nearly approach the ideal specifications and are readily compounded in the field, some maintenance men prefer a readymixed product even though its properties are inferior to the standard coating.

The ready-mixed, so-called maintenance coatings are usually based on the more crystalline, less soluble Neoprene AC rather than the sulfur-modified Neoprene KNR. Such compositions may contain curing agents which limit the can-stability of the product to some

Figure 7-6. Section of compressor barge coated with liquid neoprene.

Figure 7-7. An impeller-type pump coated with liquid neoprene.

extent. As might be concluded, the thickness of the films deposited from the one-part neoprene maintenance paints are much thinner than those deposited from the standard compounded liquid neoprene coatings. However, it is possible to load these coatings with fillers such as mica in order to secure heavy coatings.

Since the so-called maintenance coatings do not cure completely, their resistance to chemicals and abrasion is inferior to the standard coating. In spite of high cost and the previously cited disadvantages, the so-called neoprene maintenance coatings are superior to most thermoplastic protective coatings and they can be applied directly on sandblasted surfaces without the use of a separate priming operation. Of course, a separate priming system is required where exceptional adhesion is essential.

A typical neoprene maintenance coating should have a solids content of not less than 30 per cent, a specific gravity of 0.9 to 1.05, a viscosity of 1,500 to 3,000 cps at 77°F and a shelf life of at least 3 months. One gallon of this type of liquid neoprene should deposit a 2-mils thick film on 175 sq ft of surface.

As might be expected, with the great interest in household application of latex paints based on polyvinyl acetate and styrene butadiene copolymers, there is considerable interest in neoprene latices. Because of inherent high water adsorption, neoprene latex has not been used to any great extent for protection against corrosives but it has been used to line tank cars containing hot liquid caustic. It also has been mixed with hydraulic cements to form specialty trowelling compositions. While these materials cannot be claimed to be completely chemical resistant, they do have an application in the waterproofing field.

Polysulfide Rubber

While olefin polysulfides are best known for their use of solvent-resistant mechanical goods, recent modifications are of some interest in the coatings field. Blends of vinyl resins and olefin polysulfides in the form of aqueous dispersions have been used successfully as coatings for gasoline storage tanks. When finely divided, olefin polysulfides have been flame-sprayed and advocated for protection of propeller shafts and other marine equipment.

The recently developed liquid olefin polysulfide products may be blended with epoxy or phenolic resins in order to provide flexibility in these products. The liquid resin may also be used alone as solvent-resistant coatings or putties. The latter are usually cured at room temperature with lead peroxide.

Cellulose Derivatives

Ethyl cellulose, when deposited from a solution or when used as a molten material, forms a tough film with moderate chemical resistance. It has excellent compatibility with many other resins and is sometimes blended with other coating resins in order to produce toughness.

Cellulose nitrate lacks resistance to flame and chemicals but is tough and its solutions are fast drying. It is used for decorative effects but is seldom recommended for service in corrosive environments.

Cellulose acetate is much less flammable than the nitrate and has been used to a limited extent as a coating. As discussed in Chapter 5, cellulose acetate and the mixed butyl ester have limited chemical resistance.

THERMOSETTING COATINGS

Unsaturated Polyesters

Blends of styrene and so-called unsaturated polyesters can be compounded to yield a protective coating with good chemical resistance. The cured films have excellent adhesion to concrete, wood and epoxy primed steel.

Because the styrene material has a low molecular weight, coatings with extremely high solids content are possible. As might be expected, the high solids coatings deposit unusually heavy films.

Polyester coatings may be pigmented and applied by brushing, roller coating, dipping or spraying. As mentioned in Chapter 5, the cured film is resistant to aqueous solutions of salts and acids but is not suitable for service in strong alkaline environments.

Urea-Melamine Resins

The so-called amino resins are used primarily as baked coatings. When applied from organic solutions and baked at temperatures in the order of 200 to 350°F, hard, light-colored, brittle films and produced. Since these coatings have poor adhesion, they are generally blended with alkyds in order to reduce this deficiency.

The durability of alkyd-urea resin coatings is comparable to that of the alkyds. They are harder and slightly more chemical resistant than the straight alkyd coatings.

The reaction product of urea or melamine with formaldehyde may be further reacted with butyl alcohol under acidic conditions to produce the so-called butylated amino resins. These butylated resins are more soluble in aliphatic hydrocarbon solvents. Compositions with excellent adhesion are obtained when furfuryl alcohol is used in place of butyl alcohol.

Phenolic Coatings

In spite of their lack of resistance to alkalies and impact, baked phenolic coatings have been used for many years for drums and containers holding mildly corrosive materials such as aqueous formaldehyde and food products. The extremely hard, dense coating is excellent for preventing iron contamination of the stored liquid. They are applied as liquid resins dissolved in alcohol and are dried and baked at temperatures in the order of 300°F.

On-the-job catalyzed phenolic coatings have been used to a very small extent over properly primed surfaces but they are usually too brittle for general use. The main use of room temperature catalyzed phenolic resins has been as impregnants for wood and other porous materials.

Oil-soluble phenolic resins based on substituted phenols, such as a reaction product of para-phenyl phenol and formaldehyde, are used quite widely under mild corrosive conditions. These products are usually modified with drying oils and are compounded with suitable pigments for the protection of underwater structures. The chemical resistance of short oil length phenolics is not very good and the resistance decreases as oil length is increased.

Another variation is the terpene-phenolic resins which have better color and superior chemical resistance than straight phenolic resins. These products are available in a wide variety of properties and are often used for medium and short oil variations.

Epoxy Coatings

One of the greatest advances in chemical-resistant coatings during recent years was the introduction of epoxy or ethyoxyline resins. These products, which are formed by the reaction of epichlorohydrin with the condensation product of phenol and acetone, are of considerable interest in the modern coatings industry.

Epoxy coatings may be insolubilized when admixed with melamine, urea or phenolic resins by heating at 350 to 425°F. They may also be cured at room temperature with amine compounds such as ethylene diamine or amine substituted vegetable oils. Epoxy resins are sometimes reacted with drying oil acids to produce coating resins for very mild corrosive conditions.

Epoxy coatings are resistant to acids, alkalies and some solvents. They adhere very well to a wide variety of surfaces and their impact resistance is superior to that of phenolic coatings. A typical specification for a room temperature curing epoxy coating requires a compounded solution with a minimum solids of 65 per cent which yields a film 5 mils thick when 1 gallon is applied to 125 sq ft of surface. When cured, this coating should be unaffected by splash and fumes of 25 per cent sulfuric acid, 10 per cent sodium hydroxide, 10 per cent hydrochloric acid, ethyl alcohol, gasoline or motor oil and the general corrosive conditions anticipated in the petro-chemical industry.

Furan Coatings

These coatings have excellent chemical resistance but are generally considered too brittle for general use. They do have application for the impregnation of soapstone, sandstone, carbon and wood.

Selection of Coatings

Because of the wide variety of materials that are available, the choice of the proper protective coating is sometimes difficult. Fortunately, much screening can be done through the process of elimination. Thus, if the temperature requirements are below 200°F, silicones would seldom be considered. Likewise, if the corrosive conditions are not severe, for example, in the protection of industrial plant equipment in the absence of corrosive fumes, almost any protective coating might be satisfactory. Of course, if a wide variety of colors is required, the choice is limited somewhat to the products based on light-colored resins. On the other hand, if an inexpensive product must be used the choice is limited to coal-tar pitch, asphalts or oil-base paints.

If resistance to abrasion as well as chemicals is required, neoprene should be recommended. However, if hot nitric acid fumes are present, the choice would probably be limited to a vinyl, saran or chlorinated rubber-base coating.

The presence of solvents in the atmosphere would also prevent the use of many other coatings. Baked phenolic coatings have excellent resistance to organic solvents. However, when a field application of a solvent-resistant coating is required, an epoxy resin coating should be selected.

While economics may seem to favor low price coatings, it must be remembered that the cost per mil of applied coating is more important than the cost per gallon. Actually, the most important expense is the cost per unit area of protection per year. Unfortunately, the last value requires too long a time to complete the evaluation and when the results are known, it is often too late to do anything about it. Thus, the most convenient index is the cost per mil of applied coating for a unit area, providing the coating is known to be resistant to the corrosive atmosphere present.

The cost of surface preparation and application usually exceeds the cost of coating materials. Thus, the difference in price per gallon is usually not very significant when over-all costs are considered. Obviously, it pays to stress good surface preparation, workmanship and product quality. Considerable information of the quality of base coating resins is given in Table 7-1.

TABLE 7-1. PHYSICAL PROPERTIES OF FILMS FROM TYPICAL ORGANIC COATINGS

	Specific Gravity	Tensile Strength	Elongation (%)	Water Absorption – 77°F 24 hrs (%)	Maximum Service (Temp. °F)
Vinyl	1.3	2500	350	0.2	150
Chlorinated rubber	1.5	1500	20	0.3	150
Styrene-butadiene	1.1	2000	20	0.4	150
Neoprene	1.3	1600	250	0.5	200
Neoprene maintenance	1.3	1200	600	0.8	175
Epoxy	1.2	4000	5	0.1	200

Note: These properties may vary considerably depending upon the amounts of filler, pigment and plasticizer used. The stated values refer to standard black coatings compounded for maximum chemical resistance.

TABLE 7-2. COMPARATIVE RESISTANT VALUES OF TYPICAL COMMERCIAL COATING FORMULATIONS

Vinyl	TOTAL 87	Epoxy	TOTAL 80	Styrene Copolymer Blends	TOTAL 77
Sun & Weather		Sun & Weather		Sun & Weather	
Stress & Impact		Stress & Impact		Stress & Impact	
Abrasion		Abrasion		Abrasion	
Heat		Heat		Heat	
Water		Water		Water	
Salts		Salts		Salts	
Solvents		Solvents		Solvents	
Alkalies		Alkalies		Alkalies	
Acids		Acids		Acids	
Oxidation		Oxidation		Oxidation	

Neoprene	TOTAL 88	Saran	TOTAL 81	Chlorinated Rubber	TOTAL 78
Sun & Weather		Sun & Weather		Sun & Weather	
Stress & Impact		Stress & Impact		Stress & Impact	
Abrasion		Abrasion		Abrasion	
Heat		Heat		Heat	
Water		Water		Water	
Salts		Salts		Salts	
Solvents		Solvents		Solvents	
Alkalies		Alkalies		Alkalies	
Acids		Acids		Acids	
Oxidation		Oxidation		Oxidation	

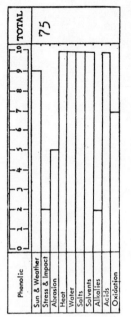

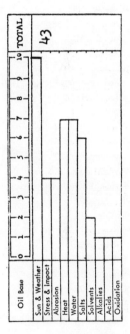

TABLE 7-3. SPECIFIC CHEMICAL RESISTANCE
FOR MAJOR TYPES PROTECTIVE COATINGS

	Vinyl 75°F-150°F		Chlorinated Rubber 75°F-125°F		Styrene-Butadiene Copolymer 75°F-150°F		Neoprene 75°F-160°F		Epoxy 75°F-200°F	
Acids:										
Acetic, 10%	F	N	F	N	F	P	F	N	E	E
Acetic, glacial	N	N	N	N	N	N	N	N	F	P
Benzene sulfonic, 10%	E	E	E	E	E	E	E	E	E	E
Benzoic	E	E	E	E	E	E	E	E	E	E
Boric	E	E	E	E	E	E	E	E	E	E
Butyric, 100%	G	N	N	N	N	N	F	N	G	F
Chloroacetic, 10%	F	N	N	N	N	N	F	N	E	E
Chromic, 10%	E	G	G	F	G	N	N	N	N	N
Chromic, 50%	G	F	P	N	P	N	N	N	N	N
Citric	E	E	E	E	E	E	E	E	E	E
Fatty acids (C$_6$ and up), 100%	E	F	N	N	E	E	F	N	E	E
Fluosilicic, 40%	E	E	E	E	E	E	E	E	E	E
Formic, 90%	F	N	N	N	N	N	G	F	E	F
Hydrobromic, 48%	E	E	E	F	E	P	N*	N*	E	E
Hydrochloric, 37%	E	E	E	E	E	G	N*	N*	E	E
Hydrocyanic, 25%	E	E	E	E	E	E	E	E	E	E
Hydrofluoric, 40%	E	E	E	E	E	G	N*	N*	E*	E*
Hypochlorous, 10%	E	E	G	G	E	F	N	N	P	N
Lactic, 25%	E	E	E	E	E	G	E	E	E	E
Maleic, 25%	G	F	G	F	E	E	G	F	E	E
Nitric, 5%	E	E	G	F	G	P	F	N	F	N
Nitric, 20%	E	E	F	N	F	N	N	N	N	N
Nitric, 40%	G	N	N	N	N	N	N	N	N	N
Oleic, 100%	E	F	N	N	E	E	F	N	E	E
Oxalic, 20%	E	E	E	E	E	E	E	E	E	E
Perchloric	E	E	F	N	E	F	E	N	E	E
Phosphoric, 85%	E	E	F	N	E	G	E	F	E	E
Picric, 10%	P	N	P	N	E	E	P	N	E	E
Stearic, 100%	E	E	E	E	E	E	E	F	E	E
Sulfuric, 50%	E	E	E	E	E	E	E	F	E	E
Sulfuric, 70%	E	G	G	F	G	N	N	N	F	N
Sulfuric, 93%	G	N	N	N	N	N	N	N	N	N
Oleum, 110%	P	N	N	N	N	N	N	N	N	N
Mixed acids, 28% HNO$_3$ 57% H$_2$SO$_4$	G	P	N	N	N	N	N	N	N	N
Alkalies:										
Ammonium hydroxide, 28%	E	F	E	E	E	E	E	E	E	E
Calcium hydroxide saturated	E	P	E	E	E	E	E	E	E	E
Potassium hydroxide, 25%	E	P	E	E	E	E	E	E	E	E
Sodium hydroxide, 25%	E	P	E	E	E	E	E	E	E	E

TABLE 7-3 (Continued)

	Vinyl		Chlorinated Rubber		Styrene-Butadiene Copolymer		Neoprene		Epoxy	
	75°F-150°F		75°F-125°F		75°F-150°F		75°F-160°F		75°F-200°F	
Acid Salts:										
Alum, 10%	E	E	E	E	E	E	E	E	E	E
Ammonium chloride, nitrate, sulfate	E	E	E	E	E	E	E	G	E	E
Copper chloride, nitrate, sulfate	E	E	E	E	E	E	G	F	E	E
Ferric chloride, nitrate, sulfate	E	E	E	E	E	E	F	N	E	E
Nickel chloride, nitrate, sulfate	E	E	E	E	E	E	E	G	E	E
Stannic chloride	E	E	E	E	E	E	G	F	E	F
Zinc chloride, nitrate, sulfate	E	E	E	E	E	E	G	F	E	E
Alkaline Salts:										
Barium sulfide	E	E	E	E	E	E	E	E	E	E
Sodium bicarbonate, 10%	E	E	E	E	E	E	E	E	E	E
Sodium carbonate, 10%	E	E	E	E	E	E	E	E	E	E
Sodium sulfide	E	E	E	E	E	E	E	E	E	E
Trisodium phosphate, 10%	E	E	E	E	E	E	E	E	E	E
Neutral Salts:										
Calcium chloride, sulfate	E	E	E	E	E	E	E	E	E	E
Magnesium chloride, sulfate	E	E	E	E	E	E	E	E	E	E
Potassium chloride, nitrate, sulfate	E	E	E	E	E	E	E	E	E	E
Sodium chloride, nitrate, sulfate	E	E	E	E	E	E	E	E	E	E
Gases:										
Chlorine, dry	E	E	F	N	P	N	N**	N**	F	N
Chlorine, wet	E	F	N	N	N	N	N**	N**	P	N
Sulfur dioxide, dry	E	E	E	E	E	E	E	E	E	E
Sulfur dioxide, wet	E	E	E	E	E	E	E	E	E	E
Hydrogen sulfide	E	E	E	E	E	E	E	E	E	E
Organic Materials:										
Acetone, 100%	N	N	N	N	N	N	N	N	E	P
Alcohol, methyl, ethyl, 100%	E	E	E	E	E	E	E	F	E	E
Aniline	N	N	N	N	N	N	N	N	F	N
Benzene	P	N	N	N	N	N	N	N	E	P
Carbon tetrachloride	N	N	N	N	N	N	N	N	E	F
Chloroform	N	N	N	N	N	N	N	N	E	F
Ethyl acetate	N	N	N	N	N	N	N	N	E	G
Ethylene chloride	N	N	N	N	N	N	N	N	E	F
Formaldehyde, 37%	E	E	E	E	E	E	E	E	E	E

TABLE 7-3.(Continued)

Organic Materials (continued)	Vinyl 75°F-150°F		Chlorinated Rubber 75°F-125°F		Styrene-Butadiene Copolymer 75°F-150°F		Neoprene 75°F-160°F		Epoxy 75°F-200°F	
Gasoline	E	F	P	N	N	N	G	F	E	G
Phenol, 5%	N	N	N	N	E	G	N	N	E	F
Refinery crudes	E	G	N	N	N	N	G	F	E	E
Trichloroethylene	N	N	N	N	N	N	N	N	E	F
Paper Mill Applications:										
Kraft liquor	E	E	E	E	E	E	E	E	E	E
Black liquor	E	E	E	E	E	E	E	E	E	E
Green liquor	E	E	E	E	E	E	E	E	E	E
White liquor	E	E	E	E	E	E	E	E	E	E
Sulfite liquor	E	E	E	E	E	E	E	E	E	E
Chlorite bleach	E	G	G	F	G	F	N**	N**	P	N
Alum	E	E	E	E	E	E	E	E	E	E
Photographic Industry:										
Developers	E	G	E	G	E	E	E	G	E	E
Silver nitrate	E	G	E	G	E	E	E	G	E	E
General use	E	G	E	G	E	E	E	G	E	E
Fertilizer Industry:										
General use	E	E	E	E	E	E	E	E	E	E
Steel Industry:										
Sulfuric acid pickling	E	E	E	E	E	E	E	E	E	E
Hydrochloric acid pickling	E	E	E	E	E	E	N*	N*	E	E
H_2SO_4HNO$_3$ acid pickling	E	E	F	N	F	P	N	N	F	P
Textile Industry:										
General use	E	E	E	E	E	E	E	E	E	E
Hypochlorite bleach	E	G	G	F	G	F	N**	N**	N	N
Food Industry:										
General use	E	E	E	E	E	E	E	E	E	E
Breweries	E	E	E	E	E	E	E	E	E	E
Dairies	E	E	E	E	E	E	E	E	E	E
Miscellaneous Industries:										
Plating	E	E	G	G	E	E	E	E	E	E
Petroleum	G	F	N	N	N	N	G	F	E	E
Tanning	E	E	E	E	E	E	E	E	E	E
Oil and soap	E	E	F	P	E	E	G	F	E	E
Water and sewer	E	E	E	E	E	E	E	E	E	E

*Permeation with concentrated solutions. Plant tests required before use.
**Surface hardening. Plant tests required before use.

Ratings: E — No attack.   P — Attacked – not recommended.
            G — Appreciably no attack.   N — Rapidly attacked.
            F — Some attack but usable in some instances.

There is no simple method for the selection of coatings. Technical knowledge, empirical know-how, experience and application ability are all important. While not infallible, the information in Table 7-2 has proved to be a helpful guide in many instances.

In this table, the relative resistance of typical commercial coatings to sunlight, weather, stress, impact, abrasion, heat, water, salts, solvents, alkalies, acids and oxidation have been compared using a value of 10 as the ultimate for each property. This table has found considerable use for screening various coatings through the application of the following rules:

1. No coating should be considered for an application when the index value for the important requirements is less than 6. Thus, epoxy, furan or phenolic coatings should be considered for exposure to solvents but these products should not be used if there is apt to be movement of the coated surface due to expansion, vibration or impact.

2. No coating should be recommended for a specific application unless the index value for the major requirement is greater than 8. Thus, when the major requirement is resistance to abrasion, only neprene should be considered.

3. No coating should be considered as a universal protective coating unless its total index value is greater than 75. Thus, furans, phenolics, alkyds, asphalts, and oil-base paints should be recommended only when requirements having low index values are considered to be unimportant for a specific application.

The application of empirical knowledge of the type presented herein should help to prevent misapplication of resinous materials for specific protective coating application. However, as previously indicated, there is no substitute for technical and practical knowledge in this field.

Specific chemical resistance values for five of the most commonly used industrial protective coatings is given in Table 7-3. It should be pointed out that omission of any specific coating should not be misinterpreted as a condemnation of that product.

As previously stated, coatings are recommended primarily for splash and fume service. Organic linings, which are suitable for continuous immersion service with corrosives, are discussed in Chapter 8.

Suggested References

"Protective Coatings for Metals," Second Edition, R. M. Burns and W. W. Bradley, Reinhold Publishing Corp., New York, 1955.

"Protective and Decorative Coatings," Vols. I-V, Jos. J. Mattiello, John Wiley & Sons, Inc., New York, 1941-46.

"Organic Protective Coatings," Wm. Von Fischer and Ed. G. Bobalek, Reinhold Publishing Corp., New York, 1953.

"Neoprenes," N. L. Catton, E. I. duPont de Nemours & Co., Inc., Wilmington, Del., 1953.

"A Primer on Protective Coatings," Raymond B. Seymour, Organic Finishing, March 1953.

"Protective Coatings," Kenneth Tator, Chem. Eng., 59, 143, Dec. 1952.

"Protective Coatings in the Plating Industry," Raymond B. Seymour, in "Metal Finishing Guidebook-Directory," 21st Annual Edition, 98 (1953).

"Synthetic Resins and Polymers," Raymond B. Seymour, in "Organic Finishing Handbook," p. 37 (1954).

"Chemical Resistant Coatings," Raymond B. Seymour, in "Organic Finishing Handbook," p. 199 (1954).

"Protective Coating Fundamentals for Southern Industry," Raymond B. Seymour, Southern Chemical Industry, VI, No. 1, Jan-Feb 1954.

"Chemical Resistant Cement Reference Sheet No. 20—Epoxy Cement," Raymond B. Seymour and Robert H. Steiner, Chem. Eng. Prog., April 1953.

"Plastics Equipment Reference Sheet No. 22—Plasticized Vinyl Resins," Raymond B. Seymour and Robert H. Steiner, Chem. Eng. Prog., June 1953.

"Plastics Equipment Reference Sheet No. 23—High Styrene-Butadiene Copolymers Coatings," Raymond B. Seymour and Robert H. Steiner, Chem. Eng. Prog., July 1953.

"Plastics Equipment Reference Sheet No. 24—Chlorinated Rubber Coatings," Raymond B. Seymour and Robert H. Steiner, Chem. Eng. Prog., Aug. 1953.

"Plastics Equipment Reference Sheet No. 25—Neoprene Rubber," Raymond B. Seymour and Robert H. Steiner, Chem. Eng. Prog., Sept. 1953.

"Organic Coating Technology," H. F. Payne, John Wiley & Sons, Inc., New York, 1954.

"Epoxys for Cements and Coatings," R. B. Seymour and R. H. Steiner, Chem. Eng., 61, No. 4, 244-52 (1954).

"Asphaltic Mastics," R. B. Seymour and R. H. Steiner, Chem. Eng., 61, No. 5, 232 (1954).

"Laboratory and Plant Evaluation of Liquid Neoprene Coatings," R. B. Seymour, Corrosion, 10, No. 4, 116-21 (1954).

"Chlorinated Rubber Corrosion-Resistant Coatings," F. K. Shankweiler, G. W. Bruxelles, and R. E. Whitney, Corrosion, 8, 130-39 (1952).

"Application Techniques, Physical Characteristics and Chemical Resistance of Polyvinyl Chlor-Acetates," Corrosion, 10, No. 10, 349 (1954).

"Alkyd Resins," R. H. Kienle, Ind. Eng. Chem., 41, 726, April 1949.

"Development of Equipment for Alkyd Resins Manufacture," A. G. Hovey, Ind. Eng. Chem., 41, 730, April 1949.

"Theories and Facts Concerning Alkyds," Kenneth A. Earhart, Ind. Eng. Chem., 41, 716, April 1949.

8. ORGANIC LININGS

It was recommended in Chapter 7 that the use of protective coatings be limited to the protection of corrodible surfaces from splash and fumes. In contrast, the applications discussed in this chapter are designed for continuous exposure to corrosives under conditions of complete or partial immersion.

The basic difference between coatings and linings is their relative thickness. As pointed out in the preceding chapter, coatings are usually applied in thicknesses of from 5 to 10 mils. Linings may vary in thicknesses from 3/32 to 3/8 inch, depending upon the materials used and the anticipated corrosive environment. Films have thicknesses in between coatings and linings, i.e., 10 to 60 mils.

Linings may be applied by four fundamentally different methods.

1. In one of the most commonly used techniques, dense, homogeneous sheets are adhered to a tank wall through the use of specially designed adhesive systems. Joints between sheets may be overlapped and thermally welded or butt jointed and protected by a welded cover strap. In no case is the adhesive exposed directly to the liquid corrosive.

2. Multiple layers of a liquid coating are built up by brushing, spraying, or dipping techniques. This method utilizes application techniques discussed in the preceding chapter and is especially use-

3. Molten material is applied using a straight-edge board or sqeegee. This technique is usually limited to the application of filled asphalts and highly plasticized sulfur cements.

4. Resin mortar cements or comparable products are applied to the tank wall through the use of a plasterer's trowel. The use of high-pressure spray systems for this type of application has also shown some promise.

It should be emphasized that considerable skill and experience are required for the application of organic linings. Lining applications are restricted primarily to storage and processing equipment. The installation of organic linings is seldom entrusted to ordinary plant maintenance men.

The hazards and plant down-time resulting from faulty lining installations have been recognized by corrosion engineers. Hence, few are willing to risk the possibility of misapplication of lining materials. However, such risks are still accepted in the application of some protective coatings.

Extreme care must be exercised in structure design, surface preparation, installation and subsequent care of lined equipment. Design information is given in Chapters 20 and 21 but the other items will be discussed in this chapter.

Surface Preparation

Greater precautions than those cited in Chapter 7 for protective coatings must be taken to assure adequate surface preparation of steel tanks before the application of linings. Condition No. 1, as established by the National Association of Corrosion Engineers must be secured prior to the application of linings on steel structures. This condition assures the complete removal of all loose and tight scale as well as all other types of surface contamination. Since experienced lining applicators recognize the importance of sound surface preparation, the need for this step in lining application is seldom a question. Obviously, the initial priming coat must be applied immediately after the surface has been blasted and solvent-cleaned.

Concrete must be carefully cured and free from surface contamination. All surfaces to be protected must be perfectly smooth to prevent entrapment of air behind the lining.

Production of Lining Materials

Most sheet rubber and plastic linings are prepared by compounding the ingredients on a rubber mill or in a Banbury mixer and then calendering to form thin sheets with thicknesses in the order of 20 mils. These sheets are then plied up to various thicknesses, depending upon the anticipated service conditions.

Natural rubber tank linings may vary in thickness from 1/8 to 1/2 inch. The thinnest sheet is used only for light-duty service. The most commonly used thickness is 3/16 inch. However, 1/4 inch thick linings are used behind brick-word in steel pickling tanks and 3/8 inch thick sheets are used for heavy-duty service where severe abrasion as well as corrosives may be encountered.

Saran rubber sheet is generally installed as 1/8 inch thick sheet but 3/16 inch thickness is also available. Plasticized polyvinyl chloride sheet is available as 1/32, 1/16, 3/32, 1/8 and 3/16 inches in thickness but the most widely used sheet is 3/32 inch thick. Some plastic linings are made by press-laminating several thicknesses of compounded sheet or by extrusion of the compounded material in sheet form.

Application Methods

As stated previously, installation of all sheet linings require sandblasting and solvent cleaning of the metal surface. The sheet is then adhered to the surface by the use of specific adhesive systems. Application techniques vary considerably depending upon the nature of the material used, but one coat of a suitable metal primer must be applied to the clean metal surface as soon as possible to prevent rusting.

For most applications, it is customary to cut the sheets to shape and coat them with a suitable adhesive. Usually two or three coats of adhesive are applied to the sheet and one or two coats to the previously primed metal surface. In some systems thermoplastic resin adhesives are used, while thermosetting plastics, which cure with heat to produce temperature-resistant bonds, are used in others. The application of an adhesive to sheet rubber is illustrated in Figure 8-1.

Figure 8-1. Priming of sheet lining prior to application.

Sheet lining is usually applied to the tank surface using a gradual scraping or rolling action to eliminate entrapment of air as shown in Figure 8-2. With thermoplastic materials, such as plasticized polyvinyl chloride, preheating of the sheet simplifies the application procedure.

The joints between individual sheets may be sealed by two basically different methods. With vulcanizable rubbers, these joints are usually produced by overlapping the sheets and stitching the heat-softened edges together with special tools as shown in Figure 8-3. Thermoplastic sheet materials are usually joined by thermally welding a cover strap over the tightly butted edges.

After the joints are heat sealed, they are usually inspected with a high-voltage spark tester to insure freedom from pinholes. Pinholes or any other imperfections are usually marked with a crayon and repaired immediately.

Vulcanizable linings are usually cured under steam pressure. However, some highly-filled linings may be cured with hot water. Autoclaves are seldom available in the field and hence, hot water curing must be used for most field installations.

As explained in Chapter 21, outlets in steel tanks must be designed so that the lining extends from the outlet and covers the flange space. Heavy thicknesses of sheet are often used at the entrance and immediately below manholes or other openings where possibility of physical damage exists.

Figure 8-2. Tank lining operation showing use of a straight edge to cement rubber sheet to a cylindrical tank.

Large diameter pipe is lined in much the same manner as tanks. Small diameter pipe is usually lined by forming the tube on a mandrel, priming the exterior and then inserting the tube in the primed pipe. Contact between the primed tube and the pipe is assured by placing the pipe in an upright position and gradually filling with warm water.

The multiple-layer method using protective coatings for tank linings utilizes methods discussed previously in Chapter 7. Vinyl plastisols or plastigels are sometimes applied by dipping or troweling techniques with subsequent oven curing.

Molten materials are usually applied as multiple layers and preferably using an alternate color system to assure complete coverage. It is well to apply the first few layers as thin films in order to minimize the difficulties which may result from air or moisture entrapment on the surface. Exceptional care must be exerted to eliminate bubbles, since these and other imperfections usually continue through subsequent layers.

Solvent-type troweling compositions have been advocated occasionally for tank linings but because of the danger of solvent entrapment, their use is generally avoided. When both nonpolar sol-

Figure 8-3. Joining of adjacent sheets by lapping through heat welding and mechanical stitching.

vents and acids are encountered, lead or resin cement troweled-type linings are usually recommended. Both should be protected by brick lining whenever possible. Resin cement linings must be applied and inspected with extreme care. Some techniques employ a thermoplastic or elastomeric layer between the steel shell and the rigid resin cement lining. Others make use of expanded metal grids which are spot-welded to the steel surface before the application of the resin mortar cement.

Care of Organic Linings

Most organic linings are designed for corrosive liquid service at temperatures below 150°F. As illustrated in Chapter 9, linings should be protected by brick sheathings for high temperature service or when there is danger of mechanical damage. Attack by corrosives can be minimized by supporting the tank on piers and by painting the exterior with a suitable protective coating. If the lining is not protected by a brick sheathing, extreme care must be exercised when the tank is emptied or cleaned. No sharp implements should be allowed to come in contact with the surface of the organic lining.

Any evidence of lining damage should be inspected as soon as possible. Small cuts or imperfections can often be repaired in the field. Delays in repairing damaged tanks may result in complete destruction of the steel or concrete shell.

MATERIALS USED FOR LININGS

Plasticized Sulfur

Most attempts to use sulfur cements as lining materials have been unsuccessful. However, it has been standard practice for many years to use a highly-plasticized sulfur cement lining as the inner layer of a triple-layer asphaltic lining for the protection of concrete vessels.

Polyethylene

Some success has been obtained as the result of an attempt to flame-spray polyethylene. While flame-sprayed compounded polyethylene will adhere to sandblasted steel, special adhesive systems are preferred for heavy sprayed linings. Superior results have been claimed for blends of polyethylene with small amounts of polyisobutylene or butyl rubber.

Small welded polyethylene tanks such as described in Chapter 16 have been used successfully as inner liners. These liners are not cemented to the tank. The metal structure acts primarily as a support for the plastic innerliner.

Polyisobutylene

Carbon-filled polyisobutylene sheet linings are used quite extensively on the European continent but have not been promoted to any great extent in the United States. Observation of European practices and small-scale experiments have shown that these linings are practical and that they are suitable for use with many corrosives which attack natural rubber. However, there are few applications where polyisobutylene has any advantage over plasticized polyvinyl chloride linings.

Asphalt

Hot applied asphalt has been used successfully on concrete both by itself and as part of the previously discussed triple-layer type construction. Asphalt lining is always applied over primed concrete and is protected by a brick sheathing. Solvent-type asphalt trowel cements have also been proposed but since residual solvents may be entrapped, they are not usually recommended.

Compounded filled asphalt-base sheets which are applied by flame techniques have been used successfully for many years on steel, both with and without brick sheathing. Coal-tar pitch and coumarone-indene resins have been used as coatings but as a rule are not applied in sufficient thickness to qualify as organic linings.

Acrylates

Attempts to use polyalkyl acrylates as commercial elastomers have met with some degree of success. Rubbery copolymers of butyl acrylate and acrylonitrile are available commercially but they have not been used as chemical-resistant sheet linings.

Polyvinyl Chloride

Solutions of plasticized vinyl chloride-vinyl acetate copolymers have been used to a small extent as field-applied linings. Since plastisols and plastigels can be applied in much greater thickness they are more economical than those applied from solution. However, oven-curing at 325 to 360°F is required for satisfactory application of such linings.

Plasticized polyvinyl chloride sheet linings have been used successfully in the American chemical industry for about twenty years. The sheet, which has a Shore durometer hardness of 85 to 95, a tensile strength of over 2000 psi and an elongation of about 350 per cent withstands many corrosives which attack natural rubber. Two typical steel tanks with plasticized polyvinyl chloride sheet lining are shown in Figure 8-4.

Plasticized polyvinyl chloride sheet linings which are usually supplied in 3/32 inch thickness will withstand moderate concentrations of nitric and other oxidizing acids which rapidly attack rubber. They are used for plating tanks and for stainless steel pickling tanks. The latter process uses a mixture of hydrofluoric and nitric acids at 165°F and requires a carbon brick sheathing or further protection.

Attempts to use unplasticized polyvinyl chloride as an adhered lining have not been satisfactory due to the great difference in co-

Figure 8-4. Reaction vessels (2,000 gal. capacity) coated with vinyl, lined with plasticized vinyl sheets.

efficient of expansion between the two materials. However, as described in Chapter 16, insert liners have been used successfully when the space between the lining and the steel was filled with an asphaltic mastic.

Some success has also been attained using a composite sheet of plasticized and unplasticized polyvinyl chloride. In this case, the softer side of the sheet is adhered to the steel shell and the lining has the appearance and resistance of unplasticized polyvinyl chloride.

Saran Rubber

A copolymer of vinylidene chloride and acrylonitrile when plasticized and admixed with carbon black can be extruded to form dense sheets. These sheets can be applied using the techniques previously described. Saran rubber linings are suitable for service with non-oxidizing salts and acids at temperatures up to 135°F, but are not recommended for use with alkaline solutions. The interior of a saran rubber-lined ion exchange resin tank is shown in Figure 8-5.

Polyfluorocarbons

As stated in Chapter 7, polyfluorocarbon coatings produce excellent anti-adhesive surfaces but as yet are not satisfactory for chemical-resistant applications. However, prefabricated polyfluorocarbon insert liners have given good service behind brickwork in several installations. An electronically sealed drum liner of polychlorotri-

Figure 8-5. Interior of 2,000-gal. water treatment tank lined with saran rubber.

fluoroethylene film is shown in Figure 8-6. It should also be noted that recently developed polyfluorocarbon elastomers have shown promise as organic linings.

Polyurethane

Because of their superior resistance to abrasion, glycol extended polyurethanes obtained by the reaction of liquid polyesters and organic isocyanates have been used in Germany in place of natural rubber. These materials are commercially available in the United States. However, because of their lack of resistance to acids and alkalies, they probably will be important only as specialty tank lining materials.

Natural Rubber

It has been estimated that over 70 per cent of all elastomeric tank

(Courtesy of Kellogg Company)

Figure 8-6. Electronically sealed drum liner of polychlorotrifluoro-
ethylene film.

linings are based on natural rubber. As indicated in Chapter 5, soft
rubber is resistant to most non-oxidizing corrosives in the absence
of nonpolar solvents. The exterior of an extremely large storage tank
lined with natural rubber is shown in Figure 7-3, p. 90.

Some success has been obtained in the application of compounded
rubber latex as a tank lining. However, because of the high water
absorption of the deposited rubber layer, its use is limited to field
and small-scale applications. A 48-inch diameter steel pipe section
with spray-applied compounded natural rubber latex lining is shown
in Figure 8-7.

Hard rubber, although somewhat more resistant to chemicals than
soft rubber, is more difficult to apply. This objection has been overcome in part by the use of a triple-layer sheet in which the outer
layers are hard and the inner layers are soft rubber. Most natural

Figure 8-7. Pipe section (48-in. diameter) lined with seamless natural rubber lining.

rubber linings must be vulcanized with high-pressure steam. However, highly filled natural rubber sheet may be cured with hot water.

Butyl Rubber

Copolymers of isobutylene and isoprene have excellent resistance to ozone and gas diffusion. They are used as specialty chemical-resistant sheet linings.

Chlorosulfonated Polyethylene

Chlorosulfonated polyethylene can be heat-cured and has superior resistance to flow at 150 to 175°F. It also exhibits good adhesion to steel and concrete. While this product has many possibilities in future applications, too little experience is available at this time to justify further discussion.

Styrene Rubber

The chemical resistance of GR-S sheet linings is essentially the

the same as those based on natural rubber. However, their use has been limited to periods of emergency when natural rubber linings were not available.

Acrylonitrile Rubber

Compounded butadiene-acrylonitrile copolymers have been applied as sheet linings in instances where resistance to aliphatic hydrocarbons was required. As indicated in Chapter 5, the acid and alkali resistance of these linings is inferior to those based on GR-S or natural rubber.

Neoprene

Cured neoprene sheet linings have been used in place of natural rubber for service with all corrosives except hydrochloric acid. In addition, neoprene has greater resistance to elevated temperatures, sunlight, and aliphatic solvents such as mineral oil. Neoprene may be applied from a solution in an organic solvent or as an aqueous dispersion. These applications are primarily heavy application of protective coating techniques as described in Chapter 7.

Polysulfide Rubber

While polysulfide rubbers have poor resistance to acids and alkalies, they have been used in the form of sheet and aqueous dispersion when solvent resistance was a prerequisite. Compounded cements based on the more recently developed liquid polysulfide rubber have some use for applications requiring solvent resistance.

Unsaturated Polyesters

"Fiberglas"-reinforced unsaturated polyester insert linings have been used occasionally in steel and concrete vessels. However, because of their limited resistance to acids and alkalies, as outlined in Chapter 5, the use of general-purpose polyesters will probably be limited to noncorrosive applications. Chemical resistant unsaturated polyesters are now available and should find application as insert linings for specialty use.

Phenolic Resins

Although baked phenolic coatings have given satisfactory service for tanks containing mildly corrosive materials, attempts to apply heavy phenolic linings have not been successful.

Epoxy Resins

Some success has been obtained with troweled-on epoxy resin cement linings. The principal drawback to this application has been the shrinkage which occurs during the curing of the resin. As in the case of chemical-resistant polyesters, glass reinforced epoxy resins are of interest as insert linings for specialty use.

Furan Resins

The chemical resistance of furan resins is superior to almost all other organic polymers except the polyfluorocarbons. However, as in the case of epoxy resin, the inherent shrinkage makes the application of these resin cements difficult.

Some degree of success has been obtained through several patented modifications. For example, the insertion of an elastomeric layer between the tank wall and the "Fiberglas"-reinforced furan lining is said to reduce cracking. Another type of construction which has shown promise is based on the application of an asbestos-filled silicate mortar to an expanded metal structure previously spot-welded to the vessel. This metal grid work serves as a base for the reinforced furan lining.

Trowel-applied furan resin cement membranes have also been applied successfully between courses of brick linings. In this technique, which is restricted primarily to circular vessels, the metal or concrete surface is protected by multiple coats of an epoxy resin. The first course of brick or tile is then installed with a backjoint of resin cement using the techniques discussed in Chapter 22.

It is customary to apply a coat of epoxy resin on the brick or tile surface and then to apply a 1/8-inch thick furan resin cement. The chemical resistant glass cloth is embedded in the cement before it hardens.

After the cement layer has cured thoroughly, a second course of brick is installed. It is customary to butter the brick on five sides with a furan resin cement to produce a solvent- and corrosion-resistant lining.

Silicate Linings

The asbestos-filled cement lining reinforced with metal grids referred to under furan resins has been used successfully for lining fluid catalyst cracking units in the petroleum industry. These units operate successfully at temperatures of 700 to 900°F. Because of its high water absorption, this lining has limited application unless protected by more resistant materials as outlined in the previous paragraph.

Comparative Data

Comparative data on the physical properties of organic linings are given in Table 8-1. The relative utility of various lining materials are compared graphically in Table 8-2 and their relative chemical resistance to both hot and cold corrosives is given in Table 8-3.

PLASTIC MATERIALS OF CONSTRUCTION

TABLE 8-1. PHYSICAL PROPERTIES OF ORGANIC LININGS

	Soft Rubber	Hard Rubber	Neoprene	Plasticized Polyvinyl Chloride	Triple Layer Asphalt	Furan Resin Cement Linings
Tensile strength, psi. @ 77°F	3,000	7,500	2,500	2,500	–	1,200
Elongation, %	700	5	500	350	–	<1
Specific gravity	0.9	1.7	1.2	1.3	1.0	1.4
Compressive strength, psi	–	14,000	–	–	–	14,000
Max. Service Temp., °F						
high	150	160	180	150	100	230
low	–80	+35	–20	–25	–30	–20
Resistance to flame	Poor	Poor-fair	Fair	Good	Poor	Fair
Resistance to abrasion	Excellent	Fair	Excellent	Good	Poor	Fair-good

TABLE 8-2. RELATIVE UTILITY OF VARIOUS LINING MATERIALS.

Gaskets

Almost all plastics that are available as sheet linings are useful for making gaskets. Some products such as polytetrafluoroethylene which do not adhere well, make excellent gasket materials. It is customary to use polyfluoroethylene sheet either by itself or as a complete shield for asbestos gasket material.

Gaskets can be formed in place using neoprene or polysulfide rubber putties or cements. The most widely used gasket materials are polyethylene, plasticized polyvinyl chloride, polyvinyl alcohol, saran rubber, polyfluorocarbons, silicone rubber, soft natural rubber, butyl rubber, acrylonitrile rubber, neoprene and polysulfide rubber.

Use of Linings at Elevated Temperatures

As indicated in Table 8-1, with the exception of furan resin cement linings, none are satisfactory for use at temperatures above

TABLE 8-2 (Continued).

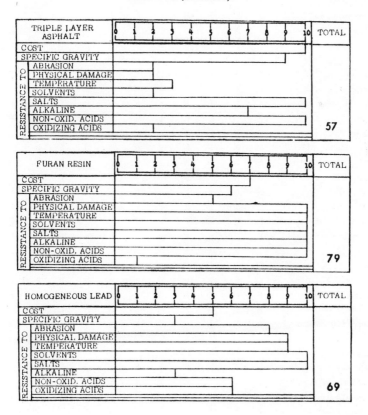

TABLE 8-3. COMPARATIVE RESISTANCE OF LINING MATERIALS

	Soft Rubber 75°F-150°F		Hard Rubber 75°F-150°F		Neoprene 75°F-160°F		Plasticized Polyvinyl Chloride 75°F-150°F		Triple Layer Asphalt 75°F-150°F		Furan Resin Cement Linings 75°F-250°F	
Acids:												
Acetic, 10%	P	N	E	E	F	N	F	N	N	N	E	E
Acetic, glacial	N	N	E	G	N	N	N	N	N	N	E	E
Benzene sulfonic, 10%	E	E	E	E	E	E	E	E	E	E	E	E
Benzoic, saturated	E	E	E	E	E	E	E	E	E	E	E	E
Boric, saturated	E	E	E	E	E	E	E	E	E	E	E	E
Butyric, 100%	N	N	E	G	F	N	F	N	N	N	E	E
Chloroacetic, 10%	P	N	E	E	F	N	F	N	N	N	E	E
Chromic, 10%	N	N	P	N	N	N	E	G	G	F	N	N
Chromic, 50%	N	N	N	N	N	N	G	F	N	N	N	N
Citric, 10%	E	E	E	E	E	E	E	E	E	E	E	E
Fatty acids (C$_6$ and up), 100%	P	N	E	G	F	N	E	F	N	N	E	E
Fluosilicic, 40%	E	E	E	E	E	E	E	E	E	E	E	E
Formic, 90%	P	N	G	N	G	F	N	N	F	N	E	E
Hydrobromic, 48%	E	F	E	E	N*	N*	E	F	E	E	E	E
Hydrochloric, 37%	E	E	E	E	N*	N*	E	F	E	E	E	E
Hydrocyanic, 25%	E	E	E	E	E	E	E	E	E	E	E	E
Hydrofluoric, 40%	E	F	E	E	N*	N*	E	F	E	E	E	E
Hypochlorous, 10%	F	P	F	F	N	N	F	F	F	F	P	N
Lactic, 25%	E	E	E	E	E	E	E	E	E	E	E	E
Maleic, 25%	E	E	E	E	G	F	G	F	G	F	E	E
Nitric, 5%	P	N	F	N	F	N	G	G	E	E	F	N
Nitric, 20%	N	N	N	N	N	N	F	N	E	F	N	N
Nitric, 40%	N	N	N	N	N	N	N	N	G	N	N	N
Oleic, 100%	N	N	E	G	F	N	N	N	E	F	E	E
Oxalic, 20%	E	E	E	E	E	E	E	E	E	E	E	E
Perchloric, 40%	E	E	E	E	E	E	E	E	E	E	E	E
Phosphoric, 85%	E	E	E	E	E	E	E	E	E	E	E	E
Picric, 10%	P	N	P	N	P	N	P	N	P	N	E	E
Stearic, 100%	N	N	E	G	G	F	N	N	E	F	E	E
Sulfuric, 50%	E	E	E	E	E	F	E	F	E	E	E	E
Sulfuric, 70%	F	N	F	N	N	N	N	N	E	G	E	F
Sulfuric, 93%	N	N	N	N	N	N	N	N	G	N	G	N
Oleum, 110%	N	N	N	N	N	N	N	N	G	P	N	N
Alkalies:												
Ammonium hydroxide, 28%	G	F	E	F	E	E	G	G	G	F	E	E
Calcium hydroxide, satd.	E	E	E	E	E	E	G	F	F	P	E	E
Potassium hydroxide, 25%	E	E	E	E	E	E	G	F	F	P	E	E
Sodium hydroxide, 25%	E	E	E	E	E	E	G	F	F	P	E	E

TABLE 8-3 (Continued).

	Soft Rubber 75°F-150°F	Hard Rubber 75°F-150°F	Neoprene 75°F-160°F	Plasticized Polyvinyl Chloride 75°F-150°F	Triple Layer Asphalt 75°F-150°F	Furan Resin Cement Linings 75°F-250°F
Acid salts:						
Alum 10%	E E	E E	E E	E E	E E	E E
Ammonium chloride, nitrate, sulfate, 10%	E E	E E	E G	E E	E E	E E
Copper chloride, sulfate, 10%	E E	E E	G F	E E	E E	E E
Ferric chloride, sulfate, 10%	E E	E E	F N	E E	E E	E E
Nickel chloride, sulfate, 10%	E E	E E	E G	E E	E E	E E
Stannic chloride, 100%	E F	E G	G F	E E	E E	E E
Zinc chloride,sulfate,10%	E E	E E	G F	E E	E E	E E
Alkaline salts:						
Barium sulfide, 10%	E E	E E	E E	G F	F N	E E
Sodium bicarbonate, 10%	E E	E E	E E	E E	E E	E E
Sodium carbonate, 10%	E E	E E	E E	E G	G P	E E
Sodium sulfide, 10%	E E	E E	E E	G F	F N	E E
Trisodium phosphate,10%	E E	E E	E E	G F	N N	E E
Neutral Salts:						
Calcium chloride, nitrate, 10%	E E	E E	E E	E E	E E	E E
Calcium sulfate, satd.	E E	E E	E E	E E	E E	E E
Magnesium chloride, sulfate, 10%	E E	E E	E E	E E	E E	E E
Potassium chloride, nitrate, sulfate, 10%	E E	E E	E E	E E	E E	E E
Sodium chloride, nitrate, sulfate, 10%	E E	E E	E E	E E	E E	E E
Gases:						
Chlorine, wet	F N	F N	N** N**	F F	E F	P N
Chlorine, dry	G F	G F	N** N**	G F	E E	F N
Hydrogen sulfide	G F	E E	E E	E E	E E	E E
Sulfur dioxide, wet	E F	E E	E E	E E	E E	E E
Sulfur dioxide, dry	E E	E E	E E	E E	E E	E E
Organic Materials:						
Acetone, 100%	G F	E E	N N	N N	N N	E E
Alcohols, methyl, ethyl, 95%	E E	E E	E F	G G	G G	E E
Aniline	N N	N N	N N	N N	N N	P N

TABLE 8-3 (Continued).

	Soft Rubber 75°F-150°F		Hard Rubber 75°F-150°F		Neoprene 75°F-160°F		Plasticized Polyvinyl Chloride 75°F-150°F		Triple Layer Asphalt 75°F-150°F		Furan Resin Cement Linings 75°F-250°F	
Organic Materials (continued)												
Benzene	N	N	N	N	N	N	N	N	P	N	E	E
Carbon tetrachloride	N	N	N	N	N	N	N	N	N	N	E	E
Chloroform	N	N	N	N	N	N	N	N	N	N	E	E
Ethyl acetate	N	N	N	N	N	N	N	N	N	N	E	E
Ethylene chloride	N	N	N	N	N	N	N	N	N	N	E	E
Formaldehyde, 37%	G	F	E	F	E	E	E	E	E	E	E	E
Gasoline	N	N	G	N	G	F	E	F	N	N	E	E
Phenol, 5%	F	N	G	F	N	N	N	N	N	N	E	E
Trichloroethylene	N	N	N	N	N	N	N	N	N	N	E	E
Paper Mill Applications:												
Kraft liquor	E	E	E	E	E	E	G	F	F	P	E	E
Black liquor	E	E	E	E	E	E	G	F	F	P	E	E
Green liquor	E	E	E	E	E	E	G	F	F	P	E	E
White liquor	E	E	E	E	E	E	G	F	F	P	E	E
Sulfite liquor	E	F	E	E	E	E	E	G	E	G	E	E
Chlorite bleach	F	N	G	N	N	N	E	F	N	N	P	N
Chlorine dioxide, acid solution	N	N	N	N	N	N	E	G	N	N	N	N
Photographic Industry:												
Developers	E	G	E	G	E	G	E	E	E	G	E	E
Silver nitrate	G	F	E	G	E	G	E	E	E	G	E	E
General use	E	G	E	G	E	G	E	E	E	G	E	E
Fertilizer Industry:												
General use	E	E	E	E	E	E	E	E	E	E	E	E
Steel Industry:												
Sulfuric acid pickling	E	E	E	E	E	E	E	E	E	E	E	E
Hydrochloric acid	E	E	E	E	N**	N**	E	F	E	F	E	E
H_2SO_4-HNO_3 pickling	N	N	N	N	N	N	E	F	N	N	P	N
Textile Industry:												
General use	E	G	E	G	E	E	E	E	E	E	E	E
Hypochlorite bleach	F	N	G	N	N**	N**	E	F	N	N	P	N
Food Industry:												
General use	E	E	E	E	E	E	E	E	E	E	E	E
Breweries	E	E	E	E	E	E	E	E	E	E	E	E
Dairies	E	E	E	E	E	E	E	E	E	E	E	E

TABLE 8-3 (Continued).

	Soft Rubber 75°F-150°F	Hard Rubber 75°F-150°F	Neoprene 75°F-160°F	Plasticized Polyvinyl Chloride 75°F-150°F		Triple Layer Asphalt 75°F-150°F		Furan Resin Cement Linings 75°F-250°F	
Miscellaneous Industries:									
Plating	G	F	G	G	E	E	E	E	G	F	E	E
Petroleum	N	N	N	N	G	F	G	F	N	N	E	E
Tanning	E	E	E	E	E	E	E	E	E	E	E	E
Oil and soap	N	N	F	N	G	F	E	F	N	N	E	E
Water and sewer	E	E	E	E	E	E	E	E	E	E	E	E

*Permeation with concentrated solution. Plant tests required before use.
**Surface hardening. Plant tests required before use.

Ratings: E – No attack
G – Appreciably no attack
F – Some attack but usable in some instances
P – Attacked—not recommended
N – Rapidly attacked

200°F. This disadvantage is overcome by using brick sheathings for additional protection. Figure 8-8 shows the temperature drop through 4 and 8 inches of brick sheathing over a 3/16-inch elastomeric lining on a steel tank.

Additional information on masonry sheathings is given in Chapter 22.

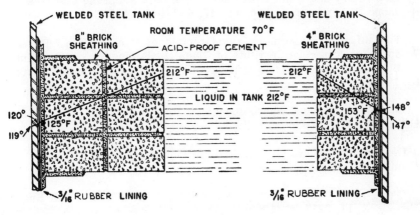

Figure 8-8.

Suggested References

"Plastics Materials of Construction,"Raymond B. Seymour, Corrosion, 9, 5, 152-9 (1953).

"Plastics Meet the Acid Test," Raymond B. Seymour, Modern Plastics, Aug. 1950.

"Engineering with Rubber," W. E. Burton, Chapt. 15, 23, McGraw Hill Publishing Co., New York, 1949.

"Symposium on Rubber," H. E. Fritz & J. R. Hoover, Am. Soc. Testing Materials, Proc. p. 113, July 1932.

"Plastics Equipment Reference Sheet No. 16—Furane Cement," Raymond B. Seymour and Robert H. Steiner, Chem. Eng. Prog., Dec. 1952.

"Plastics Equipment Reference Sheet No. 22—Plasticized Vinyl Resins," Raymond B. Seymour and Robert H. Steiner, Chem. Eng. Prog., June 1953.

"Plastics Equipment Reference Sheet No. 25—Neoprene Rubber," Raymond B. Seymour and Robert H. Steiner, Chem. Eng. Prog., Sept. 1953.

"Laboratory and Plant Evaluations of Liquid Neoprene Coatings," Raymond B. Seymour, Corrosion, 10, 4, 116-21 (1954).

"Vulcanizable Elastomers as Materials of Construction," B. M. G. Zwicker, American Institute of Chemical Engineers, Symposium on Polymeric Materials of Construction, Springfield, Mass., May 18, 1954.

"Methods Employed in Compounding Research," I. Drogin, India Rubber World, 127, 365 (1952).

"Neoprenes," N. L. Catton, E. I. duPont de Nemours & Co., Inc., Wilmington, Del., 1953.

"Polysulfide Polymers," E. M. Fettes, J. S. Jorczak, Ind. Eng. Chem., 42, 11, 2217-23 (1950).

"Polysulfide Liquid Polymers," E. M. Fettes and J. S. Jorczak, Ind. Eng. Chem., 43, 2, 324-28 (1951).

"Vulcollan—The New Polyester Rubber," F. Popper, Rubber Age, 73, 81-2 (1953).

"Chemical Engineers' Handbook—Materials of Construction," Sec. 21, 3rd Ed., J. A. Lee, H. L. Maxwell, E. C. Fetter, H. H. Dunkle, 1457-1558, McGraw-Hill Book Co., Inc., New York, 1950.

"Nitrile Rubber for Oils and Solvents," J. P. McNamee, Chem. Eng., 61, 9, 230 (1954).

"Resistant Rubbers and Elastomers," F. F. Jaray and A. E. Lever, Corrosion Prevention and Control, 1, 344 (1954).

"Plastics in Plants Manufacturing Textile Fibers," W. A. Haldeman and E. F. Wesp, Symposium on Plastics as Materials of Construction, American Chemical Society, Division of Paint, Plastics and Printing Ink Chemistry, New York, Sept. 1954.

"Plastics in Plants Manufacturing Heavy Chemicals," G. A. Griess, Symposium on Plastics as Materials of Construction, American Chemical Society, Division of Paint, Plastics and Printing Ink Chemistry, New York, Sept. 1954.

9. CHEMICAL-RESISTANT MORTAR CEMENTS

One of the least known applications of plastics for corrosion resistance is that of chemical-resistant mortar cements, which were designed primarily to replace hydraulic cement mortars for joining acid-proof brick and tile in acid, alkali, salt or solvent service.

Acid-proof masonry construction provides an economical abrasion and heat-resistant tank lining. As pointed out in Chapter 8, a few organic linings can be used continuously at temperatures above 160°F and none can withstand the mechanical abuse such as that encountered in a continuous pickling line. It must be emphasized that an impervious membrane must always be used between the tank shell and the masonry structure to prevent attack by acid seepage resulting from permeability of the brick, accidental damage, or faulty workmanship.

As might be expected, high temperature resistance is of paramount importance and, as a result, most of the bases used for mortar cements are thermosetting plastics. With the exception of those based on sulfur and asphalt, most chemical-resistant mortar cements can be applied using appropriate modifications of the traditional bricklayer and tilesetter techniques. There are also many other specific applications which utilize the unique chemical and physical properties of these products.

Plasticized sulfur and asphalt cements are applied by melting the solid material to obtain a free-flowing liquid which is then poured between spaced bricks to form the masonry structure. Plasticized sulfur cements are usually supplied as cast ingots, wafers or chips. Most of the other types of cements are supplied as two-package systems which are combined to produce the mortar just before use. These mortars set by chemical action to produce hard, impervious products.

It should be emphasized that mortar cements contain little or no solvent and are usually applied in joints at least 1/16 inch in width. They should not be confused with adhesives or glues which are frequently solutions of plastics and are almost always used to obtain very thin glue lines. These cements are discussed in Chapter 13.

The major types of commercial chemical-resistant cements discussed in this chapter are sulfur, asphalt, coal tar, polyester, phenolic, epoxy, furan and silicate cements. Silicate cements are, of course, not plastic-based in the most rigorous definition of the term but are included in this discussion to provide a complete picture of the field. The resistance of these cements to specific chemicals and

136   PLASTIC MATERIALS OF CONSTRUCTION

their important physical properties are summarized in Table 9-5 and 9-3, respectively.

Sulfur Cements

Plasticized sulfur cements are essentially mixtures of sulfur and inert fillers with minor amounts of plasticizers. The addition of the plasticizer is important in reducing the inherent brittleness and shrinkage of simple sulfur-silica or carbon mixtures.

In contrast to the resin cements which will be discussed later, sulfur cements are applied as hot-melt materials. They have been used industrially for over half a century.

The major advantages of sulfur cements over resin cements are their low cost and superior resistance to oxidizing agents. Their disadvantages are low temperature limitation and poor resistance to alkalies and nonpolar organic solvents.

Sulfur cements are applied by a simple melting and resolidifying process. The changes which take place in this process are physical rather than chemical in nature.

Sulfur cements are available commercially with either graded silica or carbon fillers. The latter type is primarily used for service in hydrofluoric or fluosilicic acids or where an electrically conductive cement is required.

Several different plasticizers have been used in sulfur cements. The amount of plasticizer may be varied over a wide range depending upon the degree of ductility required for the end-use. In addition to reducing shrinkage and brittleness, the plasticizer also minimizes the loss of strength caused by repeated temperature changes. The composition range of typical cements is shown in Table 9-1.

TABLE 9-1

	Silica Filled	Carbon Filled
Sulfur	55 – 70%	60 – 70%
Graded silica	25 – 45	—
Graded carbon	—	25 – 35
Plasticizer	0.5 – 10	0.5 – 10

Other additives occasionally included in sulfur cement formulations in trace quantities are bactericides which prevent attack by sulfur bacteria in underground installations and nonmetallic sulfides which improve the flow characteristics of highly plasticized molten cements.

The choice of the proper filler in compounding sulfur cements is very important in achieving the maximum strength properties and also in minimizing settling of the aggregate while the cement is in the molten state. Soluble materials and corrodible metals such as sodium chloride and iron filings are present in certain commercial sulfur cements to improve the rate of sealing in cast-iron water pipe joints. Such ingredients naturally are attacked by corrosive solutions and cements of this type should never be used in the construction of acid-resistant structures.

Heating equipment recommended for melting sulfur cement consists of a steel or cast iron kettle of 2 to 5 gallons capacity, suspended in a metal jacket so that the sides as well as the bottom of the kettle are heated uniformly. Heat is generally supplied by a burner using compressed liquid fuel.

Cements are usually supplied as cast ingots weighing from 2 to 5 pounds. The ingots are broken up and placed in the melting pot and melted over a low uniform fire while stirring continuously with a metal rod or ladle until the cement becomes water-thin and readily pourable. The recommended temperature range is 265 to 290°F and can be recognized by a shiny, mirror-like surface. If heated over 300°F, some cements will thicken and will not be satisfactory for use until allowed to cool to the proper temperature range.

If the sulfur cement ignites because of overheating, the source of heat should be removed and a lid placed on the kettle to exclude air. If a lid is not available, strips of wet burlap or cloth should be placed over the kettle to smother the flames. If the flame is extinguished immediately, the cement can still be used; otherwise the material should be discarded. If the molten cement foams because of entrapped air or moisture, heating and stirring should be continued until a smooth liquid remains. As the sulfur cement is used, additional ingots can be added so that the kettle is nearly full at all times.

The chemical resistance of plasticized sulfur cements is summarized in Table 9-9. These cements have excellent resistance to all non-oxidizing inorganic acids and fair resistance to oxidizing acids such as dilute nitric and chromic acids. Silica-filled cements cannot be used in the presence of hydrofluoric or fluosilicic acids although carbon-fillers are completely satisfactory.

Sulfur cements are attacked by alkaline solutions. Even mild alkalies such as sodium bicarbonate will have some effect at elevated temperatures. Their resistance to organic solvents is poor except with very polar materials such as methanol, ethanol, glycol and glycerol.

Neutral or acidic salts have no effect on sulfur cements, but metallic sulfides may be formed during electrolytic processes. In general, sulfur cements are not recommended for lining electroplating tanks.

The strength properties of sulfur cements will vary considerably depending on the degree of plasticization. A penetration test has been devised to measure quantitatively the effect of plasticizer on the ductility of the cement. The method consists essentially of driving a rod of 1/8-inch diameter into a 2-inch cast cube of the cement under constant rate of loading in a compression testing machine. The forces required for a penetration of 1/8, 1/4 and 3/7 inch are recorded. The effect of increasing the plasticizer content on the ductility of the cement is shown by the curve in Figure 9-1. It should be noted that the sample containing no plasticizer broke before any significant penetration was achieved. Such a cement might also crack or lose adhesion if subjected to extreme stress in a brickwork structure.

Recently, a fundamental study of the properties of plasticized sulfur cements has been concluded and published. This work included studies on stress-strain curves and ultimate compressive and tensile strengths under conditions of variable pouring temperatures and variable age of samples. The effect of remelting on the ultimate properties of sulfur cements was also investigated.

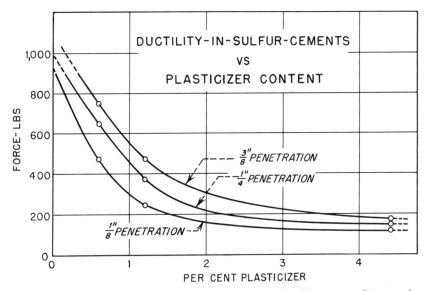

Figure 9-1. The relation of ductility and plasticizer content of sulfur cements. (Tests made by measuring force in pounds required for penetration of a 1/8-in. rod to 1/8, 1/4 and 3/8 in. depth)

Plasticizer %	Force (Lbs)		
	1/8 in.	1/4 in.	3/8 in.
0	900+	900+	900+
0.6	475	650	750
1.2	250	375	475
4.4	120	150	175

Compression creep studies made by mounting SR-4 strain gages on cylindrical compression specimens also indicated that sulfur cements definitely flow under stress. Load was applied at a rate of 1,600 lbs per minute until stress levels of 1,000, 2,000 and 3,000 psi were attained. These loads were held constant for 1 hour before release. The strains developed during compression and recovery were determined. Figure 9-2 showing a plot of the strain in microinches versus time, clearly indicates the degree of flow.

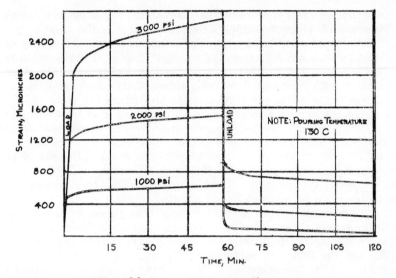

Figure 9-2. Creep test curves on sulfur cement.

ASTM Committee C-3 has adopted tentative specifications for sulfur mortar under the designation C-287-52T. The physical requirements are:

Tensile strength at 48 hr age, min., psi	400
Compressive strength, 2 in. cubes, 48 hrs, age, min., psi	4000
Modulus of rupture at 48 hrs age, min, psi	1000
Tendency of aggregate to settle, maximum variation from unity	0.6
Proportion of original strength retained after thermal shock, min., %	20.0
Moisture absorption, max., %	1.0
Sieve analysis of aggregate:	
Retained on # 40 sieve, max., %	5.0
Retained on #100 sieve, min., %	10.0
Retained on #200 sieve, min., %	35.0

The methods of test are outlined below:

1. Sampling and Preparation of Sample. If the sulfur mortar is furnished in the form of ingots or lumps, at least one entire piece shall be used and a minimum of 5 lbs shall be used for the sample. The sample shall not be melted over 1 hr and held at a temperature of 265 to 290°F for at least 15 min., while being stirred with a laboratory-type mixer. This stirrer shall be of such type and operate at a speed to lift the aggregate, but shall beat no air into the melt. All test specimens shall be cast from this sample.

2. Storage of Test Specimens. All test specimens shall be stored at a temperature of 60 to 80°F.

3. Tensile Strength. Cast six briquet test specimens in molds conforming to section 2(e) of the Standard Method of Test for Tensile Strength of Hydraulic Cement Mortars (ASTM Designation: C 190).

The specimens shall conform to the dimensional requirements shown in Figure 3 of Method C 190. Cover the center of the mold with a small lubricated plate having the edges next to the mold rounded of to a radius of approximately 1/8 in. Melt and pour the sample in accordance with the procedure described in Paragraph (a). Pour the molten sulfur mortar into both sides of the mold and puddle it to fill the space under the plate completely. Allow the plate placed across the center of the mold to remain in place for at least 15 minutes after the briquet has been poured. Remove all rough edges from the surface of the briquet that is to come in contact with the tension testing apparatus. Break the six briquet specimens at the age of 48 hours, using a rate of loading of 600 psi per minute.

4. Compressive Strength. Cast six 2-in. cube test specimens. The molds shall be made of brass or other suitable metal, in gangs of three, and shall be of the type used to make three 2-in. cubes at one time in accordance with the Standard Methods of Test for Compressive Strength of Hydraulic Cement Mortars (ASTM Designation: C 100) and the Standard Methods of Testing Gypsum and Gypsum Products (ASTM Designation: C 26). A brass base plate and cover plate, attached with studs and wingnuts, shall be used. Two 3/8-in. holes shall be bored in the cover plate for pouring. The mold and plates shall be greased before assembly. Fill the mold up to 3/16 in. from the top with sulfur mortar of 265 to 290°F. Fill in the shrinkage hole as it forms. Then place the cover plate on top of the mold and fill the remainder of the mold with sulfur mortar through the 3/8-in. pouring holes. Use a small funnel in the pouring so that shrinkage will take place in the funnel. Age the six specimens for 48 hours; then determine their compressive strength by means of a testing machine conforming to Section 2 (k) of Method C 109, using a rate of loading of 3000 psi. per minute.

Alternatively, 2 by 4 in. cylinders may be cast in suitable molds. Another mold that may be used consists of a seamless steel tube 1.7 in I.D. (2.0 in O.D.) and 30 in. long. A vertical slot is milled in the pipe and lugs are welded on the outside so that they can be tightened to close the slot. Test specimens of sulfur mortar 1.75 in. in diameter by 4 in. long are cut from the 30 in. molded cylinder with a carborundum wheel. Since the ends may not be true, a capping mixture consisting of 50 parts by weight of plaster of Paris and 50 parts by weight of high early strength portland cement may be used to "square" the ends, or the cylinders may be capped with sulfur mortar in the usual manner instead of the plastic of Paris mixture. Different results will be obtained from cubes and cylinders. The 2 in. cube will have roughly one fourth higher strength than the 2 by 4 in. cylinder. Also, the 1.75 by 4 in. cylinder will have roughly nine tenths of the strength of a 2 by 4 in. cylinder.

5. Flexural Strength Test. Prepare and test at least six test specimens. The molds shall be of brass or some other suitable metal with a 1 in. square section at least 9 in. long and with one end closed, and

shall be greased before assembly. Fill the mold with molten sulfur mortar at 265 to 290°F at a single pouring through one end. Fill the void that forms with additional material. Allow the bars to age for 48 hours; then apply center loading, over a span of 6 in., at the rate of 600 psi per minute. Calculate the modulus of rupture R by the formula R = 9P, if a span of 6 in. is used, P being the ultimate load. Any specimen varying more than 15% from the mean shall be discarded.

Note. If it is desirable to determine the modulus of elasticity, a dial gage reading to 0.001 in. may be used to measure deflection for every 5 lb. increment until the specimen fails. The modulus of elasticity shall be calculated by the formula E = 54P/D, where P/D is the slope of the stress-strain curve, and provided the slope near the origin is sufficiently constant to warrant making the calculations.

6. Tendency of Aggregate to Settle. Fill a 1 in., heat resistant glass test tube to a depth of 8 in. with molten sulfur mortar and hold at 285°F for 30 minutes. Carefully remove the test tube, hold under warm tap water until congealing begins, and then immerse in ice water. When the sulfur mortar has solidified, break the tube and extract the top and bottom thirds of the contents by the method given in Paragraph (c). The numerical ratio of the aggregate content of the bottom of the tube to that of the top shall be used as an index of the quality of the cement. The numerical factor of a coarse silica aggregate that settles rapidly is greater than unity, while that for a coke aggregate that floats is less than unity.

7. Resistance to Thermal Shock. Cast at least five tension test briquets as described in Paragraph (f), and store them for 48 hours. Two drums shall be provided containing 10 gal. of water. Maintain the temperature in one drum between 50 and 59°F and in the other drum, between 175 and 185°F. Place five briquet specimens in a wire cage constructed so as to hold the briquets spaced at least 1 in. from each other. Suspend the specimens in the middle of the hot bath for 300 sec. and immediately transfer to the cold bath for 300 sec. After five cycles, remove the five specimens and determine their tensile strength as described in Paragraph (f).

8. Moisture Absorption. Weight three 2 in. cube specimens prepared in accordance with Paragraph (g). Suspend the specimens in water at 185°F for 5 hrs., starting at least 48 hrs. after casting. Remove the specimens, wipe off the surface water with a damp cloth, and weigh them. Complete the weighing of any one specimen within 5 min. after removing the specimen from the bath. Calculate the absorption of each specimen as follows:

$$\text{Absorption, } \% = \frac{100 \ (W2 - W1)}{W1}$$

where

W1 — dry weight of specimens, and

W2 — saturated weight of specimen after 5 hr submersion in water at 185°F.

9. <u>Sieve Analysis.</u> Determine the sieve analysis of the aggregate in the sulfur mortar in accordance with the Standard Method of Test for Sieve Analysis of Fine and Coarse Aggregates (ASTM Designation: C 136). The sample of aggregate shall be obtained by extraction of the sulfur mortar with carbon disulfide. The sample shall consist of at least 20 g of the aggregate.

Uses of Sulfur Cements

Sulfur undergoes a crystalline change from the rhombic (α) form to the monoclinic (β) at 95°C (203°F). As this change is accompanied by a considerable volume expansion, sulfur cements should never be used above this temperature.

The primary use of sulfur cements in chemical plant construction is for joining acid-proof brick in the lining of reaction vessels, storage tanks, sumps, drainage lines and pickling tanks. The cements used for construction of this type are usually only slightly plasticized, since great ductility is not required. Concrete waste acid pits lined with acid brick joined with sulfur cement are shown in Figure 9-3.

Figure 9-3. Waste acid pits in a steel plant lined with acid brick joined with plasticized sulfur cement.

A method of construction has been developed to permit the use of relatively inexpensive sulfur cements at temperatures higher than 200° F. In this method, two courses of brick are used, the inner course (next to the brick wall) being joined with sulfur cement and the outer one with a high temperature resin or silicate cement.

A highly plasticized sulfur cement is used in the construction of a hot-melt lining for use behind brickwork on concrete tanks. This membrane consists of alternate 1/8-inch layers of asphalt with a 1/8-inch sandwich layer of sulfur cement. The cement used must be highly plasticized to prevent cracking of the relatively thin layer.

Sulfur cements are also used for joining brick or tile in the construction of floors for chemical plants. Sulfur cements are not resistant to strongly alkaline cleaners commonly used for industrial purposes and as a result furan resin cements have largely replaced them as joining materials for food plant floors. One of the largest uses of sulfur cement is in the jointing of cast-iron water pipe for municipal plants. This application, which is usually outside the province of corrosion engineers, is discussed in Chapter 18.

Sulfur cement is also used intthe construction of industrial sewers carrying acid wastes to join the vitrified clay liner plates in the concrete pipe as well as in conjunction with resin cements, in joining terra cotta pipe.

Along with the miscellaneous applications of sulfur cements mention may be made of the setting of steel posts and other metal equipment in concrete. Molten lead is commonly used for such purposes, but sulfur cements are much cheaper and will provide stronger bonds. Sulfur cements also find use as centers for abrasive grinding wheels. Another specialty use is in the capping of concrete test cylinders. Extensive research work has shown them to be far superior to the hydraulic cement mortars previously used for this purpose.

Asphalt and Coal-Tar Pitch Cements

Asphalts and coal-tar pitches are used as the base for low-cost, hot-melt, acid-resistant cements. They are supplied with or without fillers depending upon the service requirements. Among the fillers commonly used are silica, clay and powdered slate.

Because of the relatively high degree of cold flow exhibited by both asphalts and coal tars, their use is restricted to room temperature applications. The principal application has been in the jointing of vitrified clay pipe in sewer construction, which is discussed more fully in Chapter 19. They have also been used to some extent as caulking cements for joining brick or tile in the construction of light-duty floors and miscellaneous applications where cold flow is not a problem.

Both asphalts and coal-tar pitches are resistant to dilute non-oxidizing acids and salts and both are soluble in most non polar solvents. Asphalts are attacked by strong alkalies, but coal-tar pitches are not.

Asphalts may be either of natural origin or derived from petroleum residues. Coal-tar pitches, of course, are by-products of the
destructive distillation of bituminous coal. Usually materials melting in the range of 200 to 250°F are used.

Application methods of hot-melt cements are similar to those for
sulfur cements (pp. 136-137) with the exception that higher pouring
temperatures are required.

Other Thermoplastic Cements

Specialty cements can be prepared by the addition of fillers to
aqueous dispersions or solutions of thermoplastics in organic solvents. They have shown some promise when used as coatings or
adhesives but are not usually considered as suitable for joining brick
or tile.

Cements Based on Rubbers and Elastomers

Natural rubber and other latices can be mixed with hydraulic cements such as portland or aluminous cement to form specialty mortars. Such mortars have greater resistance to water and alternate
freezing and thawing than ordinary hydraulic cements.

Because of their superior adhesion and moisture resistance, they
have been used as underlayments in flooring and for coating underground concrete structures. They have fair resistance to alkalies
and salts but are not recommended for use in the presence of acids
or solvents.

High solids neoprene putties may be used as crack fillers and as
heavy coatings but are not usually considered for joining brick and
tile. They have shown some promise when elastomeric material is
required such as in expansion joints for brickwork.

Liquid olefin polysulfides may be filled and cured by the addition
of lead salts. The resulting products have excellent resistance to
solvents and possess fair adhesion, but are seldom considered for
joining brick and tile.

Polyester Resin Cements

One of the newest types of resin mortar cements is based on unsaturated polyester resins. Although somewhat more costly than
furan or phenolic cements, they have been used in cases where their
specific properties are required.

Commercial polyester resins are linear polymers formed by the
condensation of unsaturated dibasic acids such as maleic acid with
vinyl monomer such as styrene to form a viscous syrup. The chemical formula for a typical linear unsaturated polyester is as follows:

$$HOOC - CH = CH - COOH + HOCH_2CH_2OH$$

maleic acid   *ethylene glycol*

$$HOOC - [CH = CH - COO - CH_2 - CH_2 - OOC]_x CH = CH - COOH$$

linear unsaturated polyester resin

The liquid styrene-containing resin can be compounded with an activator to form the liquid component of the polyester cement mortar. The powder for a polyester mortar cement may consist of silica compounded with a small quantity of an organic peroxide. When the liquid and powder are mixed to produce the mortar, the activator decomposes the peroxide which initiates the polymerization of the monomeric materials. The polyester molecules are effectively cross-linked or "thermoset" by copolymerization of the unsaturated maleic acid chain segments with the growing polystyrene chains. A segment of the polymer molecule is shown below:

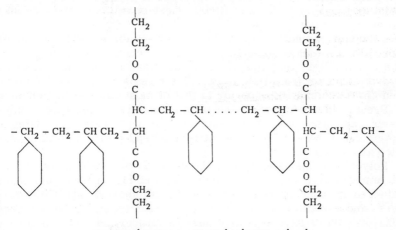

segment of styrene-unsaturated polyester molecule

The chemical resistance of polyester mortar cements depends on the ratio and composition of each component used in preparing the linear unsaturated polyester and the mortar. Since the chemical resistance of commercial polyester mortar cements varies considerably, generalizations are less readily made than in the case of other mortar cements. Obviously, the ester linkages in the final polymer are susceptible to hydrolysis by strong alkalies and hot acids.

Polyester cements are available as two-package systems. The powder and the liquid resin are usually mixed in a ratio of approximately 3 to 1 by weight. Since the catalyst is neither acidic nor alkaline, any type of clean-mixing pan or box is satisfactory. Normal precautions should be observed such as spreading out the mortar in thin layers.

The working and setting times of a typical commercial polyester cement at various temperatures are given in Table 9-2.

TABLE 9-2. WORKING AND SETTING TIMES
FOR A TYPICAL POLYESTER MORTAR CEMENT

Temp. (°F)	Working Life (min.)	Final Setting Time (hrs)
40	600	20
60	100	3
70	45	2
80	30	1
90	15	½

It should be noted that this cement sets unusually rapidly even at very low temperatures. This property is of great advantage for repointing joints in tanks and floors where operations cannot be shut down for very long periods of time.

Polyester cements are resistant to non-oxidizing acids, acidic or neutral salts and polar solvents in all concentrations. Because of the silica filler, they are not recommended for service involving hydrofluoric or fluosilicic acid. Their resistance to dilute nitric and chromic acids is superior to that of most other resin cements.

Presumably, because of the physical nature of the filler, polyester cements have better resistance than polyester laminates to hot acids. However, they are not recommended for continuous service above 200°F.

Polyester cements withstand sodium hypochlorite bleach solutions at temperatures up to 110°F below a pH of 11. These cements are attacked by aqueous solutions having a pH above 11 at all temperatures and therefore should never be used in the presence of strong alkalies. They have excellent physical properties and will adhere to most concrete and metal surfaces.

Although the resin components of these cements are usually stable at ordinary temperatures for at least six months, it is recommended that the liquid resin be stored at 60°F or lower to prevent thickening and eventual gelation. The powder should be stored in a dry area to minimize moisture pick-up.

Polyester cements are normally supplied with white fillers, but can be manufactured in any desired color. Black cement is frequently used for repointing joints in tank walls or floors in order to match the previously used furan or phenolic cement. Their principal use is for joining acid-proof brick lining plant equipment for low temperature service conditions at a pH below 11.

Urea and Melamine Cements

Light-colored specialty cements have been prepared by mixing aqueous solutions of these polymers with a filler containing an acid catalyst. These cements have excellent adhesion to a wide variety of surfaces and good resistance to aqueous salt solutions. However, they are not suitable for use in acid environments.

Phenolic Resin Cements

Chemical resistant phenolic resin cements were introduced in Germany around 1930. They have been widely used in the chemical industry in America since 1935, but are gradually being replaced in many applications by the more versatile furan cements.

Phenolic resin cements are based on low-molecular weight phenol-formaldehyde condensation products prepared under alkaline conditions. The liquid resin consists primarily of phenolic alcohols although some further reaction also probably occurs in the manufacturing process. The formation of this liquid product, which is referred to as a resol or A-stage phenolic resin can be represented by the following equations:

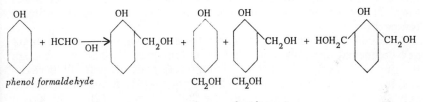

phenol formaldehyde

A-stage phenolic resin

The resinification reaction is stopped at the desired viscosity range by neutralization of the alkaline catalyst. Any excess water is then removed by vacuum distillation.

The resin mortar is prepared by combining the compounded liquid phenolic resin with an acid-containing filler. The acid catalyst causes further polymerization which results in the formation of an infusible, highly cross-linked stage. The cured resin may be represented as shown at the top of the following page.

Because of the presence of the free weakly acidic hydroxyl groups in the cured resin structure these cements are attacked by strong alkalies. The resin presents no point of attack for non-oxidizing acids, but strong oxidizing agents may attack the double bonds of the benzene ring causing disintegration of the cement.

Phenolic resin cement mortars are prepared by mixing the liquid resin and powder just prior to use. The mixing ratio of powder to liquid is about 2 to 1 by weight for the carbon-filled and 2 1/2 to 1 for the silica-filled cements.

The working and setting times at various temperatures for typical

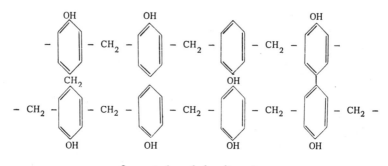

Segment of cured phenolic resin

carbon-filled and silica-filled phenolic cements as determined by ASTM Method C-308-53T are given in Table 9-3.

Phenolic resin cements have characteristically poor resistance to caustic, but show good resistance to milder alkalies, especially at lower temperatures. Their resistance to oxidizing agents such as sulfuric acid at concentrations between 60 and 90 per cent and dilute nitric acid is somewhat superior to that of furan resin cements and they are sometimes recommended for such applications at ordinary temperatures.

The low-molecular weight resins used in phenolic resin cements are somewhat unstable and tend to polymerize further even though the original alkaline catalyst is completely neutralized. This reaction is evidenced by a gradual thickening of the resin and the eventual appearance of an aqueous layer on the surface. Slightly thickened resins can still be used in preparing mortars, but they are more difficult to use when free water appears. A shelf-line of at least three months will be obtained when liquid phenolic resins are stored at temperatures of 65°F or lower.

Perhaps the largest single application of phenolic cements has been for joining of acid brick in continuous pickling lines in steel plants. Phenolic cements have performed satisfactorily while exposed for over twelve years to boiling 25 per cent sulfuric acid. They have also found wide application in recent years for casting purposes. Usually the amount of filler used is much lower than in

TABLE 9-3. WORKING AND SETTING TIMES
FOR A TYPICAL PHENOLIC CEMENT

Temp. (°F)	Working Time (min.)	Final Setting Time (days)
60	180	10
70	60	7
80	30	5
90	15	3

the troweling cements in order to obtain good casting properties. The aircraft industry in particular has found phenol cements useful as tooling resins for the production of prototypes of mechanical parts. This application is discussed more completely in Chapter 10. Silica or barytes filled phenolic cements have a characteristic brick-red color when completely cured; the carbon-filled variety is, of course, black.

As phenolic resin cements tend to decompose at 360°F, they should not be used as services above this temperature.

Epoxy Resin Cements

The "epoxy" or "ethyoxyline" resins is one of the newest thermo-setting plastics used as a base for chemical-resistant cements. The present high cost of epoxy resins limits their use to installations where their specific advantages justify the additional expense.

As depicted below, epoxy resins are produced by the alkaline condensation of p, p -isopropylidenediphenol, commonly known as "Bisphenol A," and epichlorohydrin. The proportion of the reactants can be varied to produce resins ranging from fluid liquids to high-melting solids, the former being of most interest in the formation of cements.

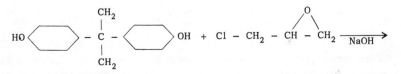

Bisphenol A   *Epichlorohydrin*

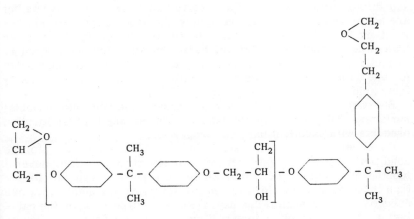

Epoxy resin

Liquid epoxy resins can be blended with inert fillers such as carbon or silica to produce trowelable mortars. The curing is accomplished by the addition of polyamine compounds such as ethylene diamine. The interaction of the amine groups with the terminal epoxy groups effectively cross-links the liquid resin to form large three-dimensional molecules.

Epoxy cements are usually supplied as ready-mixed mortars containing all the necessary ingredients except the catalyst. It is customary to add 1/2 pint of liquid catalyst to 1 gallon of the uncompounded epoxy resin mortar. It is essential that the two components be thoroughly blended. Small mechanical mixers such as the Hobart food mixers are recommended.

The completely mixed mortar should be transferred to flat pans and spread out in layers no more than 3/4-inch thick to minimize heat build-up. Mixing equipment should be cleaned thoroughly with alcohol before the cement has hardened.

TABLE 9-4. WORKING AND SETTING TIMES
OF A TYPICAL EPOXY MORTAR CEMENT

Temp. (°F)	Working Time (min.)	Final Setting Time (days)
60	120	6
75	40	4
90	20	2

This cement will set at temperatures as low as 40°F, but an extremely long period of time is required before the unit can be placed in service under these temperature conditions.

Epoxy resin cements have excellent resistance to aqueous salt solutions and non-oxidizing acids such as phosphoric, hydrochloric and dilute sulfuric acid. They are resistant to some solvents but are not as resistant as the previously discussed phenolic resin cement mortars. Their resistance to alkalies is considerably better than either phenolic or polyester cement mortars but not as good as that of furan cements. Epoxy resin cements are not recommended for use with oxidizing acids such as nitric acid or concentrated sulfuric acid.

Epoxy resin cements have excellent adhesion to concrete and metal surfaces. They shrink slightly during the setting process forming products with excellent physical properties.

Epoxy cement mortars are stable indefinitely under normal storage conditions. The catalyst, however, loses strength after several months and catalyst solutions which have been stored for longer than three months should be tested for setting power before they are used on a large scale. The heat resistance depends upon the catalyst used. Simple polyamines will cure at ordinary temperatures to produce a cement that should not be used at temperatures above

200°F. However, cements with greater resistance to temperature can be secured through the use of other catalyst systems, but these usually require heating for complete cure.

Epoxy resin cements have been used in the production of monolithic coatings for steel tanks and concrete floors. This type of application has shown promise, but no long-term service data are available at the present time.

Although the adhesion of mortar type cements is good, more fluid adhesive cements containing lower amounts of specific fillers are available for general adhesion applications. Excellent results have been obtained in joining a wide variety of rigid materials such as glass and other ceramics, all metals and almost all plastics. Bonds with shear strengths of greater than 3,000 psi can be obtained without pressure or heat. This application is discussed more fully in Chapter 13.

Unfilled or lightly filled epoxy resins are extensively used as potting compounds for electrical instruments and as casting compounds in the aircraft industry. These applications are discussed in Chapter 10.

Furan Resin Cements

At the present time these are one of the most versatile chemical resistant mortar cements in use. No other commercially available cement combines acid, alkali, salt, and solvent resistance with comparatively low cost. These cements were introduced in 1940 and their use has increased rapidly since that time.

In the manufacture of a furan resin, the components are heated with strong acids to form a viscous resin. When the desired viscosity is attained the reaction is stopped by neutralizing the acid catalyst. As illustrated by the following equations, most furan resins consist primarily of low polymers dissolved in excess furfural or furfuryl alcohol.

The polymerization of furfuryl alcohol may be represented by the mechanism shown at the top of page 152.

The liquid furan resin is mixed with a powder consisting of an inert filler, such as coke flour, silica, barytes, or asbestos containing a strong acid catalyst such as paratoluene sulfonic acid in order to prepare the resin cement mortar. Additional polymerization takes place after mixing to form a cross-linked infusible resin. The exact structure of the set or "cured" resin is not known but may be represented as shown at the bottom of page 152.

Liquid furan resins suitable for use in resin cement mortars may also be prepared by the polymerization of furfural. The polymerization may be represented by the mechanism at the top of page 153.

In many instances furfuryl alcohol and furfural are mixed and heated in the presence of acids to form a liquid resin. It is also possible to form liquid furan resins by the condensation of furfuryl alcohol and formaldehyde.

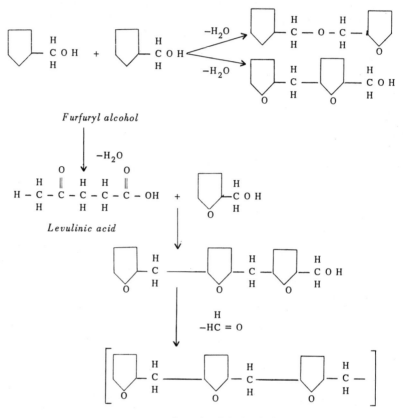

Furfuryl alcohol

Levulinic acid

Liquid polyfurfural alcohol

Proposed Mechanism for the Polymerization of Furfural Alcohol

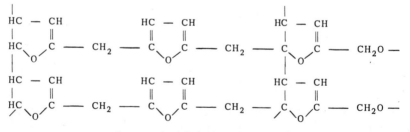

Segment of polyfurfuryl alcohol molecule

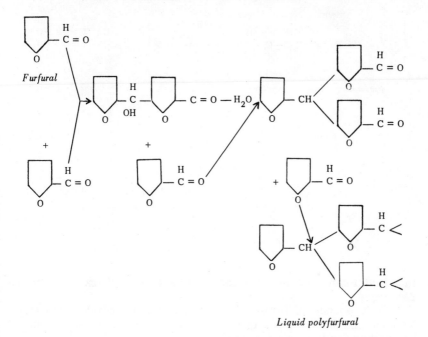

Liquid polyfurfural

In another important variation, furan resins are formed from furfural and acetone. The first step in this reaction is shown at the
top of page 154.

These products are readily prepared and economical. They will
probably replace other resin cements in other instances where the
chemical resistance and physical properties of the furfural-acetone
product is acceptable.

Regardless of the specific composition, liquid furan resins must
be mixed with a filler containing an acid catalyst in order to produce the resin cement mortar. The mixing ratio will vary from about
2 parts powder to 1 part liquid by weight for a typical carbon-filled
product to a 3:1 ratio for silica-filled cements. The ratios can be
varied somewhat depending upon the temperature and the individual
preference of the workman applying the cement.

Small batches (2 to 5 lbs) are usually mixed in an enameled mixing pan with a trowel. Mechanical mixers can be used on large jobs,
but care must be taken to clean the equipment thoroughly with acetone or methyl ethyl ketone before the cement hardens. The mortar
should be spread out in thin layers in flat mortar trays immediately
after mixing in order to dissipate exothermic heat.

Difficulties associated with inefficient mixing may be reduced
with an understanding of the following directions:

1. One pound of furan liquid resin should be weighed and placed

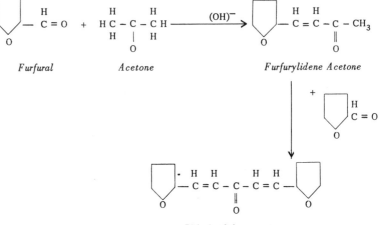

in a 1-pint can. The level of the liquid should be marked for future reference.

2. Two pounds of furan carbon-filled cement powder should be weighed and placed in a 2-quart can. The level of the powder should be marked for future reference.

3. The weighed liquid resin should be poured into a porcelain mix-ing pan approximately 10 x 14 x 2 inches in size. Most of the powder should be added and mixed with a trowel to form a smooth mortar. The remainder of the powder should be added slowly and mixed until the mortar is free from lumps or entrapped air. If the resulting mortar is either too fluid or too viscous, the ratio of powder to liquid may be modified slightly to obtain a mortar of proper consistency for troweling on brick.

4. In subsequent batches, the ingredients can be measured by vol-ume rather than by weight. If it is found that larger amounts of mortar can be used within the working time of the cement, larger containers may be used retaining the same mixing ratio as used with the smaller batches.

5. The mortar should be removed from the mixing box and spread out in layers not greater than 3/4 inch in depth in enamel trays.

6. When working at temperatures at 80 to 90°F, waste of material may be avoided by mixing small batches. The liquid resin and powder should be cooled to, but not below, 60°F before mixing. The equip-ment should also be cooled by placing the mortar mixing box and pan in ice water, being careful not to get water into the mix. Granu-lated "dry ice" may also be added. Furan resin cement mortars should not be mixed in direct sunlight.

7. When working at temperatures below 65°F, the liquid resin and powder should be kept warm but not above 80°F. If at all pos-

sible, the working area should be heated with portable blowers or stoves.

The working time of a resin-based cement has been defined by ASTM C308-53T as the time interval after the initial mixing of the powder and the liquid resin during which the mortar remains in workable condition. The methods of determination are described below:

Determination of Working Time of a Resin Cement Mortar   (ASTM C308-53T)

1. A 1,000-gram sample shall be prepared using proportionate amounts of filler and liquid resin as recommended by the manufacturer. Both filler and liquid shall be stored at 75°F, $\pm$ 5°, or at any other specified temperature for at least 16 hours before mixing.

2. An appropriate amount of liquid shall be poured in the pan and the powder added gradually to the liquid resin and the mass mixed thoroughly with the trowel until a uniform mixture is secured (this shall be complete within 3 minutes). The mixing operation is continued for 1 minute after an apparent uniform mixture is secured. The mortar shall be spread out in a layer of uniform thickness covering the entire surface of the mixing pan.

3. Approximately 15-gram portions of the resin mortar shall be removed at specific intervals and troweled onto a brick or asbestos-cement board surface. In order that sufficient data will be obtained with the minimum quantity of material, it is suggested that the first three intervals be 2 minutes in length, the next three intervals 5 minutes in length, and subsequent intervals 15 minutes in length. The sample shall be removed from a portion of the mortar located at least 2 inches from the side of the pan. The material used for test shall not be returned to the mixing pan. The working time shall be reported as the time in minutes at which the mortar can no longer be applied smoothly but tends to curl up behind the trowel.

Determination of Initial and Final Setting Times for Resin Cement Mortar's (ASTM C308-53T)

1. A 1,000-gram sample of mortar is prepared as specified under the working life test method.

2. Immediately after mixing is complete, approximately 50 grams of mortar shall be removed with the trowel and buttered on the sides of two bricks, preferably 8 1/4 x 4 x 1 3/8 inches. The brick should be laid on waxed paper and the buttered edges pushed together to form a joint approximately 1/4 inch wide. It is advantageous to establish the joint thickness by inserting a dowel rod near each end of the joint. Joint thicknesses other than 1/4 inch are acceptable, providing they are reported with the test data. Any excess material above the joint shall be struck off by use of the trowel.

3. The joint shall be examined qualitatively at 2 hour intervals

with the point of the trowel until indentation becomes difficult. The test shall be continued with a Vicat needle having a diameter of 1 mm and a plunger weight of 300 grams. This equipment is described in ASTM Method C-191-49. The point at which the indentation of the needle during a 10-minute period is less than 1 mm shall be recorded as the initial setting time.

4. Final setting: Six tensile test specimens shall be prepared in accordance with the standard ASTM method for chemical-resistant resin cement mortars. The first test shall be made 24 hours after the initial setting time and shall be continued every 48 hours until the increase in strength between tests is less than 100 psi. The final setting time shall be recorded as the time in days in which there is an increase of less than 100 psi between tests made at 48-hour intervals.

As shown in Table 9-5, the working and setting time decrease as the temperature increases. It should be noted that a preliminary set will take place between 2 and 16 hours depending upon the thickness of the joint and the ambient temperature. However, while brickwork joined with furan cements for use in an acid environment can be placed in service shortly after the initial set, it is preferable to wait until the resin has attained its final set. Since the setting time is shortened at elevated temperatures, the waiting time before placing a resin cement joined brick structure in service can be decreased through the application of dry heat such as hot air.

TABLE 9-5. WORKING AND SETTING TIMES
OF A TYPICAL FURAN RESIN MORTAR CEMENT

Temp. (°F)	Working Time (min.)	Final Setting Time (days)
60	90	12
70	60	8
80	30	6
90	15	4

For specific construction purposes, faster setting cements are available commercially. These are useful when the ambient temperature is below 60°F and for the erection of acid-brick tank walls where rapid setting is desirable to permit rapid construction of vertical or domed sections.

Furan resin cements are completely resistant to non-oxidizing acids, alkalies, salts and most solvents at temperatures up to 370°F. Silica and asbestos fillers cannot be used in the presence of strong alkaline materials or fluorine-containing acids and salts.

The adhesion of carbon-filled furan resin cements to non-glazed brick or tile surfaces is very good, and far superior to that of hydraulic cement mortars. It should be pointed out that because of the reaction of the acid catalyst, furan cements will not adhere to unprimed concrete or metallic surfaces. Several satisfactory primers are available and should be used for all such applications.

All resin cements exhibit a certain amount of shrinkage during the conversion of the fluid mortar to the cured state. The amount of shrinkage will vary from 0.3 to 2.0 per cent depending upon the nature and the amount of filler used, but will average about 0.5 per cent as measured linearly on a 10 inch test bar. This small shrinkage value is relatively unimportant when the cement is used as a joining material for brick or tile, but must be taken into account in casting and molding applications.

Carbon-filled furan cements have fairly good electrical properties, showing a volume resistivity of 12 ohm-cm. The silica-filled cements, on the other hand, are poor conductors. Both types have aroused considerable interest for the construction of special electrical apparatus. They may be blended to secure any conductivity between the two extremes.

Uncatalyzed liquid furan resins are stable at ordinary temperatures for at least five years. This is a marked advantage over some of the other resin cements which require low temperature storage conditions. The powder should be stored in a dry area to minimize moisture absorption.

Furan cement powder may be black, tan or white depending upon whether carbon, silica or barytes is used as a filler. However, it should be emphasized that all furan cements are inherently black in color when set, no matter what type of filler is used.

There are several properties of furan cements which cannot be easily described quantitatively but which are important in the selection of these products. For example, furan cements used for buttering bricks should be compounded for good consistency or containability. In contrast, furan cements that are to be used for grouting by tilesetters are usually compounded so that they will flow readily into the open joints.

Certain organic acids or catalysts used in some resin cement fillers may cause severe dermatitis on the hands and arms of the user. This effect is much stronger than simple chemical attack by the acid and is highly specific with certain individuals.

As the setting of furan cements is dependent upon an acid reaction, contamination with alkaline substances, such as portland cement dust, which is almost always present on construction jobs, will seriously interfere with the curing reaction. Some commercial cements can be permanently prevented from setting by adding as little as 0.25 per cent of portland cement.

Some furan cement powders contain "reserve acid" and will set under fairly severe conditions of contamination. However, it is recommended that the engineer insist upon the cleanest possible working conditions.

Furan cement mortars are designed primarily for joining acid-proof brick and tile for the protection of steel and concrete reaction vessels, storage tanks, sumps, piers, absorption towers, fume stacks and pickling lines. Such equipment has been used in the pulp and paper, steel, nonferrous metals, fertilizer, leather, textile, and chemical proeess industries. Standard bricklayer and tilesetter methods are applicable when appropriate modifications are made based on the characteristic properties of the cement. A large acid saturator lined with glazed tile joined with furan cement is shown in Figure 9-4.

(Courtesy of Chemsteel Construction Co.)
Figure 9-4. Large acid saturator lined with glazed acid tile joined with furan cement.

As described in Chapter 8, furan resin cements are used for the construction of tank linings. These are usually reinforced with glass fabric or expanded metal to minimize shrinkage and to obtain increased strength. Although some of these linings have given satisfactory results for several years under severe service conditions, the long-continuing shrinkage of the cement with time has led to failure because of cracking. The same difficulty has occasionally been encountered in monolithic floor applications.

Asbestos or carbon-filled furan cements have been cast or molded under low heat and pressure to form tanks, pipe, fume systems, towers and other chemical processing equipment. The cast forms can be sawed, drilled, tapped and turned with ordinary metal working equipment. Component parts can be cemented together with the same types of cement. This type of application is discussed more completely in Chapter 10.

The joining of vitrified clay pipe in industrial waste lines carrying large volumes of solvents is another specialized application of furan cements. In this case, they are frequently used in conjunction with the cheaper, but less resistant plasticized sulfur cements.

Glass cloth-reinforced furan resin cements have been used extensively in the armoring of fragile porcelain or stoneware pipe, valves and process equipment. The impact resistance of such equipment can be increased many times by this technique. The cement can also be used to adhere coated metallic flanges to porcelain or stoneware pipe.

Another small, but important use of furan cements is in repairing cracks and chips in glass-lined chemical tanks and other equipment. Because of their unusual chemical resistance, furan cements are used in many chemical processing plants as an emergency repair material. The intelligent use of furan cements and glass cloth has prevented many plant shut-downs in the chemical industry.

Silicate Cements

Silicate cements are probably one of the oldest types of chemical-resistance cements in use in the chemical industry. They were first used in Germany over 30 years ago. These cements consist of an aqueous solution of sodium or potassium silicate and an inert filler, usually graded silica. The older cements set very slowly through the evaporation of water. The newer ones contain a chemical setting agent which greatly accelerates this change. They are supplied as two-package systems, similar to the resin cements described previously in this chapter.

Silicate cements have excellent chemical resistance to all acids, except hydrofluoric or fluosilicic. They may be used at elevated temperatures. The upper limit is the temperature at which vitrification occurs. This temperature ranges from 1,300 to 1,500°F; in general, 1250°F is considered to be the upper limit. Since the physical properties decrease rapidly as the temperature is increased, a more conservative upper temperature limit of 750°F is usually recommended. In spite of good acid resistance, the lack of resistance to alkalies, high water absorption and resultant permeability limit the usefulness of silicate cements.

Typical chemical-setting silicate cements consist of a sodium silicate solution having a specific gravity of 38°Be and a $Na_2O:SiO_2$ ratio of 1:3.25. The powder consists of a graded silica filler with a small amount of a setting agent such as sodium silicofluoride. The exact nature of the action of the setting agent is not known, but presumably acid is released to form an insoluble silica gel which bonds the filler particles together. The water introduced with the silicate solution evaporates slowly over a long period of time leaving a somewhat porous structure.

Cements based on potassium silicate solutions are claimed to have lower water absorption and higher temperature resistance, but are not extensively used in the United States.

Slow setting silicate cements are supplied as ready-mixed materials. These are usually based on sodium silicate solution having a specific gravity of $35°$ Be and a $Na_2O:SiO_2$ ratio of 1:3.80.

Chemical setting silicate cements are supplied as two-package systems. The liquid solution and the filler containing a catalyst are mixed to form a mortar which can then be used in the same manner as resin cement mortars.

The working life and setting time of silicate cements can be determined by ASTM Method C-308-53T, described previously. The working and setting times of a typical silicate cement are given in Table 9-6.

TABLE 9-6. WORKING AND SETTING TIMES
OF A TYPICAL SILICATE MORTAR CEMENT

Temp. ($°F$)	Working Time (min.)	Final Setting Time (days)
60	90	4
70	45	2
80	30	1
90	10	2/3

Except for the fact that larger batches may be used, the directions for silicate mortar cements are similar to those outlined for resin mortar cements. Mixing pans and tools should be cleaned with water before the mortar has set. It is recommended that silicate cement joints be painted with strong acid solutions such as 20 per cent hydrochloric acid after the cements have attained their final set and before the structure is placed in service.

Silicate cements are recommended for use only where resin cements or sulfur cements are not applicable, i.e., with high concentrations of nitric, chromic, or sulfuric acids or at temperatures above $350°F$. Consideration must always be given to the permeability and absorption of the cements. They are used primarily for joining acid brick in the construction of towers, stacks, tank linings, sumps, drains, etc. Small nitric acid pickling tanks lined with acid brick joined with silicate cement are shown in Figure 9-5.

A specific application to which silicates are especially well suited is for joining acid brick in fume chambers and stacks handling hot,

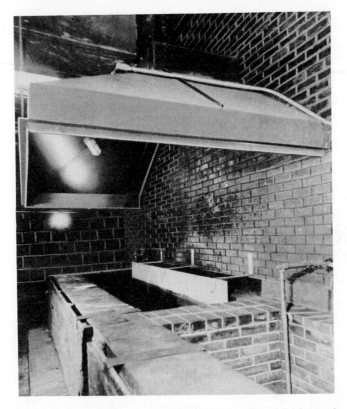

Figure 9-5. Small concrete pickling tanks lined with acid brick joined with silicate cement.

dry acid fumes and vapors. In this type of service, the permeability of the cement is not detrimental.

General Information

The physical and mechanical properties of typical chemical-resistant cements are compared in Table 9-7.

The practical properties of these cements are compared graphically in Table 9-8.

The resistance of typical chemical-resistant mortar cements to specific corrosives are compared in Table 9-9.

Additional information on specific applications of plastic materials of construction can be obtained by referring to the articles cited at the end of this chapter.

Resin cement mortars with little or no filler are used to a large extent as casting and tooling resins. This application is described in the following chapter.

TABLE 9-7. PHYSICAL AND MECHANICAL PROPERTIES OF TYPICAL CHEMICAL RESISTANT CEMENTS

ASTM Test Number	Property	Sulfur (silica-filled)	Polyester (silica-filled)	Phenolic (carbon-filled)	Epoxy (carbon-filled)	Furan (carbon-filled)	Silicate (silica-filled)
C-307-53T C-287-52T	Tensile strength, psi	650	1200	1250	1500	1200	350
C-306-53T C-287-52T	Compressive strength, psi	6000	11000	10000	16000	14000	3000
D-790-49T	Flexural strength, psi	—	6000	4000	6000	5000	—
D-790-49T C-287-52T	Modulus of rupture, psi	1800	1000	1000	1500	1000	—
D-792-50	Specific gravity	2.2	2.0	1.4	1.4	1.4	2.0
D-696-44.4	Coefficient of expansion, in./in./°F × 10^{-6}	8	5	6	6	6	7
	Adhesion						
	Wire-cut brick, psi	400	400	400	500	500	100
	Sandblasted steel, psi	—	400	—	800	—	—
D-570	Water absorption, %	0.3	0.2	0.2	0.3	0.2	8-15
	Maximum service temp., °F	200	180	360	200	375	750

TABLE 9-8. COMPARATIVE UTILITY OF TYPICAL COMMERCIAL
CHEMICAL RESIDENT CEMENTS

SULFUR (silica filled) — scale 0 to 10 — TOTAL 63

	COST	SPECIFIC GRAVITY	ABRASION	PHYSICAL DAMAGE	TEMPERATURE	SOLVENTS	SALTS	ALKALINE	NON-CXID. ACIDS	OXIDIZING ACIDS
RESISTANCE TO										

POLYESTER (silica filled) — scale 0 to 10 — TOTAL 65

COST, SPECIFIC GRAVITY, ABRASION, PHYSICAL DAMAGE, TEMPERATURE, SOLVENTS, SALTS, ALKALINE, NON-CXID. ACIDS, OXIDIZING ACIDS — RESISTANCE TO

PHENOLIC (carbon filled) — scale 0 to 10 — TOTAL 71

COST, SPECIFIC GRAVITY, ABRASION, PHYSICAL DAMAGE, TEMPERATURE, SOLVENTS, SALTS, ALKALINE, NON-CXID. ACIDS, OXIDIZING ACIDS — RESISTANCE TO

EPOXY (carbon filled) — scale 0 to 10 — TOTAL 72

COST, SPECIFIC GRAVITY, ABRASION, PHYSICAL DAMAGE, TEMPERATURE, SOLVENTS, SALTS, ALKALINE, NON-CXID. ACIDS, OXIDIZING ACIDS — RESISTANCE TO

FURAN (carbon filled) — scale 0 to 10 — TOTAL 75

COST, SPECIFIC GRAVITY, ABRASION, PHYSICAL DAMAGE, TEMPERATURE, SOLVENTS, SALTS, ALKALINE, NON-CXID. ACIDS, OXIDIZING ACIDS — RESISTANCE TO

164   PLASTIC MATERIALS OF CONSTRUCTION

TABLE 9-8 (Continued).

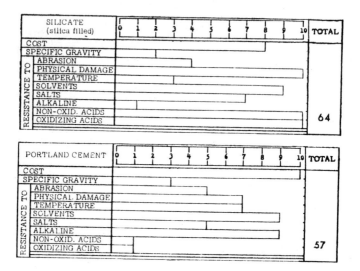

TABLE 9-9. CHEMICAL RESISTANCE OF TYPICAL
CHEMICAL RESISTANT MORTAR CEMENTS

	Sulfur 75°F-190°F		Polyester 75°F-175°F		Phenolic 75°F-250°F		Epoxy 75°F-200°F		Furan 75°F-250°F		Silicate 75°F-750°F	
Acids:												
Acetic, 10%	E	E	E	F	E	E	E	E	E	E	E	E
Acetic, glacial	G	N	N	N	E	G	F	P	E	E	E	E
Benzene sulfonic, 10%	E	E	E	E	E	E	E	E	E	E	E	E
Benzoic, satd.	E	E	E	E	E	E	E	E	E	E	E	E
Boric, satd.	E	G	E	E	E	E	E	E	E	E	E	E
Butyric, 100%	G	N	G	N	E	E	G	F	E	E	E	E
Chloroacetic, 10%	F	N	E	F	E	E	E	E	E	E	E	E
Chromic, 5%	E	G	E	G	G	P	F	N	F	N	E	E
Chromic, 10%	E	G	E	P	F	N	N	N	N	N	E	E
Citric, 10%	E	E	E	E	E	E	E	E	E	E	E	E
Fatty acids (C$_6$ and up), 100%	G	F	G	F	E	E	G	F	E	E	E	E
Fluosilicic, 40%	E*	E*	N	N	E*	E*	E*	E*	E*	E*	N	N
Formic, 90%	F	N	G	N	E	E	G	F	E	E	E	E
Hydrobromic	E	E	E	F	E	F	E	E	E	E	E	E
Hydrochloric	E	G	E	F	E	E	E	E	E	E	E	E
Hydrocyanic, 25%	E	E	E	E	E	E	E	E	E	E	E	E
Hydrofluoric, 40%	E*	E*	N	N	E*	E*	E*	E*	E*	E*	N	N
Hypochlorous, 10%	F	P	E	G	F	N	P	N	P	N	E	E
Lactic, 25%	E	E	E	E	E	E	E	E	E	E	E	E

TABLE 9-9 (Continued).

	Sulfur 75°F-190°F		Polyester 75°F-175°F		Phenolic 75°F-250°F		Epoxy 75°F-200°F		Furan 75°F-250°F		Silicate 75°F-750°F	
Acids:												
Maleic, 25%	E	F	E	E	E	E	E	E	E	E	E	E
Nitric, 5%	E	E	E	P	G	P	F	N	F	N	E	E
Nitric, 10%	E	G	G	N	P	N	N	N	N	N	E	E
Nitric, 20%	E	F	G	N	N	N	N	N	N	N	E	E
Oleic, 100%	E	F	G	F	E	E	E	E	E	E	E	E
Oxalic, 20%	E	E	E	E	E	E	E	E	E	E	E	E
Perchloric, 40%	E	E	E	F	E	E	E	E	E	E	E	E
Phosphoric, 85%	E	E	E	F	E	E	E	E	E	E	E	E
Picric, 10%	E	E	E	E	E	E	E	E	E	E	E	E
Stearic, 100%	E	F	G	F	E	E	E	E	E	E	E	E
Sulfuric, 50%	E	E	E	G	E	E	E	E	E	E	E	E
Sulfuric, 70%	E	F	F	P	E	P	F	N	E	N	E	E
Oleum, 110%	P	N	N	N	P	N	N	N	N	N	E	E
Mixed acids, 28% HNO_3 57% H_2SO_4	G	P	F	N	N	N	N	N	N	N	E	E
Alkalies:												
Ammonium hydroxide, 28%	N	N	F	N	P	N	E	E	E	E	N	N
Calcium hydroxide, satd.	N	N	N	N	F	P	E*	E*	E*	E*	N	N
Potassium hydroxide, 25%	N	N	N	N	N	N	E*	G*	E*	E*	N	N
Sodium hydroxide, 25%	N	N	N	N	N	N	E*	G*	E*	E*	N	N
Acid Salts:												
Alum, 10%	E	E	E	E	E	E	E	E	E	E	E	E
Ammonium chloride, nitrate, sulfate	E	E	E	E	E	E	E	E	E	E	E	E
Copper chloride, nitrate, sulfate	G	F	E	E	E	E	E	E	E	E	E	E
Ferric chloride, nitrate, sulfate, 10%	E	E	E	E	E	E	E	E	E	E	E	E
Nickel chloride, sulfate, 10%	E	E	E	E	E	E	E	E	E	E	E	E
Stannic chloride, 100%	E	F	E	N	E	E	E	F	E	E	E	E
Zinc chloride, nitrate, sulfate, 10%	E	E	E	E	E	E	E	E	E	E	E	E
Alkaline Salts:												
Barium sulfide	N	N	G	P	P	N	E	E	E	E	N	N
Sodium bicarbonate, 10%	E	F	E	E	E	E	E	E	E	E	F	N
Sodium carbonate, 10%	E	N	G	P	E	N	E	E	E	E	N	N
Sodium sulfide	N	N	G	P	P	N	E	E	E	E	N	N
Trisodium phosphate, 10%	G	N	G	P	G	N	E	E	E	E	N	N
Neutral Salts:												
Calcium chloride, nitrate, 10%	E	E	E	E	E	E	E	E	E	E	E	E

TABLE 9-9 (Continued).

	Sulfur 75°F-190°F		Polyester 75°F-175°F		Phenolic 75°F-250°F		Epoxy 75°F-200°F		Furan 75°F-250°F		Silicate 75°F-750°F	
Neutral Salts:												
Magnesium chloride, nitrate, sulfate, 10%	E	E	E	E	E	E	E	E	E	E	E	E
Potassium chloride, nitrate, sulfate, 10%	E	E	E	E	E	E	E	E	E	E	E	E
Sodium chloride, nitrate, sulfate, 10%	E	E	E	E	E	E	E	E	E	E	E	E
Gases:												
Chlorine, dry	F	N	G	N	F	N	F	N	F	N	E	E
Chlorine, wet	N	N	G	N	P	N	N	N	P	N	E	E
Hydrogen sulfide	E	E	E	E	E	E	E	E	E	E	E	E
Sulfur dioxide, dry	E	E	E	E	E	E	E	E	E	E	E	E
Sulfur dioxide, wet	E	E	E	E	E	E	E	E	E	E	E	E
Organic Materials:												
Acetone, 100%	N	N	N	N	E	E	E	P	E	E	E	E
Alcohol, methyl, ethyl, 95%	E	E	E	E	E	E	E	E	E	E	E	E
Aniline	N	N	P	N	F	P	F	N	P	N	F	N
Benzene	N	N	G	N	E	E	E	P	E	E	E	E
Carbon tetrachloride	N	N	E	N	E	E	E	F	E	E	E	E
Chloroform	N	N	G	N	E	E	E	F	E	E	E	E
Ethyl acetate	N	N	P	N	E	E	E	G	E	E	E	E
Ethylene dichloride	N	N	N	N	E	E	E	F	E	E	E	E
Formaldehyde, 37%	E	E	E	E	E	E	E	E	E	E	E	E
Phenol, 5%	N	N	N	N	E	E	E	F	E	E	E	E
Trichloroethylene	N	N	N	N	E	E	E	F	E	E	E	E
Papermill Applications:												
Kraft liquor	N	N	N	N	N	N	E*	G*	E*	E*	N	N
Black liquor	N	N	N	N	N	N	E*	G*	E*	E*	N	N
Green liquor	N	N	N	N	N	N	E*	G*	E*	E*	N	N
White liquor	N	N	N	N	P	N	E*	G*	E*	E*	N	N
Sulfite liquor	E	E	E	E	E	E	E	E	E	E	G	G
Chlorite bleach	F	N	E	F	F	P	P	N	P	N	N	N
Alum	E	E	E	E	E	E	E	E	E	E	E	G
Photographic Industry:												
Developers	E	F	E	E	E	E	E	E	E	E	G	F
General use	G	F	E	E	E	E	E	E	E	E	G	F
Silver nitrate	E	E	E	E	E	E	E	E	E	E	G	F
Fertilizer Industry:												
General use	E	E	E	E	E	E	E	E	E	E	F	F
Steel Industry:												
Sulfuric acid pickling	E	E	E	E	E	E	E	E	E	G	G	F
Hydrochloric acid pickling	E	E	E	E	E	E	E	E	E	E	G	F
H_2SO_4-HNO_3 acid pickling	G	F	F	P	F	N	F	P	P	N	G	F

TABLE 9-9 (Continued).

	Sulfur 75°F-190°F		Polyester 75°F-175°F		Phenolic 75°F-250°F		Epoxy 75°F-200°F		Furan 75°F-250°F		Silicate 75°F-750°F	
Textile Industry:												
General use	F	P	E	E	E	E	E	E	E	E	G	F
Hypochlorite bleach	F	N	E	F	F	P	P	N	P	N	N	N
Food Industry:												
General use	F	P	E	E	E	E	E	E	E	E	F	F
Breweries	F	P	E	E	E	E	E	E	E	E	F	F
Dairies	F	P	E	E	E	E	E	E	E	E	F	F
Miscellaneous Industries:												
Plating	E	G	E	E	E	E	E	E	E	E	G	F
Petroleum	F	N	E	F	E	E	E	E	E	E	G	F
Tanning	E	E	E	E	E	E	E	E	E	E	G	F
Oil and soap	F	P	G	F	F	F	E	E	E	E	F	N
Water and sewer	E	E	E	E	E	E	E	E	E	E	F	F

*Carbon filled

Ratings: E – No attack
G – Appreciably no attack
F – Some attack but usable in some instances
P – Attacked – not recommended
N – Badly attacked

Suggested References

"Plastics Equipment Reference Sheet No. 16—Furane Cement," R. B. Seymour and R. H. Steiner, Chem. Eng. Prog., Dec. 1952.

"Plastics Equipment Reference Sheet No. 17—Phenolic Cement," R. B. Seymour and R. H. Steiner, Chem. Eng. Prog., Jan. 1953.

"Chemical Resistant Cement Reference Sheet No. 18—Sulfur Cements," R. H. Steiner and W. R. Pascoe, Chem. Eng. Prog., Feb. 1953.

"Chemical Resistant Cement Reference Sheet No. 19—Silicate Cements," R. B. Seymour and R. H. Steiner, Chem. Eng. Prog., March 1953.

"Chemical Resistant Cement Reference Sheet No. 20—Epoxy Cement," R. B. Seymour and R. H. Steiner, Chem. Eng. Prog., April 1953.

"Chemical Resistant Cement Reference Sheet No. 21—Bleach-Resistant Cement," R. B. Seymour and R. H. Steiner, Chem. Eng. Prog., May 1953.

"Furane Cements," R. B. Seymour and R. H. Steiner, Chem. Eng., Dec. 1951.

"Phenolic Cements," R. B. Seymour and R. H. Steiner, Chem. Eng., Jan. 1952.

"Sulphur Cements," R. B. Seymour and R. H. Steiner, Chem. Eng., Feb. 1952.

"Silicate Cements," R. B. Seymour and R. H. Steiner, Chem. Eng., March 1952.

"Physical Properties of Plasticized Sulfur Cements," A. C. Loewer, W. J. Eney, R. B. Seymour and W. R. Pascoe, Am. Soc. Testing Materials, Proc., 1951.

"Torsion Testing Equipment for Cylindrical Cement Specimens," E. K. Muhlhausen, A. C. Loewer, Jr., and W. J. Eney, Soc. Exp. Stress Analysis, Proc., XI, 1 (May 1952).

"The Chemical Resistance of Phenolic Resins," R. B. Seymour, Corrosion, May 1951.

"The Furans," A. P. Dunlop and F. N. Peters, Reinhold Publishing Corp., New York, pp. 785-790, 1953.

"Soluble Silicates," J. G. Vail, Reinhold Publishing Corp., New York, Vol. II, pp. 434-443, 1952.

"Epoxy Cements and Coatings," R. B. Seymour and R. H. Steiner, Chem. Eng., April 1954.

"Corrosion Resistant Cements," V. Evans, Corrosion, Prevention and Control, 1, 339 (1954).

10. CASTING RESINS

Chemical-resistant mortar cements and many of the plastics described in previous chapters can be utilized for casting purposes. The principal requirement is that the product can be converted from a liquid or semi-liquid form to a solid with a minimum amount of shrinkage.

Some of the applications of casting resins are as follows: potting (stabilization of freely moving units), production of plastic items when quantity or size makes molding impractical, filling of voids, the manufacture of dies for shaping plastics or metals and the manufacture of chemical resistant equipment such as tanks and piping.

As in previous chapters, the utility of the plastic materials, rather than the specific applications, will be stressed. Also, as in previous cases, this chapter should be considered as a general discussion and not as an exhaustive treatment of the subject.

Sulfur

Since sulfur cements may be melted and cooled with relatively little shrinkage, they find considerable use as casting compositions. Carbon-filled sulfur cements have been used to prepare electrically conductive cores which can be removed by melting after being coated or plated.

Both carbon and silica-filled sulfur cements have been used as hubs for grinding wheels and for capping concrete test cylinders. In the latter application, the concrete always fractures while the cap remains intact. Silica-filled sulfur cements have been used for setting wrought iron posts, parking meters, road markers and machinery in concrete. Their use as jointing materials in water pipe will be discussed in Chapter 18.

Polyethylene—Polyisobutylene

Some of the lower molecular weight types of polyethylene have been used to a small extent as melts but microcrystalline wax and other readily melted products are usually preferred. Mixtures of polyethylene and microcrystalline wax have been used as hot-melt coatings for paper. In some instances, small amounts of polyisobutylene have been added to polyethylene or hydrocarbon waxes in order to improve casting properties of the molten compositions. Large structures have been cast from proprietary compositions based on polyethylene, polyisobutylene and paraffins.

Asphalt

Natural occurring filled asphalt, such as that mined at Lake Trinidad, has been used for centuries as a hot-melt type casting resin. During the past fifty years, filled asphalt has been manufactured for use as a casting material for joining vitrified clay pipe, etc. These products have limited use since they exhibit a tendency to cold flow. This characteristic is advantageous in sewer pipe lines but is usually undesirable in most other applications. Large quantities of asphalt are used for the production of storage battery boxes.

Coumarone-Indene Resins

The applications of coumarone-indene plastics and coal-tar pitch as casting materials are similar to those of asphalt. However, coumarone-indene casting compositions are more expensive than either asphalt or coal tar pitch. The latter is apt to decompose somewhat when overheated.

As described in Chapter 19, a filled polymeric hydrocarbon is used extensively as a root-resistant joint filler for sewer pipe. Such products can be modified to meet a wide variety of specifications.

Polystyrene

Attempts to use polystyrene as a melt plastic have not been successful. Blends of chlorinated biphenyl and polystyrene have been compression molded but the presence of relatively small amounts of polystyrene in chlorinated biphenyls increases the viscosity of the hot melts excessively. Solid chlorinated biphenyls have been used to some extent as melt castings. Blends of these products and polymethyl methacrylate have been proposed for novelty castings but such products have not been used to any great extent industrially.

Acrylates

Solutions of polymethyl methacrylate in its monomer can be polymerized at room temperature in the presence of a catalyst to produce clear castings. Until recent years, almost all methacrylate sheet plastic was obtained by casting techniques. Comparable sheet can now be manufactured much more economically by the extrusion process.

The polymerization in situ process is still employed for the production of dentures and novelties. The former process is an adaptation of the methacrylate sheet casting technique in the presence of appropriate pigments. Promoters are usually added to the catalyst in order to hasten polymerization. Biological specimens, ornaments, small trophies and replicas may be mounted in clear methacrylate plastic by casting techniques.

Polyvinyl Chloride

Although commercial vinyl film has been cast from solutions of polyvinyl chloride, it is not usually considered as a castable resin. However, in recent years, the development of plastisol and plastigel techniques has made vinyl casting more practical.

Plastisols are essentially dispersions of finely divided vinyl resins in liquid plasticizers. The addition of gelling agents produces creamy trowelable compositions. Either liquid plastisols or the more viscous plastigels can be placed in molds and heated at 325 to 375°F to produce irreversible plasticized vinyl castings. This process is used widely for the production of novelties, such as doll heads and for coating plating racks. It is also of interest to note that molds cast from plastisols are used for casting phenolic and epoxy resins.

Polyurethanes

Polyurethanes may be cast in situ as cellular plastics or foams, as discussed in Chapter 11, as well as higher density products. Such castings are usually prepared from organic isocyanates and organic polyesters containing free hydroxyl groups.

The shrinkage which occurs during the casting of these resins can be controlled. The product also exhibits outstanding adhesion to a wide variety of surfaces. They have been used to a small extent as space-filling, formed-in-place reinforcement for hollow structures.

Natural Rubber

Liquid depolymerized rubber can be cured at room temperature to produce flexible products. These compositions have been proposed for use where flexible potting compositions are required.

Polysulfide Rubbers

The use of mixtures of sulfur and olefin polysulfides as castable melts has been limited. In recent years, liquid olefin polysulfides have been available commercially.

These products can be cured in the absence of solvent by the addition of specific catalyst systems to produce resilient castings. While their use has been confined essentially to specialized aeronautical and military applications, they have considerable potential when cast resilient objects with good solvent resistance are required.

Cellulose Derivatives

Ethyl cellulose or cellulose acetate butyrate may be blended with low melting products and/or plasticizers to form useful melt-type plastics. Proprietary compositions based on ethyl cellulose have been used as melts for the temporary protection of small automotive and airplane parts during shipping and storage. Metal forming dies for drop hammer and foundry applications have been cast from similar proprietary compositions.

Polyesters

Solvent-free unsaturated polyester resin-styrene blends can be catalyzed and cured at room temperature to form large castings. The limiting factor is apparently associated with the ability to dissipate the heat of polymerization, which often leads to cracking when large units are cast.

The clear polyesters have been used to mount biological specimens and other items using techniques adapted from the methacrylate casting process. Polyesters have also been pigmented and cast to form novelties and special parts when molding processes were not applicable.

Many industrial potting compounds are based on polyesters. This plastic has fair electrical properties and is often cast around electronic assemblies. Filled polyester castings, with a wide variety of properties are available commercially. Pipe cast from polyester resins is described in Chapter 17.

Urea-Melamine Resins

Proprietary casting resins based on mixtures of urea or melamine resins with appropriate fillers have been used to a limited extent. These compositions are cured at room temperature after the addition of liquid catalysts. The cast objects are characterized by good surface hardness and dimensional stability.

Phenolic Resins

Phenolic castings have perhaps the most important commercial application discussed in this chapter. As previously pointed out, liquid phenolic resins can be converted to solids by the addition of heat and/or acids. This technique has been used for many years to produce novelties and small industrial parts. Most novelties are produced by curing natural resins for long periods of time at 170 to 180°F. Pipe and fittings have been produced commercially from phenolic resins by acid catalysts. Phenolic resins are also widely used for production of chemical-resistant equipment and metalforming tools. These applications are discussed in the final section of this chapter.

Shell molding is essentially a process in which highly filled cast phenolic resins serve as the mold cavity for metal castings. Since either furan, epoxy or phenolic resins may be used, shell molding and equipment formed from cast asbestos plastic combinations will be discussed separately at the end of this chapter.

Physical properties of typical cast phenolic resins are compared in Table 10-1:

TABLE 10-1. COMPARISON OF FILLED CAST PHENOLIC RESINS.

Property	No Filler	Tooling Resin	Walnut Shell Flour	Asbestos	Carbon
Shrinkage, mils/in.	7	4	6	4	6
Tensile strength, psi.	6,000	5,000	5,000	4,000	4,000
Compressive strength, psi.	8,000	11,000	3,000	4,000	5,000
Impact, Izod ft lb/in. notch	0.28	0.3	0.25	0.25	0.3
Specific gravity	1.21	1.26	1.18	1.21	1.20
Thermal expansion, in./in./°F $\times 10^{-6}$	5.1	6.2	5.1	1.5	5.1
Maximum operating temp., °F	160	265	160	265	265

Epoxy Resins

As previously described, liquid epoxy resins are somewhat simi-lar to phenolic resins. However, epoxy resins utilize amine curing catalysts rather than acids. Epoxy casting resins also exhibit less shrinkage than phenolic resins and hence, find application where cast phenolics are not suitable. They are of special interest as potting or encapsulating materials for fragile electrical assemblies which will be subjected to intense vibration, and as tooling resins.

High-temperature curing epoxy resin compositions are also widely used. The curing agents include phthalic anhydride, sodium phenoxide and complex amines. A restrike die made of epoxy resin cast over a polyester resin core is shown in Figure 10-1.

Furans

Liquid furan resins can be converted to solids by casting tech-niques similar to those discussed for phenolic resins. However, all furan castings are characteristically black and polymerization is more difficult to control than in the phenolic casting process. As previously noted, because of their industrial importance, cast asbes-tos-filled furan resins are discussed separately later in this chapter.

Shell Molding

The often quoted statement that progress is limited only by imagi-nation is applicable to the cast plastics industry. Unfortunately, progress in this field is sometimes impeded by a narrow viewpoint which does not accept the use of plastics with nonplastic materials.

Some of the most significant advances in the plastics art have been made by those who attempted to utilize all materials on a func-tional basis. Among these advances, laminates, plastic impregnated graphite, plastic rubber blends and shell molding are included. The last is one of the most important recent developments in both the plastics and metals industries.

Shell molding, like unplasticized polyvinyl chloride and polyure-thanes, is a German development. The process, sometimes named

(Courtesy of Shell Chemical Company)

Figure 10-1. A restrike die made of epoxy resin cast over a polyester core.

after its inventor, Johannes Croning, was used during World War II and noted by American technical teams on their post-war tours of German industry.

In this process, an intimate mixture of 5 to 19 parts by weight of finely divided thermosetting resin and 90 to 95 parts dry sand is placed in a dump box. A hot pattern coated with a parting agent is placed in the box and permitted to contact the resin sand mixture uniformly for a specific length of time.

The contact with the hot surface softens the resin so that a fairly uniform sand-resin shell is formed around the pattern. The pattern and shell are removed and then heated in an oven to complete the cure of resin.

After curing, the shell which varies between 1/8 and 3/8 inch in thickness may be cut and removed from the pattern. If cutting is essential, the two or more parts are clamped or adhered together, forming the mold for subsequent casting operations. Otherwise, the shell is used in the form in which it was removed from the pattern.

The shell mold requires little support for small or light castings but large molds must be prevented from breaking by the use of external support, such as gravel. When the hot metal is added to the shell mold, charring and decomposition of the resin take place. However, the shell retains its form long enough to produce exceptionally true castings.

Castings produced by the shell process have an excellent finish and reproduce the pattern characteristics well. Obviously, the cost of the sand-resin mix is greater than foundry sand but some economies are realized as a result of fewer rejects, more efficient use of space and a reduction in finishing costs.

Up to the present time, phenolic resins have been used almost exclusively as resins for the shell molding process. Urea and melamine resins hold considerable promise for use with low melting alloys. Polyester, epoxy and furan resins could also be used in this process, but phenolic resins continue to be of prime importance because of Croning's original work.

The growth of the shell molding process in the United States is extremely interesting. In spite of the process being known in 1945, less than a million pounds of resin were used for this purpose up until 1950. However, 3 million pounds of resin were consumed in 1952. and over 10 million pounds in 1953. It has been estimated that over 100 million pounds of shell molding resins will be consumed by over 2,000 foundries in 1960. These potential quantities assume greater significance when one remembers that less than 75 million pounds of phenolic molding resins were used in 1953.

Tooling Resins

One of the most rapidly expanding fields of application of industrial plastics is the use of resins for the fabrication of tools in the metal-forming industries. In this case, the term "tools" includes any form, die, jig or fixture used to form, fabricate, check or hold components in position during the manufacture of structural shapes. It should be mentioned that plastic tools are also used to a great extent in the reinforced plastics industry.

The various types of tools which have been constructed of plastics include stretch forming dies, draw dies, drop hammer dies, hydro-forming dies, blanking dies, drill jigs, routing fixtures, installation fixtures and checking fixtures. Much of the pioneering work was carried out by the aircraft industry for the low cost production of airplane components. However, many of the improved techniques have been adopted by the automotive and other metal-working industries. Obviously, it is beyond the scope of this book to describe the functions of the many varied types of tools now being used.

The three major types of resins which have been used for tooling purposes are phenolics, polyesters and epoxies. Phenolics were the first resins studied and because of their low cost and high strength are still the most widely used. However, the disadvantages of high shrinkage and the use of acidic catalysts somewhat offset their inherent advantages.

Polyester resins are seldom used except with fiberglas reinforcement. Again, high shrinkage is a drawback. Because of their low shrinkage factor and excellent dimensional stability, epoxy resins, with or without fillers or fibrous reinforcements, are of great interest.

The first step in the fabrication of a plastic tool is the construction of a plaster, wooden or sheet metal replica of the object to be formed. After a suitable parting agent such as wax has been applied to the surface of the replica, the tooling resin containing the required catalyst is poured and allowed to harden. When large or extremely durable tools are required, the replica is usually constructed by laying up several layers of glass cloth in a relatively thin layer of epoxy resin. This technique is described in greater detail in Chapter 14.

The body or core of the tool may be cast of cheaper materials such as phenolic or melamine resins. A considerable savings in weight may be achieved by using foamed-in-place phenolic or isocyanate resins as the core material. Although the resins used are all room-temperature curing, the tool is usually heated at elevated temperatures to insure complete cure.

The advantages of plastic tooling are many. Savings in time and labor of up to 80 per cent are realized by the use of plastics instead of cast metal tools. In addition, the weight of the completed tool may be reduced by as much as 90 per cent. This weight reduction results in much lower handling costs and permits the use of lighter weight presses.

The forming of sheets of aluminum, soft steel and hard stainless steel in thicknesses up to 64 mils on plastic tooling is now standard practice in many modern shops.

It should be emphasized that plastic tooling will not replace metal tools and dies completely but will find a definite place in this industry.

Resin-Asbestos Equipment

As discussed in Chapter 14, phenolic resin laminates have been considered for use in the chemical process industry. However, most commercial phenolic laminates utilize cellulosic reinforcing members. Polyester laminates are reinforced by glass fiber or mat which is more chemically resistant. Unfortunately, however, the chemical resistance of most polyesters is inferior to that of phenolic, epoxy and furan resins.

These objections were overcome in Germany in 1922 through the development of readily cast liquid phenolic-asbestos compositions. This process, which was commercialized in the United States in 1932, utilizes inexpensive molds in which the acid-washed asbestos-liquid phenolic mixtures are cast.

In the casting process, a partial cure takes place at ordinary temperatures, after which the articles are finally cured in ovens at elevated temperatures. By a utilization of these techniques, it is possible to produce cylindrical vessels up to 10 feet in diameter and rectangular vessels up to 12 feet in length. Cylindrical and rectangular structures of almost unlimited depth and length are possible by joining together the flanged sections.

The original asbestos-phenolic equipment was suitable for service at temperatures up to 265°F in the presence of salts, many solvents and non-oxidizing acids, with the exception of hydrofluoric acid. Subsequently, asbestos was replaced by carbon in order to secure equipment with resistance to fluorides.

After the introduction of furan cements, liquid furan resin-asbestos casting compositions were used. Equipment produced from furan-carbon mixtures is resistant to alkalies as well as non-oxidizing acids, solvents and salts.

As shown in Figures 10-2 and 10-3, equipment based on filled phenolic or furan resins has been used for valves, piping, fittings, fume exhaust systems, tanks, reaction vessels, fan housings, pumps

(Courtesy of Haveg Corporation)

Figure 10-2. Cyclone separator fabricated of cast phenolic resin-asbestos.

178   PLASTIC MATERIALS OF CONSTRUCTION

(Courtesy of Haveg Corporation)

Figure 10-3. Dished head of a cast phenolic resin-asbestos tank.

and absorption towers. All three types have a specific gravity of approximately 1.6. The published coefficient of expansion is 18 x 10^{-6} in./in. of length per $°F$. Other physical properties are given in Table 10-2.

Design data for typical standard-size cylindrical and rectangular tanks of cast phenolic resin-asbestos mixtures are presented in Tables 10-3 and 10-4 respectively.

The commercial utilization of resin-asbestos compositions is a classic example of the employment of a plastic and a nonplastic material in order to secure superior physical properties for the solution of a specific problem.

TABLE 10-2. COMPARATIVE PHYSICAL PROPERTIES OF CAST PHENOLIC EQUIPMENT

Property	Phenolic-Asbestos	Phenolic-Carbon	Furan-Asbestos
Tensile strength, psi	2,500	2,500	4,000
Compressive strength, psi	10,500	8,000	11,500
Flexural strength, psi	5,600	4,500	7,500
Thermal conductivity, Btu/sq ft/$°F$/hr/ft	0.203	0.607	0.203

TABLE 10-3. DESIGN DATA FOR STANDARD
PHENOLIC RESIN-ASBESTOS CYLINDRICAL TANKS

Internal Diameter (ft)	Depth (ft)	Wall Thickness (in)	Bottom Thickness (in)
1	1 – 10	1/2	5/8
2 A	1 – 4½	1/2	5/8
2 A	4½ – 15	5/8	3/4
5 B	1 – 4½	5/8	3/4
5 B	4½ – 9½	3/4	1
5 B	9½ – 14	1	1¼
10 B	1 – 4	3/4	1
10 B	4 – 7	1	1¼
10 B	7 – 10	1¼	1½
10 B	10 – 12	1½	1⅝

A – Supporting bands required.
B – Supporting staves and hoops required.

TABLE 10-4. DESIGN DATA FOR STANDARD
PHENOLIC RESIN-ASBESTOS RECTANGULAR TANKS

Depth (ft)	Width (ft)	Length (ft)	Wall Thickness (in)	Bottom Thickness (in)	Number of External Reinforcing Ribs
1	1	1 – 15	1/2	5/8	0
2	2	1 – 2⅓	1/2	5/8	0
2	2	2⅓ – 7½	7/8	7/8	0
2	2	7½ – 14½	5/8	3/4	3
4	4	1 – 6	5/8	3/4	5
4	4	6 – 8	3/4	1	5 – 6
4	4	8 – 14	1	1¼	6
6	6	1 – 3	5/8	3/4	9
6	6	3⅓ – 3¾	3/4	1	9
6	6	4 – 12	1	1¼	9–10

Chemical equipment with comparable design, but with greater resistance to chemicals, has been fabricated by casting resins in a permanent form of thermoplastic material. For example, thin polychloroether or polytetrafluoroethylene plastic sheet may be thermally formed and welded as the inside of a storage vessel.

A similar shape, measuring at least 2 inches greater in all dimensions, can be formed from a glass textile reinforced thermosetting resin is discussed in Chapter 14. An asbestos-furan, asbestos-phenolic or a carbon-furan resinous cement is cast in the space formed when the smaller tank is inserted within the larger. The cast resin is then allowed to cure at room temperature, after which it is heat-cured. The final structure has the outstanding chemical resistance of the inner liner and the strength of the filled cast resin. Unlike the lined equipment discussed in Chapter 8, it is resistant to chemicals throughout its entire structure.

Cast plastics account for a relatively small volume of plastic materials. However, some of the products cannot be made by any other technique. These methods should not be overlooked by those attempting to solve problems through the use of plastics. Another interesting application of plastics to produce structural foams is described in Chapter 11.

Suggested References

"Plant Equipment From Synthetic Resins," D. H. Killefer, Ind. Eng. Chem., 25, 1217 (1933).

"Phenol-Asbestos Plant Equipment," W. H. Adams, Jr., Modern Plastics, 18, 4, 53 (1940).

"Cast Phenolic Resins," W. R. Thompson, Chem. Industries, 48, 450-6 (1941).

"Colloid Chemistry," Vol. 6, J. Alexander, Reinhold Publishing Corp., New York, 1946.

"Cast Plastics and Casting Processes," P. E. Erbe and J. T. Grey, Modern Plastics, 24, No. 3, 153 (1946).

"Surface Reactions of Copolymers—Methyl Methacrylate and $\alpha\beta$-Unsaturated Carboxylic Acids," Raymond B. Seymour and Ira Branum, Ind. Eng. Chem., 41, 1479 (July 1949).

"Surface Reactions of Copolymers—Methyl Methacrylate and Maleic Anhydride," Raymond B. Seymour, Ira Branum, Jr., and F. W. Hayward, Ind. Eng. Chem., 41, 1482 (July 1949).

"Phenolic Resins in Chemical Plants," Raymond B. Seymour, International Chemical Engineering, 385, (August 1951).

"Shell Molding," Anon., Plastics World, 16-20 (November 1953).

"The Chemistry of Commercial Plastics," R. L. Wakeman, Reinhold Publishing Corp., New York, 1947.

"Better Tools From Molded Laminates," L. Wittman, Modern Plastics, 24, 10, 132 (1947).

"Plastic Tooling," L. Wittman, Materials & Methods, 27, 87 (1948).

"Plastic Punches Facilitate Metal Forming," G. H. Prudden, Machinery, 136, (July 1944).

CASTING RESINS 181

"Plastic Foundry Match Plates," F. Schumacher, Modern Plastics, 27, 3, 95 (1949).

"Asbestos Resin Compositions in the Chemical Industry," P. L. McWhorter, Corrosion, 10, 4, 141 (1954).

"Shell Molding and Shell Mold Castings," T. C. Du Mond, Reinhold Publishing Corp., New York, 1954.

"Plastics Engineering in the Electrical Industry," H. Rudoff, T. J. Jordan and J. A. Coffman, Symposium on Plastics as Materials of Construction, American Chemical Society, Division of Paint, Plastics and Printing Ink Chemistry, New York, Sept. 1954.

"Alloying with Epoxys," John Charlton, Modern Plastics, 32, 1, 155 (1954).

"Metal Working Swings to Plastic Tools," Modern Plastics, 32, 1, 85 (1954).

"Why Epoxy Resins for Laminated Tooling?," J. Delmonte, Materials & Methods, 40, 2, 93 (1954).

11. CELLULAR PLASTICS

The previously discussed casting resins are usually dense and void-free since such a type of structure is essential for maximum strength. However, there are occasions when low density is advantageous even though the product must be cellular in order to obtain such properties. The lightweight of natural cellular products is an advantage which has been recognized for many years. As a result, products like balsa wood have been utilized where lightweight structural materials are required.

When strength and chemical resistance have not been important, attempts have been made to utilize structures related to natural sponges. These developments have resulted in sponge-like structures based on rubber, vinyls and cellulose. Structural foams or sponges may be produced by several different processes, the prime requirement being the production of a noncollapsible cell-like structure.

In some processes, air is whipped into the liquid resin and conversion to a solid takes place without loss in cellular structure. In other methods, a chemical blowing agent is either added or is produced as a part of the polymerization process.

In spite of the obvious potentials of foams and sponge-like materials for thermal insulation purposes, these products have not been utilized to any great extent until recent years. However, as it is apparent from the subsequent discussion, all plastic and elastomeric materials are potential foams.

The Cellular Plastics Division of the Society of the Plastics Industry has been formed to establish standards for this product. In spite of the newness of this application, the Division should be able to prevent misapplications which may result from a lack of knowledge of the product.

Some specific applications of plastics in the formation of cellular products are discussed below.

Sulfur

Inexpensive sponge-like products have been produced from hot melts of salt and sulfur. When the filled products are cast in specific shapes, a sponge-like structure is obtained by subsequent extraction of the salt with water.

Polystyrene

Polystyrene may be readily dissolved in volatile solvents such as methyl chloride and as a result, can be converted to rigid foam-like products having non-interconnecting cells and a wide variety of physical properties. Polystyrene may be expanded to forty times its original volume to produce foams weighing as little as 1.5 lbs/cu ft. Such products have a "K" factor as low as 0.27 Btu/hr/sq ft/°F/in. of thickness.

While styrene foam is produced in relatively large quantities, much of the output has been consumed for displays and novelty uses. At the present time, packaging and sandwich construction account for greatly increasing amounts. Styrene foams have considerable industrial potential, particularly for low temperature installations. They are said to be satisfactory for use at a temperature range from −250 to 175°F.

Polystyrene foam, like most other plastic foams, can be fabricated by the use of wood working tools. It may be cut with high-speed band saws or by hot wire. It may be heat-formed and adhered to a variety of surfaces using a number of adhesives including solvent, curing (such as epoxy resins) and hot-melt types.

Since styrene foams are generally formed from solutions of styrene and methyl chloride, some of this solvent remains in the cells and is released during fabrication. Hence, special precautions must be taken to provide good ventilation when working. The insulation of a brine pipeline with preformed polystyrene foam is shown in Figure 11-1.

Polystyrene molding powder which foams when heated is now available commercially. It may be formed in a heated mold or allowed to foam as a slab of uncontrolled dimensions. Small sections of sandwich construction with these materials are shown in Figure 11-2.

Vinyls

Since vinyl plastisols do not require a liquid solvent, they can be used to produce resilient foams without the danger of toxic solvent residues. It is customary to add a chemical blowing agent or carbon dioxide to the plastisol and to chill the mixture. As the cold mixture is then gradually heated, the blowing agent decomposes to form gaseous products which cause the mixture to expand. As indicated in Chapter 5, heat curing at temperatures above 325°F is required to fuse the plasticizer and vinyl resin.

Vinyl foams have been produced with densities varying from 2.5 to 12 lbs/cu ft. as might be expected, the compressibility varies with the density. Compressibilities in the range of 2 to 60 psi have been obtained. Vinyl foams are said to have a "K" factor of as low as 0.20 Btu/hr/sq ft/°F/in. They have been proposed as resilient, low temperature insulating materials and for use in the manufacture of orthopedic and prosthetic devices.

Polyurethanes

Foamed-in-place products which expand to as much as thirty times

(Courtesy of Dow Chemical Company)

Figure 11-1. Insulation of brine pipelines with foamed polystyrene.

their original volume can be produced from diisocyanates and compounds containing active hydrogen such as hydroxyl groups. In these reactions, the foaming is dependent upon the carbon dioxide which is released as a product of the reaction.

These isocyanate foams have excellent adhesion to a wide variety of surfaces and may be produced as rigid or flexible products with densities ranging from 2 to 20 lbs/cu ft. Isocyanate foams which may have a "K" factor as low as 0.20 Btu/sq ft/hr/°F/in. thickness have been used for aircraft construction. They are supplied commercially as two-package units which are mixed on the job.

The application of a diisocyanate foam producing plastic to provide insulation for a valve is shown in Figure 11-3 to 11-6. The rapid rate of formation of the foam can be observed from the timer in the sequence of action photographs.

Foams based on diisocyanates are somewhat more expensive than other foam products. Since they are highly adhesive and are essen-

(Courtesy of Koppers Company)

Figure 11-2. Plywood and aluminum sandwich sections with foamed polystyrene.

tially neutral, and readily applied, they have considerable potential as engineering materials for thermal insulation on pipe, valves and other intricately shaped chemical equipment. They may be used at temperatures as high as 235°F and as low as −300°F.

Because of their excellent electrical properties, isocyanate foams have also been used extensively for the potting of electronic equipment. The aircraft industry has used them in sandwich construction to increase the rigidity of light structural items such as rudders, ailerons and wingstabs. Radar domes constructed of reinforced polyester resins have been filled with foamed isocyanates for increased strength. Usually foams with a density of 6 to 8 lbs/cu ft are used for reinforcement purposes.

Flexible cellular diisocyanate plastics may be foamed on the job or prefoamed in the plant. Because of the possible toxicity of unreacted organic isocyanates, a prepolymer is usually preferred for field applications. However, providing adequate ventilation and technical assistance are available, foamed articles can be prepared directly from the organic diisocyanates and polyesters.

Commercial equipment is now available for continuous mixing of the prepolymer and catalyst for the formation of isocyanate foams. The two ingredients can also be fed separately to the nozzle and sprayed in specially designed equipment.

(Courtesy of E. I. du Pont de Nemours & Co.)

Figure 11-3. Figures 11-3 through 11-6 show insulating a valve with a foamed-in-place isocyanate resin. Above, mixing of catalyst with isocyanate prepolymer.

Rubber

Cellular material may be produced from either natural or synthetic rubber using chemical blowing agents and heat. In recent years, rubber foam has been produced commercially by whipping air into compounded rubber latex in the presence of a latent acid setting agent. These foams are then poured into molds and heat-cured.

Cellulose Acetate

Solutions of cellulose acetate in volatile solvents have been flash evaporated to produce cellulose acetate foams with closed cell structures. These products have densities as low as 6 lbs/cu ft and "K" factors as low as 0.31 Btu/hr/sq ft/°F/in. thickness.

Cellulose acetate foam has been produced commercially for several years. It is available in the form of blocks and has been used in aircraft structures.

Polyesters

Polyester foams have not been used to any great extent in the United

(Courtesy of E. I. du Pont de Nemours & Co.)

Figure 11-4. Pouring catalyzed resin into transparent temporary form.

States. However, reaction products of polyesters and diisocyanates produce both rigid or resilient foams which have been used to considerable extent in Germany, and which are now produced in the United States.

Urea and Melamine

Liquid urea and melamine resins may be acid catalyzed and then frothed by chemical action or air. These resins may be cured to produce foams in the form of shreds or blocks with densities varying from 0.5 to 15 lbs/cu ft. They have "K" factors as low as 0.18 Btu/hr/sq ft/°F/in. thickness and may be used at temperatures up to 130°F.

Phenolics

Phenolic foams, first introduced in 1945, can also be formed in place. They are produced by adding an acid catalyst to a liquid phenolic resin in the presence of a gas former. Like phenolic casting resins, they may be cured at room temperature. Some progress has been made in spraying phenolic foam components with a dual nozzle spray gun.

Figure 11-5. Beginning of foaming action.

Figure 11-6. Completed foam. Form can be removed after 30 minutes.

Phenolic resin foams are dark in color and contain residual acid catalyst. They have been proposed for structural space filling and for foam packaging for shipment of glassware, etc.

Recently developed phenolic resin microscopic balloons are also cellular plastics. These balloons, which are filled with nitrogen, vary in size from 0.0002 to 0.0036 inch in diameter and have a bulk density of approximately 9 lbs/cu ft. "Microballoons" are admixed with oil and gradually rise to the surface to form a thin floating layer which prevents excessive evaporation of oil during storage. As indicated in Chapter 5, phenolic resins are not affected nor attacked by petroleum oil or materials expected to be present under storage conditions.

As might be anticipated, pores of cellular material are often impregnated with plastics to form dense objects. This application of plastics is discussed in Chapter 12.

Suggested References

"Developments in Plastic Foams," W. C . Goggin and O. R. McIntire, Plastics (Chicago), 8, 18 (April 1947).

"Polyurethane Resins," J. Bjorksten, H. Tovey and H. L. Dollard, Modern Plastics, 31, 8, 143 (1954).

"Polyurethanes," O. Bayer, Modern Plastics, 24, 10, 149 (1947).

"A New Plastic Low Temperature Insulation," E. C. Van Buskirk and C. C. Surland, Chem. Eng. Prog., 44, 803 (1948).

"Styrofoam for Low Temperature Insulation," O. R. McIntire and R. N. Kennedy, Chem. Eng. Prog., 44, 727 (1948).

"Polystyrene Foam," R. N. Kennedy, SPE Journal, 9, 10, 11-13 (1953).

"Phenolic Foam," J. D. Nelson, SPE Journal, 9, 10, 14-15 (1953).

"Sandwich Materials," K. Rose, Materials & Methods, 39, 3, 117-132 (1954).

"Plastics in Plants Manufacturing Heavy Chemicals," G. A. Griess, Symposium on Plastics as Materials of Construction, American Chemical Society, Division of Paint, Plastics and Printing Ink Chemistry, New York, Sept. 1954.

12. PLASTIC IMPREGNANTS

The utility of many porous nonplastic materials can be increased by impregnation with a casting-type plastic. In some instances a plastic in the form of a solution or suspension may be used. In such cases, no change in molecular size occurs and the plastic molecules must be held primarily by adhesive forces. Sometimes this is an advantage when only a temporary effect is desired.

In contrast, the sealing effect of the impregnant used with most porous materials is dependent upon an increase in molecular size of the resin used. The discussion in this chapter will be restricted to plastic materials which polymerize after being impregnated in the voids of nonplastic materials. Those products which may polymerize in situ are styrene, acrylates, polysulfide rubber, polyesters, urea, melamine, phenolic, epoxy and furan resins.

Many impregnation procedures require the use of high-vacuum equipment to obtain complete penetration of the voids by the liquid resin or resin-forming material. In a typical process, the object to be treated is subjected to a high vacuum in a suitably designed vessel to exhaust the air. The liquid resin is then added while the system remains under vacuum. Commercial equipment is available for impregnation by this technique.

Commercial metal castings are often rejected because of porosity. If they are not expected to operate at temperatures above 300°F, this deficiency can usually be overcome through plastic impregnation. Similar techniques are used to produce impervious graphite and to make porous stone more useful. The plastics that have shown promise for this application are discussed below. Specific commercial applications are described at the end of the chapter.

Styrene

Styrene polymerizes quite readily at moderate temperatures in the presence of catalysts. Thus, a catalyzed styrene solution may be used to impregnate fabric, textile or wood and allowed to polymerize in situ. Possible solvent extraction of the polymer can be prevented by employing a small amount of a cross-linking agent such as divinyl benzene. The impregnant produces a three-dimensional polymer which is more resistant to heat and solvents.

Some success has been obtained by impregnating porous materials with maleic anhydride and a catalyst with subsequent impregnation with styrene. The rapid formation in situ of a styrene-maleic anhydride heteropolymer results, which may subsequently be in-solubilized by reaction with metal salts. Solutions of styrene-maleic anhydride copolymer may also be impregnated in porous materials and subsequently reacted with polyhydric alcohols such as poly-ethylene glycol.

Acrylates

Methyl methacrylate or ethyl acrylate monomers may be mixed with catalysts such as benzoyl peroxide and polymerized in situ using processes similar to those described for styrene. Interesting ef-fects can be secured through the use of higher molecular weight alkyl esters such as octyl or dodecyl which yield more flexible prod-ucts.

Olefin Polysulfides

Liquid olefin polysulfides have higher molecular weights than mono-meric styrene or methyl methacrylate. Nevertheless, solutions of the liquids and catalysts can be impregnated in paper, asbestos or textiles. The subsequent increase in molecular weight within the nonplastic product yields oil-resistant products which are some-times more interesting than the polymer itself.

Polyesters

Alkyd resins and oil paints have been used as impregnants for porous castings. As might be expected, the conversion to useful products is slow even when the impregnated unit is baked. In addi-tion, the impregnated product has limited resistance to heat and chemicals.

When polyester resins became available commercially, they re-placed alkyds and oil paints as impregnants to a large extent. The viscosity and rate of cure of these resins can be regulated over a wide range.

No solvents or fumes are evolved during the polymerization of such catalyzed products in porous castings. In addition, the resultant polyesters usually adhere well to the metal castings. Polyesters are also largely used industrially for the impregnation of other po-rous products.

Urea Resins

Because urea solutions exert a swelling effect on cellulosic ma-terials, urea treatment is a standard technique in many woodworking industries. Hence, it was quite logical to substitute liquid urea-formaldehyde polymers to obtain stronger products as a result of further polymerization.

Partial polymers of both urea and melamine are used with wood, paper, cotton and wool. Impregnated wood is much denser and more water resistant than untreated material. Wet strength properties are imparted to paper by the addition of melamine resins in the beater. Melamine or urea treated wool develops shrink resistance and impregnated textiles possess unique surface properties.

Phenolic Resins

Phenolic sealants are comparable to urea and melamine impregnants but are not used interchangeably. Phenolic resins have been used for the impregnation of wooden chemical equipment such as filter plates to extend the useful life of the equipment.

Epoxy Resins

At present, epoxy sealants are used interchangeably with phenolic resins. Since epoxy resins are cured on the alkaline side, they may also be used to impregnate alkaline materials such as concrete or limestone, which would neutralize the acid catalyst in phenolic resins.

Furans

Liquid furan resins are catalyzed by acids and may be used to impregnate plaster of Paris castings. Since they are not affected by alkalies, acids or solvents, they have been used to impregnate wooden filter frames and other wooden equipment in chemical process plants.

Impregnated Sandstone

Laboratory tabletops, hoods and similar structures manufactured from resin-impregnated sandstone were introduced commercially in 1942. The resinous impregnant consisted of a mixture of approximately three parts of furfural and one part furfuryl alcohol catalyzed with aqueous sulfuric acid.

In manufacturing impregnated sandstone, the stone is immersed in freshly prepared catalyzed furan solutions under vacuum, removed and heated at 250 to 350°F in order to polymerize the mixture in situ. The resulting product may be machined and sawed, and is resistant at ordinary temperatures to most alkalies, solvents, salts and acids, with the exception of nitric, chromic and concentrated sulfuric acid.

Impervious Graphite

The use of preformed carbon and graphite as structural materials is well known. Both are essentially inert in oxidizing atmospheres at elevated temperatures but their high porosity restricts their use in many applications. Actually, while graphite is more heat stable than carbon, both have a porosity value of approximately 25 per cent.

As might be concluded from previous discussions on impregnation, the porosity of both carbon and graphite can be reduced by impregnation with liquid thermosetting resins followed by polymerization in situ by heat. Since impervious graphite is the more useful of the two impregnated products, this discussion will be restricted to the product obtained by the impregnation of graphite.

Copper, brass and aluminum have superior heat conductivity but steel, lead and stainless steel are all poorer conductors of heat than impervious graphite. This property is particularly advantageous when the product is used as a heat exchanger.

Most of the impervious graphite used commercially is impregnated with phenolic resins. Previously, furan resins were used, but these have been replaced to some extent in the interest of standardization and higher temperature service. Modified phenolic resins are used where resistance to caustics and severe oxidizing agents is required.

The chemical resistance of impregnated graphite is less dependent upon the nature of the resin than might be expected. The reason for this lies in the facts that only a limited surface area of the resin is exposed to the corrosive environment and that the strength of the structure is primarily a function of the graphite. In fact, some equipment, such as heat exchangers designed for operation with nitric acid, can be reimpregnated after the resin has been partially destroyed.

While impervious graphite is satisfactory for service with most non-oxidizing acids, salts and solvents up to the boiling point, it cannot be used with concentrated sulfuric acid at temperatures above 175°F. It should not be used with bromine, chlorine dioxide, or nitric acid without consultation with a qualified corrosion engineer. It is available commercially in the form of heat exchangers, steam jets, towers, absorbers, pumps, valves and pipe. Additional information on impervious graphite pipe is given in Chapter 17.

The comparative properties of impregnated and unimpregnated carbon and graphite are given in Table 12-1.

Condensed information on the chemical resistance of impervious graphite is given in Table 12-2.

Impervious graphite has been used successfully for the manufacture of tanks, towers, piping, pumps, valves, heat exchangers

TABLE 12-1. PHYSICAL PROPERTIES OF
TYPICAL CARBON AND GRAPHITE PRODUCTS

	Carbon	Graphite	Impervious Carbon	Impervious Graphite	Porous Carbon	Porous Graphite
Density, lb/cu ft	98	97	110	117	65	65
Tensile strength, psi	900	800	1,800	2,500	140	80
Compressive strength, psi	8,000	45,000	10,000	9,000	600	400
Coefficient of expansion, $\times 10^{-7}/°F$	13	13	29	24	25	20
Thermal conductivity, Btu/hr/sq ft/°F/ft	3.5	76	3	86	1.3	35

TABLE 12-2. CHEMICAL RESISTANCE OF IMPERVIOUS GRAPHITE

	C	H		C	H
Acids:			*Acid Salts (continued)*		
Acetic, 10%	E	E	Copper chloride, sulfate	E	E
Acetic, glacial	E	E	Ferric chloride, sulfate	E	E
Benzene sulfonic	E	E	Nickel chloride, sulfate	E	E
Benzoic	E	E	Stannic chloride	E	E
Boric	E	E	Zinc chloride, sulfate	E	E
Butyric	E	E	*Alkaline Salts:*		
Chloroacetic	E	E	Barium sulfide	E	E
Chromic, 10%	E	N	Sodium bicarbonate	E	E
Chromic, 50%	N	N	Sodium carbonate	E	E
Citric	E	E	Sodium sulfide	E	E
Fatty acids (C$_6$ and up)	E	E	Trisodium phosphate	E	E
Fluosilicic	E	E	*Neutral Salts:*		
Formic	E	E	Calcium chloride	E	E
Hydrobromic	E	G	Calcium sulfate	E	E
Hydrochloric	E	E	Magnesium chloride, sulfate	E	E
Hydrocyanic	E	E	Potassium chloride, nitrate, sulfate	E	E
Hydrofluoric	G	N	Sodium chloride, nitrate, sulfate	E	E
Hypochlorous	G	N	*Gases:*		
Lactic	E	E	Chlorine, wet	G	N
Maleic	E	E	Chlorine, dry	G	N
Nitric, 5%	E	N	Sulfur dioxide, wet	E	E
Nitric, 20%	N	N	Sulfur dioxide, dry	E	E
Nitric, 40%	N	N	Hydrogen sulfide	E	E
Oleic	E	E	*Organic Materials:*		
Oxalic	E	E	Acetone	E	E
Perchloric	G	N	Alcohols, methyl, ethyl	E	E
Phosphoric	E	E	Aniline	E	E
Picric	E	E	Benzene	E	E
Stearic	E	E	Carbon tetrachloride	E	E
Sulfuric, 50%	E	E	Chloroform	E	E
Sulfuric, 70%	E	E	Ethyl acetate	E	E
Sulfuric, 93%	N	N	Ethylene chloride	E	E
Oleum	N	N	Formaldehyde, 37%	E	E
Mixed acids, 28% HNO$_3$, 55% H$_2$SO$_4$	N	N	Gasoline	E	E
Alkalies:			Phenol	E	E
Ammonium hydroxide	E	E	Refinery crudes	E	E
Calcium hydroxide	E	E	Trichloroethylene	E	E
Potassium hydroxide	E	E			
Sodium hydroxide	E	E	*Paper Mill Applications:*		
Acid Salts:			Kraft liquor	E	E
Alum	E	E	Black liquor	E	E
Ammonium chloride, nitrate, sulfate	E	E	Green liquor	E	E

TABLE 12-2 (Continued).

Paper Mill Applications (continued)	C	H	Textile Industry:	C	H
White liquor	E	E	General use	E	E
Sulfite liquor	E	E	Hypochlorite bleach	G	N
Chlorite bleach	P	N			
Alum	E	E	Food Industry:		
Photographic Industry:			General use	E	E
Developers	E	E	Breweries	E	E
Silver nitrate	E	E	Dairies	E	E
General use	E	E			
Fertilizer Industry:			Miscellaneous Industries:		
General use	E	E	Plating	E	E
Steel Industry:			Petroleum	E	E
Sulfuric acid pickling	E	E	Tanning	E	E
Hydrochloric acid	E	E	Oil and soap	E	E
H_2SO_4–HNO_3 pickling	F	N	Water and sewer	E	E

Ratings:
E – no attack
G – appreciably no attack
F – some attack but usable in some instances
P – attacked–not recommended
N – rapidly attacked
C – cold 75°F
H – hot 300°F

and other chemical process equipment. It is another example of how plastics and other materials can be used together to produce products with properties superior to those of the individual components.

Plastic impregnants discussed in this chapter maintain stability in porous structures. The applications discussed in Chapter 13 require greater adhesive forces since the plastic must permit the joining of articles that were previously separated.

Suggested References

"Development of Karbate Materials and Their Applications," M. R. Hatfield and C. E. Ford, Trans, A. I. Ch. E., XLII, 121 (1947).

"Physical Properties of Plaspreg," J. Delmonte, ASME Paper, No. 45 A-42, (Nov. 1945).

"Carbon and Graphite," J. P. Oliver, Chem. Eng., 59, 9, 276 (1952).

"Carbon and Graphite Materials and Parts," P. O'Keefe, Materials & Methods, 35, 119 (April 1952).

"Carbon and Graphite," W. M. Gaylord, Ind. Eng. Chem., 45, 2182 (1953).

13. INDUSTRIAL ADHESIVES

With the exception of the coatings discussed in Chapter 7, specific plastic materials are a sizable component of the various structures previously discussed. In contrast, adhesives usually constitute a very small fraction of the entire mass under consideration, since best results are obtained when the thickness of the glue line is held to a minimum.

In its broadest sense, adhesion may be defined as the affinity of two materials for each other when joined together. Almost all polymeric materials are adhesives even though some may serve as appropriate parting agents for specific applications. Until recent years, most adhesives were based on natural occurring products but synthetic plastics are growing rapidly in importance in this application.

An attempt will be made in this chapter to show the general utility of plastics in the adhesive field, but a comprehensive treatise on the subject is not intended. Additional information can be secured from the suggested references at the end of the chapter.

In general, polar plastics are suitable adhesives for polar materials. Nonpolar plastics usually adhere well to nonpolar materials. Some products like polyethylene and polytetrafluoroethylene actually produce anti-adhesive surfaces for polar materials. Likewise, while some silicone formulations may be adhesive in nature, others can produce water-repellent surfaces.

As in other plastic applications, adhesives may be applied as melts, dispersions in nonsolvents and as solutions. Many industrial adhesives consist of a liquid thermosetting plastic which is converted to a solid in situ by the application of heat or the addition of an appropriate catalyst.

Some plastics show adhesive characteristics by themselves but compounding with other appropriate additives is usually required to develop commercial utility. Many of the more useful commercial adhesives are proprietary compositions consisting of several components. Some specific applications are described below.

Sulfur Cements

In addition to their use as jointing materials, hot melts consisting of plasticized sulfur and selected aggregates have found specialized use as adhesives. The less ductile products are used for adhering ceramic insulators, capping concrete test cylinders and as centers for abrasion wheels. Highly plasticized sulfur cements are much more versatile and have been used as an intermediate bond between flexible materials such as "Thiokol" and rigid surfaces like portland cement.

Polyisobutylene

In contrast to the semi-hard polyethylene, polyisobutylene is tacky and exhibits "legs" when spread between the thumb and index finger. Because of this inherent tack, polyisobutylene is often used as one of the components of pressure-sensitive adhesives.

Butyl rubber has similar properties but is not used to any great extent as an adhesive. Polyethylene film presents a nonadhesive surface for polar materials. Low molecular weight polymers of ethylene are actually used as mold lubricants for processing polyvinyl chloride.

Asphalt

In the broadest sense, asphalt, coal-tar pitch and coumarone-indene resins serve as adhesives or binders for aggregates in linoleum, mastic floor tile and in road paving. Asphalt solutions and emulsions are used for bonding asphaltic sheet and tile to concrete and for adhering felt, paper and cork to metal. They are also used as additives with other polymers in adhesive formulations.

Polystyrene

Like polyethylene, polystyrene has little use as an adhesive. Some success has been reported when it was used as a binder for magnetic powder cores in telephone coils. It has also been used to join ceramic and metal parts in electrical fixtures. Aqueous suspensions of polystyrene and liquid plasticizers have been proposed as adhesives for paper and textile products but the copolymers of styrene and butadiene have greater potential for such applications.

Acrylates

In spite of their inherent potential, the use of polymers of acrylic and methacrylic acid esters as adhesives has been limited. As might be expected, solutions of polymethyl methacrylate in organic solutions are used to join molded and cast articles from methacrylate polymers.

Recently, copolymers of methacrylic acid with methyl methacrylate or butadiene have shown promise as adhesives for rubber to steel. The latter are of considerable interest in applications such as engine vibration mounts.

Polyvinyl Chloride and Copolymers

Polyvinyl chloride and polyvinylidene chloride are not very soluble and, like other highly nonpolar plastics, have little potential as adhesives. The copolymers of vinyl chloride and vinyl acetate have improved solubility and adhesive properties but the introduction of stronger polar groups is required for good adhesion. When a few polar groups are present in the copolymer chain, improved adhesive properties are noted. Thus, the plastic formed by the copolymerization of vinyl chloride and vinyl acetate with a few per cent maleic anhydride has excellent adhesive properties.

Polyvinyl Acetate

Aqueous dispersions of polyvinyl acetate are widely used as adhesives for bonding cotton fibers, inorganic pigments, paper, cork, wood and leather. These adhesives exhibit tack but tend to flow at elevated temperatures and are not noted for moisture resistance.

Polyvinyl acetate has been used for binding abrasives in grinding wheels, as a binder for powdered metals and for binding metal to glass. In many instances cross-linking agents such as glyoxal or metallic salts such as zinc chloride are added and the specimens are cured at 250°F while being held in place.

Aqueous polyvinyl alcohol solutions are excellent adhesives but tend to lose their bond in the presence of moisture.

Polyvinyl Acetals

Solutions of polyvinyl formal and butyral have been used commercially as adhesives for wood, pigments, leather and textiles. The so-called "Redux" process for joining metal utilizes powdered polyvinyl acetal and phenolic resins. In this process, powdered polyvinyl acetal is sprinkled over a surface which has previously been coated with the phenolic resin. Outstanding adhesive properties are developed by heat curing under pressure.

Polyvinyl Ether

Polyvinyl ethers have excellent potential as commercial adhesives. They have been used in Europe and to some extent in the United States as adhesives for paper and textiles.

Silicones

As might be anticipated from a study of their chemical structure, silicones will adhere to glass and ceramic materials. Adhesives based on silicones are often used to join silicone rubber or silicone impregnated fabric to other objects. In some instances, less expensive inorganic silicates are satisfactory for adhering glass and ceramic surfaces. Silicone adhesives have inherent resistance to heat and should find considerable application as specialty adhesives.

Polyamides

Natural occurring proteins, such as casein, soybean proteins, blood albumin, peanut protein, zein, gluten and animal proteins have been used as adhesives for many years. Animal glues are still important articles of commerce but a discussion of such products is beyond the scope of this chapter.

Casein adhesives were patented in 1876 and until recently this protein was the base of many of the strongest and most weather-resistant commercial glues. In contrast, because of its general insolubility, the use of nylon as an adhesive is somewhat limited. It is used as a hot melt and as a blend with phenolic resins. Sometimes neoprene is also added to this mixture.

Polyurethanes

As illustrated in Chapter 5, organic diisocyanates react readily with polyhydric alcohols to form polyurethanes. These products have exceptional adhesion to many surfaces. Some of the urethane adhesives are actually formed by reacting organic diisocyanates such as tolylene diisocyanate with polyesters containing hydroxyl groups. These adhesives have excellent electrical properties and weatherability. As stated in Chapter 11, they are suitable for use at temperatures as low as $-300°F$.

Optimum results are obtained when unreacted diisocyanates are present. Based on observations in Germany, it may be predicted that the reaction products of diisocyanates will become extremely important as adhesives in American industry.

Natural Rubber

Because of its inherent tackiness, natural rubber has been used as an adhesive for centuries. It has been estimated that over 5 per cent of the natural rubber now produced is consumed in adhesive formulations. Rubber latex may be compounded to yield pressure-sensitive adhesives and adhesives for leather, textile and paper.

Most rubber cements are based on solutions in hydrocarbon solvents such as naphtha. Such cements are also used as adhesives for leather, textile and paper as well as for pressure-sensitive tapes. The latter usually contains polyisobutylene and softeners in addition to the natural rubber.

Rubber Derivatives

Thermoprenes and other cyclized or isomerized rubbers form the basis for many industrial adhesives. These products and those obtained by heating rubber and phenol in the presence of acids are outstanding as rubber-to-metal adhesives.

Rubber hydrochloride has adhesive qualities but is seldom used except to seal films to other surfaces. Chlorinated rubber is widely used as a rubber-to-metal adhesive and primer for coatings.

Synthetic Rubber

Solutions of styrene rubber have some adhesive properties but are not used in place of natural rubber except for specialized application. It has been the custom to add tackifiers, such as a reaction product of para-tertiary butyl phenol and acetylene, in order to secure improved adhesive qualities for styrene rubber. Blends of acrylonitrile rubber and other resins such as phenolics and coumarone-indenes produce excellent adhesives for fabrics and metal.

All types of neoprene exhibit some tackiness and adhesive properties. However, readily crystallizable products such as "Neoprene AC" have proved to be superior. "Neoprene AC" is often dissolved in naphtha and compounded with terpene phenolic resins or thermoplastic resins to produce exceptionally good metal-to-metal adhesives. Products of this type can also be used to adhere rubber or fabric to many different surfaces.

Polysulfide Rubber

Hot melts of "Thiokol" and sulfur have been used as special adhesives for several years. "Thiokol" may be softened on a mill to yield a putty-type adhesive. The new liquid "Thiokols," which may be converted catalytically to solids at room temperature, have been used as high solids flexible adhesives.

Starch

By definition, most nonprotein vegetable glues are based on starch, starch derivatives, starch hydrolysates or related carbohydrates. Most starch adhesives are based on tapioca, saga, corn, white or sweet potato and waxy maize.

Starch may be converted to adhesives for specific end use by roasting or by acid, alkali or enzymatic hydrolysis. Natural gums such as gum arabic and tragacanth are polygluronic acids.

Adhesives based on starch are widely used industrially for adhering paper, wood and textiles. However, the use of starch and natural gums is declining to some extent due to replacement by synthetic products.

Cellulosics

Unlike starch, cellulose is insoluble in common solvents. Solutions of its esters in organic solvents have been used as industrial adhesives for many years.

The use of collodion, a solution of cellulose nitrate in ether and alcohol, was known prior to Hyatt's proposed application of this product as a plastic. Proprietary cellulose nitrate adhesives have been used for joining aluminum and steel alloys. One of the better known proprietary household cements is a solution of cellulose nitrate. Adhesives based on cellulose nitrate are also used extensively in the shoe and paper industries.

As might be expected, formulations based on cellulose acetate are used as adhesives for paper, leather and textiles. Solutions of ethyl cellulose in toluene-alcohol mixtures have been used to adhere ethyl cellulose sheeting to various surfaces. The water-soluble cellulose ethers have been used as pigment adhesives and as a replacement for starch. It may be predicted that products such as carboxy methyl cellulose will find additional applications as water-soluble adhesives as formulators become better acquainted with the properties of these derivatives.

Polyesters

Alkyd resins have some adhesive characteristics. They have been used for cementing abrasive aggregates to paper and for adhering optical parts, as well as for sealers in plumbing fittings and for bonding metal laminates in electrical equipment. Greater resistance to solvents and heat is obtained by using the so-called sytrene alkyd polyesters.

Polyester cements and adhesives are used to patch polyester boats and other structures. The manufacture of reinforced polyesters through the use of fiber mat and textiles (discussed in Chapter 14) is actually an adhesive application.

Urea-Melamine Resins

Urea resins have replaced animal and vegetable glues to a large extent in the plywood and veneer industries. Urea resins are catalyzed with ammonium salts and press-cured at 70 to 250° F. Room temperature adhesion may be brought about by coating separate surfaces with acid catalyst and liquid urea resins. Good adhesive strength is developed when the two treated surfaces are brought together. Urea and melamine adhesives are often extended with equal amounts of low cost materials such as wood flour.

Plywood joined with urea resins has relatively poor resistance to hot water. There is also a tendency for crazing to occur at the glue line. Improvements have been attained by fortification with resorcinol or melamine adhesives. Obviously, the all melamine-formaldehyde adhesives have greater resistance to boiling water than the urea adhesives. An interesting specialty urea adhesive is prepared by reacting urea formaldehyde resins with furfuryl alcohol.

Phenolic Resins

Phenolic resins are doubtlessly the most useful, reliable and durable of all synthetic adhesives. Much of the plywood industry is dependent upon these resins. However, these products must be cured at a temperature 80°F higher than that required for urea adhesives. Room temperature phenolic adhesives are applied by the same technique as that described for urea adhesives. A specific substituted phenol, cashew nut oil, reacts readily with formaldehyde or paraformaldehyde to form an adhesive useful for bonding asbestos in brake linings.

Resorcinol is much more reactive than phenol and will react with formaldehyde or paraformaldehyde at room temperature. Some proprietary adhesives consist of a solution of partically polymerized resorcinol and formaldehyde. Powdered paraformaldehyde is added at the time of use and the adhesive cures rapidly after application to the members to be joined. This type of resorcinol adhesive has been used with wood, rubber and plastics. The use of phenolic resin to produce laminates such as discussed in Chapter 14 is also essentially an adhesive application.

Epoxy Resins

One of the most interesting classes of adhesives developed in recent years is based on the so-called epoxy resins. One type of epoxy cement consists of a solid resin which contains a high temperature active catalyst. The adhesive is applied as a hot melt and cured at elevated temperatures.

Adhesives having greater utility because of ease of application consist of liquid epoxy resins which are mixed with amine catalysts and cured at ordinary temperatures. These epoxy adhesives show considerable promise since they will join a variety of surfaces including metals, plastics and ceramics. A shear strength as high as 3,000 psi is readily obtained with epoxy adhesives.

Furan Resins

Adhesives based on furfuryl alcohol or furfural are economical and in excellent supply. However, in spite of the interest of chemurgists in these products, furan adhesives are not used in large volume. It should be noted that in contrast to phenolic adhesives, furan resins have long shelf life and excellent resistance to alkalies.

Solutions of phenolic resins in furfural are employed as bonding agents for abrasive wheels. Graphite particles in impervious graphite are bonded by polyfurfuryl alcohol formed in situ. As previously noted in Chapter 7, over 10,000,000 pounds of furan cements are produced annually. In their well known application, furan resin mortar cements form tenacious bonds to ceramic surfaces. The relative usefulness of various synthetic adhesives are compared in Table 13-1.

Like other segments of the plastics industry, structural plastic adhesives are relatively new. Their use in this field will continue to increase as plastics are properly selected and utilized for this application. The plastic application discussed in the following chap-

TABLE 13-1. RELATIVE EFFECTIVENESS OF
VARIOUS PLASTICS AS ADHESIVES

	Cost	Adhesion To				Resistance To					Total
		Wood	Metal	Ceramics	Rubber	Water	Nonpolar Solvents	Alkalies	Acids	Fungus	
Asphalt	10	5	5	3	7	6	1	8	8	10	63
Coumarone-indene	9	5	6	3	7	8	1	10	8	10	67
Polystyrene	8	3	2	2	5	8	1	10	8	10	57
Polyethylacrylate	6	4	3	5	6	8	2	5	7	10	56
Polymethyl mathacrylate	6	3	2	3	6	8	3	8	7	10	56
Polyvinyl chloride	7	7	6	7	6	8	6	10	9	10	76
Vinyl chloride–acetate copolymer	7	8	6	7	5	8	5	9	9	10	74
Polyvinyl acetate	8	7	7	7	3	3	3	4	6	10	74
Polyvinyl alcohol	5	2	2	4	6	1	7	1	3	10	41
Polyvinyl acetal	4	7	8	7	7	8	5	3	5	10	64
Saran	7	7	6	7	7	8	7	8	9	10	76
Silicone	5	6	7	7	8	10	7	6	6	10	72
Urethane	2	10	10	9	10	7	8	4	4	10	74
Alkyd	8	7	5	6	7	7	2	2	5	10	59
Natural rubber	7	4	4	3	8	7	3	10	8	10	64
Isomerized rubber	5	4	8	4	7	9	3	10	9	10	69
Butyl rubber	6	3	6	2	8	8	3	10	9	10	65
Chlorinated rubber	6	5	7	4	7	6	3	10	9	10	67
Styrene rubber	7	7	6	5	8	7	3	10	9	10	72
Acrylonitrile rubber	6	6	8	6	9	7	5	8	8	10	73
Neoprene	6	7	7	5	8	8	3	10	8	10	72
Polysulfide rubber	5	5	4	2	4	6	8	3	5	10	52
Cellulose nitrate	6	5	1	5	5	3	2	2	4	10	43
Cellulose acetate	5	3	1	3	5	2	3	1	3	9	35
Cellulose acetate butyrate	4	3	1	4	5	2	3	1	3	9	35
Methyl cellulose	5	1	1	3	3	1	6	3	3	9	35
Ethyl cellulose	5	3	1	3	5	2	3	3	3	9	37
Carboxy methyl cellulose	4	1	2	3	2	1	6	1	4	9	33
Unsaturated polyester	7	8	2	5	7	7	6	1	6	10	59
Urea resin	7	9	2	2	2	6	9	5	5	10	57
Melamine resin	6	10	2	2	2	7	9	5	5	10	58
Phenolic resin	7	8	2	6	7	8	10	7	8	10	73
Epoxy resin	4	10	8	8	8	8	9	9	8	10	82
Furan resin	6	7	1	8	7	8	10	10	8	10	75

Ratings: 1, 2 – Poor
           3, 4 – Fair
           5, 6 – Moderate
           7, 8 – Good
           9, 10 – Excellent

The plastics in Table 13-1 have been rated from 1 to 10 for each property, with 10 being the highest possible value.

ter is essentially an adhesive application since laminates consist of fabrics or sheets held together by plastics. However, plastic laminates are a distinct and an important application which must be considered separately in order to prevent confusion. Additional information on the subject of adhesives may be found in the references cited at the end of this chapter.

Suggested References

"Technology of Adhesives," John Delmonte, Reinhold Publishing Corp., New York, 1947.

"Adhesion and Adhesives," N. A. deBruyne and R. Houwink, Elsevier, New York, 1951.

"Adhesives," F. Brande, Chemical Publishing Co., New York, 1943.

"Modern Wood Adhesives," T. D. Perry, Pitman Publishing Co., New York, 1944.

"SPI Handbook," Society of the Plastics Industry, New York (1947).

"Plastics Engineering Handbook," Society of the Plastics Industry, Reinhold Publishing Corp., New York, 1954.

"How to Bond Plastics," M. Meyers, Plastics (Chicago), 264 (May 1945).

"Bonding Metal to Wood," C. M. Grafton, Modern Plastics, 22, 1, 103 (1944).

"Adhesives for Metals and Non Metals," K. Rose, Metals & Alloys, 20, 959 (1944).

"Modern Plywood," T. D. Perry, Pitman Publishing Co., New York, 1944.

"Plastics in Industry," Plastes, Chemical Publishing Co., New York, 1941.

"Structural Plastics," H. C. Engel, C. B. Hemming and H. R. Merriman, McGraw Hill Publishing Co., New York, 1950.

"Industrial Adhesives," J. L. Perkins, Modern Plastics, 16, 9, 52 (1939).

"Resorcin Resins and Adhesives," P. H. Rhodes, Modern Plastics, 22, 4, (1944).

"Engineering Materials Manual," T. C. DuMond, Reinhold Publishing Corp., New York, 1951.

"Adhesive Bonding of Metals," George Epstein, Reinhold Publishing Corp., New York, 1954.

"Nature of Adhesion," F. W. Reinhart, J. Chem. Educ., 31, 128 (1954).

"Adhesive Bonding," Helmut Thielsch, Materials & Methods, 40, 5, 113 (1954).

14. REINFORCED PLASTICS

As noted in Chapter 13, because of their adhesive properties many types of plastics have been used as bonding agents for woven or matted fibrous materials. Products such as asbestos, glass fabrics, cotton and paper have been impregnated with resinous materials to produce plastic laminates.

Reinforced plastics possess properties superior to those of the individual components. The plastic components are usually inherently brittle thermosetting plastics while the fibrous reinforcements are porous and flexible. A combination of the two produces tough, rigid, impact, resistant structural materials.

In contrast to most other engineering materials, reinforced plastics are both nonhomogeneous and anisotropic in nature. Thus, physical properties may vary considerably depending upon the direction in which they are determined. These facts must be kept in mind when designing structures.

Although chopped glass fibers, unwoven asbestos and certain granular materials offer some reinforcing properties, the discussion in this chapter will be limited to laminated products reinforced with woven or matted fabrics. Since almost all plastics can be reinforced the emphasis here will be on reinforced thermosetting plastics.

Plastic laminates, like metals, are available as sheets, rods, tubes, and fabricated structures. These products have been used successfully for bearings, gears, chemical processing equipment such as tanks, fume exhaust systems, piping, fans, fan housings and electrical equipment.

The properties of laminates are functions of the resin, the curing cycle and the reinforcing material. Many properties are also dependent upon the adhesion between the resin and the reinforcing material. In general, plastic laminates are light in weight, have good dimensional stability, high dielectric strength, low heat conductivity and low water absorption.

Thermoplastics

Woven "Fiberglas" has been used for reinforcing various thermoplastics such as asphalt for the protection of concrete floors and tanks. This type of construction is of particular importance for corner construction and for the protection of pipeline exteriors from corrosion. However, as previously stated this discussion will be limited to reinforced thermosetting plastics which will be described on a generic basis.

Silicones

Because of their outstanding resistance to higher temperature, silicone resins have been used for laminate construction with fiberglas textiles. Commercially available silicone-glass fiber laminates have been reported to have served satisfactorily at temperatures as high as 480°F. They have low water absorption and excellent electrical properties. Their physical properties are comparable to other plastic laminates but the silicones are much more costly.

Polyesters

One of the most important types of reinforced plastics is based on glass fiber reinforced polyester resins. These materials were developed during World War II for the manufacture of flak resistant sheet armor and aircraft parts. After the war, their use almost ceased because of the many difficulties encountered in the production of both the glass reinforcements and the resins. As basic improvements were made in raw materials, interest was revived and this type of plastic is now enjoying the most rapid growth in the entire plastics field. The annual production in 1947 was less than 2 million pounds but over 25 million pounds were produced in 1953.

The major use of polyesters at the present time is in the production of aircraft components, boats, automobile bodies and other products in which the extremely high strength to weight ratio of these laminates is of utmost importance. Their major applications in the chemical field, are in the production of tanks, pipe and fume systems.

As discussed in Chapter 5, most commercially available polyester laminates are not resistant to alkalies, strong oxidizing agents, solvents or aqueous salt solutions above 140°F. However, laminates based on specialty resins with good resistance to flame and chemicals are commercially available.

Reinforced plastics may be produced by contact molding, vacuum or pressure bag techniques, flexible plunger techniques, vacuum injection, matched die molding and by hand lay-up techniques. The choice of method depends to a large extent on the number of parts to be produced and the complexity of the shape.

A large number of identical pieces are usually required before the expense of the matched die or flexible plunger techniques can be justified. As little as one piece can be made economically by many of the other methods. However, most chemical-resistant equipment is made by the bag molding or hand lay-up procedures.

In the production of polyester laminate duct work, a female mold of wood, reinforced plastic, sheet metal or plaster is prepared and coated with wax and a suitable parting film. A layer of catalyzed polyester resin containing sufficient activator to cause rapid curing at room temperature is applied by brushing or spraying. Additional layers of glass cloth or glass mat are then applied and impregnated with resin until the desired thickness is attained.

In the bag-molding procedure, a bag constructed of polyvinyl alcohol film is stretched over the entire assembly. Vacuum or pressure is then applied through a suitable valve arrangement to pull the film tight, thus forcing out entrapped air and excess resin. The hand lay-up procedure differs from bag-molding only in that excess resin and much of the entrapped air are removed by rolling or squeegeeing with hand tools.

Tanks, duct work and other structures may also be constructed from flat press-molded sheets by cementing the corners with an overlay of glass cloth or by adhering right-angle members made of the same material. When epoxy resin cements are used, the strength of the corner joints may actually exceed that of the flat sheet.

As pointed out in the preceding discussion, both glass cloth and glass mat are used as reinforcements. Cloth will produce laminates with greater tensile strength and greater glass content, but these laminates have lower flexural strength and tend to craze on flexing, especially when used with low pressure or hand lay-up techniques.

Glass mat has the advantages of lower cost and faster build-up, but has the objectionable feature of contributing to "wicking action" whereby exposed fibers present a path for transmitting liquids through the structure. Some laminators make use of sandwich construction whereby mat is used for the inner layers and cloth is used on the surfaces.

So-called "roving mats," introduced recently, which consist of loosely woven glass rovings show great promise since they combine the strength of cloth reinforcement with the low cost and rigidity of mat construction.

The properties of typical reinforced polyester plastics are summarized later in this chapter. However, it must be pointed out that the range of properties is at least as great as that found in steel.

The glass content may be as low as 25 per cent for laminates made with chopped strand mat and as high as 75 per cent for square woven roving laminates. Likewise, the tensile strength may vary from 15,000 psi for chopped strand mat laminates to 130,000 psi for those reinforced with parallel roving. Obviously, the high values with the latter are obtained by testing in the direction of the glass fibers.

Values for flexure, compression and impact for various polyester glass laminates exhibit similar differences. For example, unnotched Izod impacts as low as 12 and as high as 70 ft lbs/in may be obtained for laminates reinforced with chopped strand mat and parallel roving respectively.

As shown in Chapter 4, the coefficient of linear expansion of polyester resins is in the range of 5 to 10×10^{-5} and the coefficient for glass is approximately 3×10^{-6} per °F. However, the value for "Fiberglas" reinforced polyesters is in the range of 5 to 18 x 10^{-6} per °F.

General-purpose polyester resin laminates are satisfactory for the construction of exhaust systems for non-oxidizing acid fumes but should not be used for containers for liquid corrosives. Vessels constructed from chemical-resistant grade glass fibers and chemical resistant polyester resins have given satisfactory service as containers for hot acid and salt solutions.

Considerable caution must be taken when recommending reinforced polyester laminates for chemical-resistant applications. Success or failure depend not only on the proper selection of the resin and reinforcing material but also on the design and fabrication of the equipment.

Flame-resistant resins with chemical resistance somewhat superior to general-purpose resins are now available commercially. Some specific applications of reinforced polyester resins are shown in the accompanying illustrations.

Figure 14-1 shows the lamination process for the production of flat "Fiberglas" reinforced polyester sheet. Figures 14-2, 14-3 and 14-4 show the sheet being used to construct a geodesic dome atop the Ford Rotunda in Dearborn, Michigan.

A series of glass reinforced sections of an exhaust prior to assembly are shown in Figure 14-5.

(Courtesy of Bakelite Co., Div. of Union Carbide & Carbon Corp.)

Figure 14-1. The production of glass reinforced polyester sheet on laminating press.

Figure 14-2. Geodetic dome constructed from glass reinforced polyester sheet.

(Courtesy of Bakelite Co.; Div. of Union Carbide & Carbon Corp.)

Figure 14-3. Process of assembling reinforced polyester sheets on dome.

214   PLASTIC MATERIALS OF CONSTRUCTION

(Courtesy of Bakelite Co., Div. of Union Carbide & Carbon Corp.)

Figure 14-4. Beginning of construction using reinforced polyester sheets to cover an aluminum framework for the construction of a Geodesic dome.

The hood and duct section shown in Figure 14-6 were constructed by hand lay-up techniques from reinforced polyester plastic.

Figure 14-7 shows an 18-inch diameter fume exhaust line carrying hydrogen chloride gas, chlorine gas, traces of organic chemicals and moisture in an electrochemical plant. A 24-inch diameter flame resistant duct system is shown in Figure 14-8.

Urea and Melamine

Urea resins can be used as bonding agents for laminates but melamine resins are preferred because of their superior properties. Paper, cloth and fiberglas laminates utilizing melamine resins have been produced commercially. The poor acid resistance of these resins has excluded them from many corrosion-resistant application. However, melamine resin bonded cotton fabric laminates have been used successfully for plating barrels and for alkaline service.

The flame resistance of melamine laminates is essentially as good as that of the polyester laminates. The melamine laminates are high in cost and yield volatile by-products during the curing cycle. Melamine laminates have excellent electrical properties and are often used in applications where these properties are advantageous.

Phenolic

The oldest and possibly the best known plastic laminates are based on phenolic resins. These products are widely used for decorative,

Figure 14-5. Glass reinforced polyester duct work including weather cap, elbows, transition pieces, tees, crosses, and ten-foot duct sections.

mechanical, chemical and electrical applications.   Because technologists have been more familiar with them than with some of the newer resins, phenolic laminates have been produced from a wide variety of paper and fabric reinforcing materials.

Phenolic laminates are readily machined and possess excellent resistance to heat, light and long-term exposure. The density of phenolic laminates is between that of structural wood and aluminum. However, many of their physical properties are superior to both of these products.   For example, a typical fabric-base phenolic laminate may have a compressive strength of 40,000 psi, compared with values of 5,000 and 15,000 for wood and aluminum, respectively.

As shown in Table 14-1, the type and amount of reinforcing agent has a great effect on the strength of a phenolic plastic laminate.

Figure 14-6. Glass reinforced polyester hood and duct section.

(Courtesy of Hooker Electrochemical Company)

Figure 14-7. Flame resistant polyester fume duct (18 inches) carrying HCl, Cl_2, moisture and traces of organics.

(Courtesy of Hooker Electrochemical Company)

Figure 14-8. Reinforced flame resistant polyester fume system (24-in. diameter) handling sulfuric acid fumes.

TABLE 14-1. EFFECT OF FILLER ON
STRENGTH OF PHENOLIC PLASTIC LAMINATE

Filler		Flexural	Impact Strength
Type	(%)	Strength (psi)	Izod ft lbs/in. notch
None	–	13,300	0.25
Wood flour	50	9,770	0.31
Cotton fabric	50	12,000	2.4
Cotton cord	50	12,900	7.2
Glass mat	50	35,000	8.7

As shown in Table 14-2, the heat resistance of phenolic laminates is superior to that exhibited by many other widely used products of this type.

TABLE 14-2. RELATIVE EFFECT OF TEMPERATURE
ON FLEXURAL STRENGTH OF GLASS-REINFORCED PLASTICS

Type Laminate	Room Temp.	30 min. at 300°F	30 min. at 500°F
Phenolic	53,000	52,000	42,000
Triallyl cyanurate polyester	49,000	42,000	24,000
General-purpose polyester	48,000	9,000	—
Low-pressure silicone	30,000	16,000	14,000

Phenolic resin laminates are relatively inexpensive but their color range is limited. Phenolic laminates may be readily machined, punched, sawed, sheared, turned, drilled, tapped, threaded and milled. They have good resistance to water, salts and non-oxidizing acids. As pointed out in Chapter 5, they are attacked by alkaline solutions.

Typical applications of phenolic laminates are shown in the accompanying illustrations. Figure 14-9 shows a phenolic laminate anodizing basket. Phenolic laminated pipe nipples are shown in Figure 14-10. An aircraft fuel tank flapper valve is shown in Figure 14-11.

Epoxy Resins

Epoxy resin laminates are affected less by moisture than their polyester counterparts. Also, as indicated in Chapter 5, laminates based on epoxy resins have good resistance to alkaline and salt solutions as well as acids. Epoxy resin laminates shrink less than 3 per cent and do not evolve volatile products while being cured.

The use of epoxy resins for laminating purposes has been hampered to some extent by their high cost and the lack of fast curing resins. These deficiencies have been corrected to some extent and laminates of this type are finding wider application in chemical processing plants.

Furan Resins

As indicated in Chapter 8, furan resin cement glass fiber laminates have been used as solvent and acid resistant tank linings. This same type of construction has been proposed for the manufacture of chemical process equipment. Although they are dark in color and exhibit high shrinkage during curing, furan resin laminates have excellent chemical resistance and hence are used to some extent in chemical industry.

(Courtesy of Synthane Corp.)
Figure 14-9. A phenolic laminate anodizing basket.

The physical properties of typical commercial plastic laminates are compared in Table 14-3.

Relative cost and physical and resistance properties of laminates are shown graphically in Table 14-4 and specific chemical resistance data are presented in Table 14-5.

Until recent years most structural plastics were based on cast resins as described in Chapter 10 or on plastic laminates. More recently, several of the thermoplastics have been used for the fabrication of self-supporting structures. Background information on such plastics is outlined in Chapter 15.

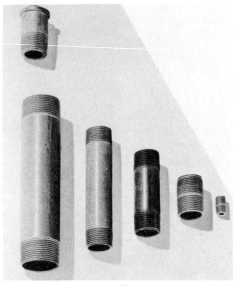

(Courtesy of Synthane Corp.)
Figure 14-10. Various size phenolic laminate pipe nipples used primarily for insulating properties in gas meter connections and for handling corrosives.

(Courtesy of Synthane Corp.)
Figure 14-11. Phenolic laminated flapper valve used in aircraft fuel tanks.

TABLE 14-3. PHYSICAL PROPERTIES OF TYPICAL COMMERCIAL PLASTIC LAMINATES

Resin	Reinforcement	NEMA* Grade	Direction of Test	Impact Izod Notch (ft lb/in.)	Tensile Strength (psi)	Compressive Strength (psi)	Specific Gravity	Max. Service Temp.(°F)	% Water Absorption 1/8"Thick Specimen
Silicone	Glass cloth	G-6	Length	6	–	40,000	1.65	400	0.35
			Width	5	–	9,000	–	–	–
Unsaturated polyester	Glass cloth	–	Length	16	40,000	30,000	1.75	300 (dry)	0.4
			Width	–	–	–	–	–	–
Melamine	Glass cloth	G-5	Length	6	37,000	70,000	1.90	300	2.0
			Width	5	30,000	25,000	–	–	–
Phenolic	Paper	XX	Length	.4	16,000	34,000	1.34	250	1.3
			Width	.35	13,000	23,000	–	–	–
Phenolic	Cotton fabric	L	Length	1.35	14,000	35,000	1.35	225	1.6
			Width	1.10	10,000	23,000	–	–	–
Phenolic	Asbestos	AA	Length	3.6	12,000	28,000	1.70	275	2.5
			Width	3.0	10,000	21,000	–	–	–
Phenolic	Glass cloth	G-3	Length	6.5	23,000	50,000	1.65	290	2.0
			Width	5.5	20,000	17,500	–	–	–
Phenolic	Nylon	N-1	Length	3.0	8,500	20,000	1.15	165	0.4
			Width	2.0	8,000	–	–	–	–

*National Electrical Manufacturers Association

TABLE 14-4. PROPERTIES OF PLASTIC LAMINATES.

Polyester Glass Laminates	0 1 2 3 4 5 6 7 8 9 10	TOTAL
Initial Cost		
Weather		66
Flame **		
Impact		
Solvents		
Water		
Salts		
Alkalies*		
Acids		
Oxid, Acids		

Chemical Resistant Polyester Glass Laminates	0 1 2 3 4 5 6 7 8 9 10	TOTAL
Initial Cost		
Weather		70
Flame **		
Impact		
Solvents		
Water		
Salts		
Alkalies*		
Acids		
Oxid, Acids		

Phenolic Laminates	0 1 2 3 4 5 6 7 8 9 10	TOTAL
Initial Cost		
Weather		67
Flame		
Impact		
Solvents		
Water		
Salts		
Alkalies*		
Acids		
Oxid, Acids		

Epoxy Glass Laminates	0 1 2 3 4 5 6 7 8 9 10	TOTAL
Initial Cost		
Weather		69
Flame **		
Impact		
Solvents		
Water		
Salts		
Alkalies*		
Acids		
Oxid, Acids		

TABLE 14-4 (Continued).

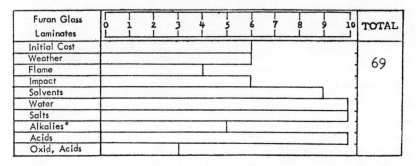

TABLE 14-5. CHEMICAL RESISTANCE OF PLASTIC LAMINATES

	General Purpose Polyester Glass Laminates 75-150°F		Chemical Resistant Polyester Glass Laminates 75-200°F		Phenolic Glass Laminates 75-200°F		Epoxy Glass Laminates 75-200°F		Furan Glass Laminates 75-250°F	
Acids:										
Acetic, 10%	E	E	E	E	E	E	E	E	E	E
Acetic, glacial	N	N	E	F	E	G	N	N	E	E
Benzene sulfonic, 10%	E	E	E	E	E	E	E	E	E	E
Benzoic	E	E	E	E	E	E	E	E	E	E
Boric	E	E	E	E	E	E	E	E	E	E
Butyric, 100%	G	N	G	F	E	E	G	F	E	E
Chloroacetic, 10%	E	F	E	E	E	E	E	E	E	E
Chromic, 5%	G	N	G	P	G	P	F	N	F	N
Chromic, 50%	F	N	F	P	F	N	N	N	N	N
Citric	E	E	E	E	E	E	E	E	E	E
Fatty acids (higher than C_6)	G	F	E	E	E	E	G	F	E	E
Fluosilicic	G	F	E	E	E	E	G	F	E	E
Formic, 90%	G	N	E	F	E	E	G	F	E	E
Hydrobromic	G	F	E	G	E	E	E	E	E	E
Hydrochloric	G	F	E	G	E	E	E	E	E	E
Hydrocyanic	E	E	E	E	E	E	E	E	E	E
Hydrofluoric	N	N	N	N	N	N	N	N	N	N
Hypochlorous	G	F	G	F	F	N	P	N	P	N
Lactic	E	E	E	E	E	E	E	E	E	E
Maleic, 25%	E	E	E	E	E	E	E	E	E	E
Nitric, 5%	G	P	E	F	G	P	F	N	F	N
Nitric, 20%	N	N	F	N	N	N	N	N	N	N
Nitric, 40%	N	N	N	N	N	N	N	N	N	N
Oleic	G	F	E	E	E	E	E	G	E	E
Oxalic	E	E	E	E	E	E	E	E	E	E
Perchloric	G	F	E	G	E	E	E	E	E	E
Phosphoric	G	F	E	G	E	E	E	E	E	E

TABLE 14-5 (Continued)

	General Purpose Polyester Glass Laminates 75-150°F		Chemical Resistant Polyester Glass Laminates 75-200°F		Phenolic Glass Laminates 75-200°F		Epoxy Glass Laminates 75-200°F		Furan Glass Laminates 75-250°F	
Acids (Continued):										
Picric	E	E	E	E	E	E	E	E	E	E
Stearic	G	F	E	E	E	E	E	E	E	E
Sulfuric, 50%	G	F	E	G	E	E	E	E	E	E
Sulfuric, 70%	F	P	G	P	E	P	F	N	E	N
Sulfuric, 93%	N	N	F	N	G	N	N	N	P	N
Oleum	N	N	N	N	P	N	N	N	N	N
Mixed acids, 57% H_2SO_4, 28% HNO_3	N	N	N	N	N	N	N	N	N	N
Alkalies:										
Ammonium hydroxide	F	N	G	F	P	N	F	P	G	F
Calcium hydroxide	N	N	N	N	N	N	N	N	N	N
Potassium hydroxide	N	N	N	N	N	N	N	N	N	N
Sodium hydroxide	N	N	N	N	N	N	N	N	N	N
Acid Salts:										
Alum or Aluminum sulfate	E	E	E	E	E	E	E	E	E	E
Ammonium chloride, nitrate, sulfate	E	E	E	E	E	E	E	E	E	E
Copper chloride, nitrate, sulfate	E	G	E	E	E	E	E	E	E	E
Ferric chloride, nitrate, sulfate	E	G	E	E	E	E	E	E	E	E
Nickel chloride, nitrate, sulfate	E	G	E	E	E	E	E	E	E	E
Stannic chloride	E	F	E	G	E	E	E	P	E	E
Zinc chloride, nitrate, sulfate	E	G	E	E	E	E	E	E	E	E
Alkaline Salts:										
Barium sulfide	G	P	G	F	P	N	G	F	G	F
Sodium bicarbonate	E	G	E	E	E	E	E	E	E	E
Sodium carbonate	G	P	E	E	E	E	E	E	E	E
Sodium sulfide	G	P	G	F	P	N	G	F	G	F
Trisodium phosphate	G	P	G	F	G	N	G	F	G	F
Neutral Salts:										
Calcium chloride, nitrate, sulfate	E	E	E	E	E	E	E	E	E	E
Magnesium chloride, nitrate, sulfate	E	E	E	E	E	E	E	E	E	E
Potassium chloride, nitrate, sulfate	E	E	E	E	E	E	E	E	E	E
Sodium chloride, nitrate, sulfate	E	E	E	E	E	E	E	E	E	E
Gases:										
Chlorine, dry	G	F	G	F	F	N	G	F	F	N
Chlorine, wet	P	N	F	N	P	N	F	N	P	N
Sulfur dioxide, dry	E	E	E	E	E	E	E	E	E	E
Sulfur dioxide, wet	E	G	E	E	E	E	E	E	E	E

TABLE 14-5.(Continued).

	General Purpose Polyester Glass Laminates 75-150°F		Chemical Resistant Polyester Glass Laminates 75-200°F		Phenolic Glass Laminates 75-200°F		Epoxy Glass Laminates 75-200°F		Furan Glass Laminates 75-250°F	
Organic Materials:										
Acetone	N	N	N	N	E	E	E	P	E	E
Alcohol, methyl, ethyl	E	F	E	G	E	E	E	E	E	E
Aniline	P	N	P	N	F	P	F	N	P	N
Benzene	F	N	G	N	E	E	E	P	E	E
Carbon tetrachloride	E	N	E	F	E	E	E	F	E	E
Chloroform	G	N	E	F	E	E	E	F	E	E
Ethyl acetate	P	N	G	P	E	E	E	G	E	E
Ethylene chloride	F	N	G	F	E	E	E	F	E	E
Formaldehyde, 37%	E	E	E	E	E	E	E	E	E	E
Phenol, 5%	G	N	G	F	E	E	E	F	E	E
Trichloroethylene	N	N	F	N	E	E	E	F	E	E
Papermill Application:										
Kraft liquor	N	N	N	N	N	N	N	N	N	N
Black liquor	N	N	N	N	N	N	N	N	N	N
Green liquor	N	N	N	N	N	N	N	N	N	N
White liquor	N	N	N	N	N	N	N	N	N	N
Sulfite liquor	E	G	E	E	E	E	E	E	E	E
Chlorite bleach	E	N	E	F	F	P	P	N	P	N
Alum	E	E	E	E	E	E	E	E	E	E
Chlorine dioxide	E	G	E	E	N	N	P	N	N	N
Photographic Industry:										
Developers	E	E	E	E	E	E	E	E	E	E
General use	E	E	E	E	E	E	E	E	E	E
Silver nitrate	E	E	E	E	E	E	E	E	E	E
Fertilizer Industry:										
General use	E	E	E	E	E	E	E	E	E	E
Steel Industry:										
Sulfuric acid pickling	G	F	E	E	E	E	E	E	E	E
Hydrochloric acid pickling	G	F	E	E	E	E	E	E	E	E
$H_2SO_4 - HNO_3$ acid pickling	N	N	F	P	F	N	P	N	P	N
Textile Industry:										
General use	E	E	E	E	E	E	E	E	E	E
Food Industry:										
General use	E	E	E	E	E	E	E	E	E	E
Breweries	E	E	E	E	E	E	E	E	E	E
Dairies	E	E	E	E	E	E	E	E	E	E

TABLE 14-5 (Continued).

	General Purpose Polyester Glass Laminates 75-150°F		Chemical Resistant Polyester Glass Laminates 75-200°F		Phenolic Glass Laminates 75-200°F		Epoxy Glass Laminates 75-200°F		Furan Glass Laminates 75-250°F	
Miscellaneous Industries:										
Plating	E	G	E	E	E	E	E	E	E	E
Petroleum	E	G	E	E	E	E	E	E	E	E
Tanning	E	E	E	E	E	E	E	E	E	E
Oil and soap	G	F	E	E	F	F	E	E	E	E
Water and sewer	E	E	E	E	E	E	E	E	E	E

Ratings:
E – no attack
G – appreciably no attack
F – some attack but usable in some instances
P – attacked—not recommended
N – badly attacked

Suggested References

"Engineering Laminates," A. G. A. Dietz, John Wiley & Sons, Inc., New York, 1949.

"Low Pressure Laminating of Resins," J. S. Hicks, Reinhold Publishing Corp., New York, 1947.

"Fabric Reinforced Plastics," W. J. Brown, Clever-Hume Press, London, 1947.

"Plastic Laminated with Cotton Linters," M. Gallagher and R. B. Seymour, Modern Plastics, 25, No. 12, 117 (1948).

"Reinforcement of Polyester Laminates with Fabrics," M. Gallagher, H. H. Goslen and R. B. Seymour, Modern Plastics, 27, No. 7, 111-4 (1950).

"Standards for Laminated Thermosetting Products," Publication No. LPI, National Electrical Manufacturing Assoc., 1951.

"Engineering Materials Manual," T. C. Du Mond, Reinhold Publishing Corp., New York, 1951.

"Plastic Laminates as Engineering Materials," K. Rose, Materials & Methods, 24, 653 (Sept. 1946).

"Insulation Resistance of Thermosetting Laminates," N. A. Show, Electrical Mfg., 47, 100 (March 1951).

"Mechanical and Permanence Properties of Laminates," G. M. Kline, Modern Plastics, 28, No. 12 (1951).

"Properties of Laminated Phenolics," L. E. Caldwell, Modern Plastics, 20, No. 7, 82 (1943).

"Silicone Resin Bonded Laminates," L. V. Larsen, K. A. Whelton, and J. J. Pyle, Modern Plastics, 23, No. 8, 197 (1946).

"Reinforced Polyester Plastics," R. B. Seymour and R. H. Steiner, Chem. Eng., 59, No. 12, 278 (1952).

"Effect of Chemicals on Phenol Resin Bonded Laminated Products," H. E. Riley, Ind. Eng. Chem., 28, 919 (1936).

"Chemical Resistance of Phenolic Laminates," W. R. Tyrie, Trans. Am. Soc. Mech. Engrs., 69, 795 (1947).

"Laminated Plastics," G. S. Learmonth, Leonard Hill Ltd., London, 1951.

"New Phenolic-Glass Laminates for Elevated Temperatures," J. B. Campbell, Materials & Methods, 38, No. 5, 87 (1953).

"Temperature Versus Strength for Phenolics," T. S. Carswell, D. Telfair and R. U. Haslanger, Modern Plastics, 19, 11, 65 (1942).

"Resins for Reinforced Chemical Resistant Construction," Raymond B. Seymour and Robert H. Steiner, Proceedings Ninth Annual Technical and Management Conference, Reinforced Plastics Division, Society of the Plastics Industry, Meeting at Chicago, Illinois, Feb. 3, 1954.

"Glass Fiber Polyester Laminates for Chemical Engineering," J. R. Stevenson, Brit. Plastics, 27, 326 (1954).

"Resins and Techniques," V. Parkyn, Plastics Institute Trans., 22, 99 (1954).

"Products and Applications," A. M. Dobson, Plastics Institute Trans., 22, 113 (1954).

"Fiberglas Reinforced Plastics," R. H. Sonnenborn, Reinhold Publishing Corp., New York, 1954.

"Plastics in Petroleum Production," Bryant W. Bradley, Symposium on Plastics as Materials of Construction, American Chemical Society, Division of Paint, Plastics and Printing Ink Chemistry, New York, Sept. 1954.

"Plastics in Plants Manufacturing Textile Fibers," W. A. Haldeman and E. F. Wesp, Symposium on Plastics as Materials of Construction, American Chemical Society, Division of Paint, Plastics and Printing Ink Chemistry, New York, Sept. 1954.

"Monomer Synergism in Heat Resistant Polyesters," W. Cummings and M. Botwick, Symposium on Plastics as Materials of Construction, American Chemical Society, Division of Paint, Plastics and Printing Ink Chemistry, New York, Sept. 1954.

"An Experimental Investigation of the Structural Use of Plastic Reinforced with Parallel Glass Fibers," E. F. Byars, Symposium on Plastics as Materials of Construction, American Chemical Society, Division of Paint, Plastics and Printing Ink Chemistry, New York, Sept. 1954.

"The Chemistry of Unsaturated Polyester Resins," C. P. Vale, British Plastics, 26, 327 (1953).

"Specifications for Laminated Plastics," Materials & Methods, 40, No. 5, 131 (1954).

SECTION III
THERMOPLASTIC
APPLICATIONS

15. THERMOPLASTIC STRUCTURAL MATERIALS

Thermoplastic materials have been applied as coatings, linings, and adhesives for many years, but their use as self-supporting structures has been neglected until recently. As stated in previous chapters, thermosetting resins have been used as cast plastics, impregnants and laminates but the fabrication of thermoplastics was usually considered too difficult.

The thermal welding of saran sheet as a method for fabricating simple structures was suggested almost twenty years ago but commercial development of the plastic welding art in this country was delayed until recently. The practicability of utilizing thermoplastic structures was demonstrated twenty years ago in Germany. The success of such equipment was observed by the American technical teams which visited German industries after World War II.

Much of the European development was nurtured by material shortages in a wartime economy. Nevertheless, unprecedented accomplishments were recorded using rigid unplasticized polyvinyl chloride as a permanent material of chemical construction.

Unplasticized polyvinyl chloride sheet was first imported into this country in 1947. Its growth, like that of many other technical segments of the plastics industry, has been slow. However, it should be noted that there has been a steady increase in the use of this product as well as other thermoplastics not previously considered by European engineers.

Almost all thermoplastic materials have been considered for this application but only a few have shown promise. The properties of the most useful thermoplastic structural materials are discussed generically in this chapter.

Polyethylene

Hydrocarbon plastics, such as asphalt, coal-tar pitch, coumarone-indene resins, polyisobutylene and butyl rubber have insufficient rigidity or strength to merit consideration for applications as all-plastic structures. While polyethylene also lacks rigidity, it has sufficient tensile strength to permit its wide use as extruded pipe and its limited use for self-supporting structures.

While polyethylene having an average molecular weight in the order of 8,000 is satisfactory for paper coating, average molecular weights of at least 17,000 are required for general fabrication, molding and for the extrusion of tubing, piping and sheets. The resistance to chemicals and stress cracking are functions of molecular weight.

Unsupported polyethylene deforms excessively when heated above 125°F. Plastic flow is observed the moment a load is applied at 212°F. Improvements in heat resistance have been obtained by ir-radiating polyethylene with gamma rays. Presumably, this irradia-tion produces a cross-linked product and reduces the thermoplasticity of the plastic. Irradiated polyethylene is already available in the form of thin foil but because of the high cost of irradiation, the pro-cess is not practical at present for pipe and plastic structures.

Polyethylene may be used at temperatures as low as −30°F. Un-pigmented polyethylene has poor resistance to sunlight and weather but properly pigmented and stabilized compositions are considered satisfactory.

As pointed out in Chapter 5, polyethylene has excellent resistance to inorganic acids, some alkalies and salts. Concentrated sulfuric acid, fluorine, hydrofluoric acid and chlorine may react with the surface to form a protective layer. The protective layer is essen-tially inert and prevents further deterioration. However, environ-mental cracking may take place in so-called active environments.

These active environments are alcohols, animal, vegetable and mineral oils, detergents and metallic soaps, sodium hypochlorite, liquid aliphatic and aromatic hydrocarbons, organic acids, silicones and alkalies. Polyethylene, with an average molecular weight greater than 27,000 is fairly resistant to environmental cracking. Obviously, care must be taken to prevent molecular weight degradation of poly-ethylene pipe or structures during fabrication.

Polyethylene can be readily extruded in the form of tubing, pipe and sheet without the addition of plasticizers. Thin sheets of poly-ethylene have been widely used for waterproofing underground struc-tures.

Polyethylene can be sawed, planed, drilled, filed, routed and machined using modifications of woodworking equipment. Polyethy-lene sheet can be thermally welded using the techniques discussed in Chapter 16. Providing there is little degradation in molecular weight, the weld strength of properly welded polyethylene sheet is essentially the same as the tensile strength of the sheet itself. Poly-ethylene monofilaments have also been woven into rope, but a dis-cussion of this application is beyond the scope of this chapter.

As shown in Chapter 16, polyethylene may also be heat-formed and welded to produce insert tank liners, stacks, tubing and ducts. When the thickness of the sheet is less than 3/16 inch, the resulting equipment is somewhat flexible. Advantage may be taken of this characteristic property in assembling sections before the addition of rigid supports.

Styrene Copolymer Rubber Resin Blends

Polystyrene may be thermally or solvent-welded, but the product is too brittle for general use as a structural material. However, copolymers of styrene and butadiene or blends of copolymers of styrene and acrylonitrile with butadiene-acrylonitrile rubber have good resistance to impact and have shown promise as structural materials. The latter are sometimes called styrene copolymer rubber resin blends.

These blends cannot be thermally welded satisfactorily, but sheet and pipe sections can be cemented using solvents or adhesives. As might be predicted from a knowledge of their composition, the chemical resistance of such blends is inferior to that of polyethylene. As indicated by the comparative data in Table 15-4, styrene copolymer rubber resin blends are satisfactory for dilute acid service but should not be used under strongly oxidizing conditions.

Extruded styrene copolymer rubber resin blend pipe is more rigid than polyethylene. Injection molded pieces from these blends have been used as insert fittings for polyethylene pipe. Sheets of this plastic can be produced by calendering and pressing or by extrusion techniques. Exhaust hoods and ducts have been fabricated by cementing extruded corner strips to extruded or pressed sheet. Trays and small parts have been drawn from heated sheet using vacuum-forming techniques.

Acrylates

Polymers of esters of acrylic acid are more flexible than polyethylene and hence have not been used successfully as unsupported thermoplastic structures. Polymethyl methacrylate sheets are rigid and have potential use as structural plastics. Polymethyl methacrylate sheet stock may be heat-formed to produce intricate shapes and can be joined by both thermal and solvent techniques.

However, in spite of its adaptability to standard fabrication techniques, polymethyl methacrylate has not been widely used in the fabrication of structures in the chemical industry. Methacrylate structures were often proposed when transparency was required prior to the commercial availability of clear unplasticized polyvinyl chloride sheet.

For example, clear polymethyl methacrylate plating barrels and dipping baskets have been used in the plating industry. The use of clear methacrylate sheets for glazing is beyond the scope of this discussion. Recent reductions in manufacturing cost of both the monomer and extruded sheet should increase its use as a structural material in other industrial applications.

Vinyls

Sheets manufactured from vinyl chloride-vinyl acetate copolymers and polyvinyl butyral may be heat formed but neither product has been used to any great extent as self-supporting structures in the chemical process industry. These products are not readily heat welded and there is no obvious advantage in using these materials instead of unplasticized polyvinyl chloride or saran.

Some saran sheet has been fabricated to form various chemical-resistant structures, but most of this plastic has been used in the chemical process industry in the form of extruded pipe and tubing. Saran lined steel pipe is satisfactory for service at temperatures up to 180°F. Saran monofilaments have been woven to form upholstery, screens and industrial filters. This plastic is also available as unsupported film but a discussion of such application is beyond the scope of this chapter.

As the result of approximately twenty years of successful industrial experience in Germany, there is considerable interest in structures formed from unplasticized polyvinyl chloride.

This type plastic has excellent resistance to salts, alkalies, nonoxidizing acids and dilute oxidizing acids at temperatures up to 150°F. For example, as shown in Table 15-4, unplasticized polyvinyl chloride is one of the few materials that is resistant to chlorine dioxide.

The type unplasticized polyvinyl chloride used successfully in Germany for over twenty years is less fragile than glass and stoneware but can be damaged by sharp blows. In order to overcome this objection, a product with much greater resistance to impact has been introduced commercially in the United States.

The higher impact resistant unplasticized polyvinyl chloride has been well accepted in the form of pipe in American industry. However, it is too early to conclude whether the normal or optimum impact plastic will be preferred for exhaust systems and other fabricated structures.

As a result of considerable testing and unanimous approval by 35 company members of the Thermoplastics Structures Division of the Society of the Plastics Industry, the two products have been classified as Type I and Type II. The proposed specifications for these materials are given in Table 15-1 (see page 235).

1. A specimen, at least 1 in. wide, shall be placed on edge in a container so that it is supported at an angle by the bottom and sidewall of the container, and shall be completely immersed in anhydrous liquid acetone for the duration of the test at 70 to 75°F. The length of time for the test shall be given in the specifications. There shall be no evidence of delamination or disintegration. Evidence of softening and/or swelling shall not constitute failure.

Note: A modification of ASTM Method D543 was used for chemical test. Sample size was 1 x 3 x 1/8 inches.

Type I and Type II unplasticized polyvinyl chloride are readily welded by heat and can be joined by proprietary adhesives or cements. It is important to note that the correct range of molecular weight is required for suitable weldability of unplasticized polyvinyl chloride. If the molecular weight is too high, the plastic cannot

TABLE 15-1. PROPOSED SPECIFICATIONS FOR
TYPES I AND II UNPLASTICIZED POLYVINYL CHLORIDE

(Thermoplastic Structures Division – Society of Plastics Industry)

Physical Properties

Property	ASTM Test Method	Type I	Type II
Tensile strength, psi.	D638-49T	7,000 (min.)	5,000 (min.)
Flexural strength, psi.	D790-49T	11,000 (min.)	8,500 (min.)
Flexural modulus, psi.	D790-49T	400,000 (min.)	300,000 (min.)
Impact strength, Izod, ft lb/in. notch	D256-47T	0.5 (min.)	3 (min.)
Rockwell hardness	D785-48T	R110 (min.)	R100 (min.)
Heat distortion, 264 psi, fiber stress, °F	D648-45T	158 (min.)	150 (min.)
Lamination (1)	–	2 hrs. (min.)	2 hrs. (min.)
Allowable change in flexural strength:			
in 80% sulfuric acid, 30 days – 140°F		±15%	±25%
in glacial acetic acid, 30 days–140°F		<–55% + 0%	<–80%
Allowable change in weight:			
in 80% sulfuric acid, 30days–140°F		±5%	±15% – 0%
in glacial acetic acid, 30 days–140°F		<+10% – 0%	<+20% – 0%

be softened sufficiently to permit complete fusion between the welding rod and the sheet material without thermal decomposition.

The welding of Type II unplasticized polyvinyl chloride is more difficult and considerably slower than Type I. Trained welders can usually produce a joint with a tensile strength equal to at least 80 per cent of the original using either Type I or Type II product. It is of importance to note that existing unplasticized polyvinyl chloride fabricated structures can be modified readily by trained personnel through the use of approved fabrication and welding techniques. Thus, mechanically damaged structures can be readily repaired on the job. Both Type I and II polyvinyl chloride exhibit creep or cold flow. The magnitude is a function of temperature and must be considered in the design of unplasticized polyvinyl chloride structures. This property was termed "dauerstandsfestigkeit" by the German engineers. The literal translation is "the time required to deform under long term stress."

German engineers also recognized the notch sensitivity of Type I unplasticized polyvinyl chloride and the high coefficient of expansion which is present in both Type I and Type II materials. Obviously, they made an allowance for both factors in the design of chemical equipment which has withstood the test of time.

The low resistance to gas and liquid flow by the surfaces of either Type I or Type II unplasticized polyvinyl chloride must be considered in the design of unplasticized polyvinyl chloride exhaust systems.

It is often possible to design structures which are considerably smaller than their metal counterparts because of this advantageous characteristic. As might be expected, unplasticized polyvinyl chloride, like most other unfilled plastics, are poor conductors of electricity and heat.

As stated in Chapter 17, pipe in iron pipe sizes up to 8 inches can be extruded from both types of unplasticized polyvinyl chloride. These products may be readily processed on calenders to produce sheet with uniform thickness varying from 5 to 30 mils. These sheets may be built-up and pressed at elevated temperatures to form plastic sheets with thicknesses up to 2 inches. Molded parts can be formed from both products by transfer-molding. Pipe fittings and special parts are also being produced using a modified injection molding process.

Thick unplasticized polyvinyl chloride sheet is seldom recommended for use as an adhered tank lining because movement of the plastic would be restricted and the difference in expansion rates would tend to set up internal stresses. However, unplasticized polyvinyl chloride has been used in the form of thin sheets which are laminated to plasticized polyvinyl chloride sheets and installed with standard techniques such as discussed in Chapter 8. It is also practical to fabricate heavy gauge interliners and to fill the cavity between the shell and the liner with a low melting flexible product such as an asphaltic mastic. The use of isocyanate cellular plastics have also shown promise for this application.

Polyfluorocarbons

Polytetrafluoroethylene and polymonochlorotrifluoroethylene have much higher softening points than most other thermoplastics, but can be thermally welded and molded. In spite of the high cost of polyfluorocarbon sheet, welded structures of these polymers have been fabricated when superior resistance to temperature and chemicals was required. Extruded pipe and molded valves and fittings are used in many segments of the chemical process industry.

Cellulose Derivatives

Because of its availability and ease of extrusion, considerable quantities of cellulose acetate butyrate have been used in the form of pipe. As shown in Chapter 5 and in the comparative data at the end of this chapter, this product lacks resistance to strong acids, alkalies and most solvents. It does perform satisfactorily under mild corrosive conditions, such as salt water service, gas lines, water lines and oil field piping.

Cellulose acetate butyrate sheet cannot be thermally welded. However, it can be joined by solvents or adhesives using techniques similar to those described for styrene copolymer rubber resin blends. Unlike most of the other plastics discussed in this chapter, cellulose acetate butyrate is usually plasticized.

(Continued on page 242)

TABLE 15-2. PHYSICAL PROPERTIES OF TYPICAL THERMOPLASTIC STRUCTURAL MATERIALS

	ASTM Test Method	Polyethylene	Styrene Copolymer Rubber-Resin Blends	Polymethyl Methacrylate	Polyvinyl Chloride Type I	Polyvinyl Chloride Type II	Polytetrafluoroethylene	Cellulose Acetate Butyrate
Tensile strength, psi (ultimate)	D638	1400	4500	8000	7000	5000	1800	5000
Compressive strength, psi	D695	–	10,000	15,000	11,000	8500	–	5000
Flexural strength, psi	D650	1700	8000	15,000	14,000	10,000	–	6000
Flexural modulus, psi	D650	–	300,000	450,000	400,000	300,000	–	180,000
Impact strength, Izod, ft lb/in. notch Izod, ft lb/in. notch	D256 D256	–	5 - 12	0.5	0.5 - 0.8	3 - 18	4	1.5
Thermal conductivity Btu/sec/sq ft/°F/in./10^{-4}	–	8	2	4	3.7	4.5	5	5
Thermal expansion in./in./°F $\times 10^{-5}$	D696	10	3.4	5	4	6	5.5	6
Heat distortion, °F 264 psi fiber stress	D686	107	180 - 187	190	165	155	250	180
Specific heat, Btu/lb/°F	D792	0.92	1.06	1.19	1.40	1.40	2.2	1.22
Flammability	D635	Burns Rapidly	Burns	Burns Slowly	Self Exting.	Self Exting.	Non-flammable	Burns Rapidly
Light stability	–	Fair	Fair	Very Good	Good	Good	Excellent	Good

TABLE 15-3. COMPARATIVE UTILITY OF
TYPICAL THERMOPLASTIC STRUCTURAL MATERIALS.

Polyethylene	0 1 2 3 4 5 6 7 8 9 10	TOTAL
Installed Cost		81
Weldability by heat		
Resistance to — Heat, Mechanical Damage, Electricity, Solvents, Salts, Alkalies, Acids, Oxidation		

Styrene–Rubber Blends	0 1 2 3 4 5 6 7 8 9 10	TOTAL
		73

Polymethyl Methacrylate	0 1 2 3 4 5 6 7 8 9 10	TOTAL
		71

Polyvinyl Chloride (Type I)	0 1 2 3 4 5 6 7 8 9 10	TOTAL
		84

Polyvinyl Chloride (Type II)	0 1 2 3 4 5 6 7 8 9 10	TOTAL
		82

TABLE 15-3 (Continued).

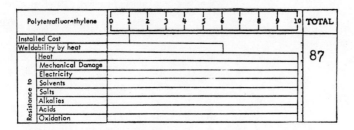

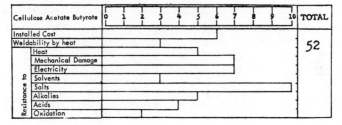

TABLE 15-4. CHEMICAL RESISTANCE OF
THERMOPLASTIC STRUCTURAL MATERIALS

	Poly-ethylene 75°F-125°F		Styrene Copolymer Rubber-Resin Blends 75°F-160°F		Polymethyl Meth-acrylate 75°F-150°F		Polyvinyl Chloride Type I 75°F-160°F		Polyvinyl Chloride Type II 75°F-150°F		Polytetra-fluoro-ethylene 75°F-250°F	
Acids:												
Acetic, 10%	E	E	E	G	G	F	E	G	E	G	E	E
Acetic, glacial	P	N	N	N	N	N	G	N	F	N	E	E
Benzene sulfonic, 10%	E	E	E	E	E	E	E	E	E	E	E	E
Benzoic	E	E	E	E	E	E	E	E	E	E	E	E
Boric	E	E	E	E	E	E	E	E	E	E	E	E
Butyric, 100%	N	N	N	N	N	N	F	N	N	N	E	E
Chloroacetic, 10%	P	N	N	N	N	N	E	G	G	F	E	E
Chromic, 5%	E	E	E	N	E	G	E	E	E	E	E	E
Chromic, 50%	E	E	F	N	F	N	E	G	G	P	E	E
Citric	E	E	E	E	E	E	E	E	E	E	E	E
Fatty acids (higher than C_6)	F	P	G	F	F	P	E	P	G	P	E	E
Fluosilicic	E	E	E	E	E	E	E	E	E	E	E	E
Formic, 90%	G	F	N	N	N	N	E	P	G	P	E	E
Hydrobromic	E	E	E	F	G	F	E	E	E	E	E	E
Hydrochloric	E	E	E	F	G	F	E	E	E	E	E	E
Hydrocyanic	E	E	E	E	E	E	E	E	E	E	E	E
Hydrofluoric	E	E	E	F	G	F	E	E	E	E	E	E
Hypochlorous	E	E	E	F	E	F	E	E	E	G	E	E

TABLE 15-4 (Continued).

	Poly-ethylene 75°F-125°F		Styrene Copolymer Rubber-Resin Blends 75°F-160°F		Polymethyl Meth-acrylate 75°F-150°F		Polyvinyl Chloride Type I 75°F-160°F		Polyvinyl Chloride Type II 75°F-150°F		Polytetra-fluoro-ethylene 75°F-250°F	
Acids (Continued):												
Lactic	E	E	E	F	E	E	E	E	E	E	E	E
Maleic, 25%	E	E	E	E	G	F	G	F	G	F	E	E
Nitric, 5%	E	E	G	N	G	N	E	E	E	E	E	E
Nitric, 20%	E	E	F	N	N	N	E	E	E	G	E	E
Nitric, 40%	E	G	N	N	N	N	E	G	F	P	E	E
Oleic	P	N	E	F	F	N	E	F	G	P	E	E
Oxalic	E	E	E	E	E	E	E	E	E	E	E	E
Perchloric	E	E	E	F	E	E	E	E	E	E	E	E
Phosphoric	E	E	E	F	E	F	E	E	E	E	E	E
Picric	E	G	E	E	N	N	P	N	P	N	E	E
Stearic	P	N	E	F	F	N	E	G	G	P	E	E
Sulfuric, 50%	E	E	E	E	E	G	E	E	E	E	E	E
Sulfuric, 70%	E	F	G	N	N	N	E	E	E	F	E	E
Sulfuric, 93%	F	N	N	N	N	N	E	F	P	N	E	E
Oleum	P	N	N	N	N	N	F	P	N	N	E	E
Mixed acids, 57% H_2SO_4 28% HNO_3	E	N	N	N	N	N	E	G	G	F	E	E
Alkalies:												
Ammonium hydroxide	E	E	E	F	G	F	E	E	E	E	E	E
Calcium hydroxide	E	E	E	F	F	N	E	E	E	E	E	E
Potassium hydroxide	E	E	E	F	F	N	E	E	E	E	E	E
Sodium hydroxide	E	E	E	F	F	N	E	E	E	E	E	E
Acid Salts:												
Alum or Aluminum sulfate	E	E	E	E	E	E	E	E	E	E	E	E
Ammonium chloride, nitrate, sulfate	E	E	E	E	E	E	E	E	E	E	E	E
Copper chloride, nitrate, sulfate	E	E	E	E	E	E	E	E	E	E	E	E
Ferric chloride, nitrate, sulfate	E	E	E	E	E	E	E	E	E	E	E	E
Nickel chloride, nitrate, sulfate	E	E	E	E	E	E	E	E	E	E	E	E
Stannic chloride	E	E	E	E	E	E	E	E	E	E	E	E
Zinc chloride, nitrate, sulfate	E	E	E	E	E	E	E	E	E	E	E	E
Alkaline Salts:												
Barium sulfide	E	E	E	G	G	F	E	E	E	E	E	E
Sodium bicarbonate	E	E	E	E	E	G	E	E	E	E	E	E
Sodium carbonate	E	E	E	E	E	G	E	E	F.	F.	E	E
Sodium sulfide	E	E	E	G	G	F	E	E	E	E	E	E
Trisodium phosphate	E	E	E	G	G	F	E	E	E	E	E	E

TABLE 15-4 (Continued)

	Poly-ethylene 75°F-125°F	Styrene Copolymer Rubber-Resin Blends 75°F-160°F	Polymethyl Meth-acrylate 75°F-150°F	Polyvinyl Chloride Type I 75°F-160°F	Polyvinyl Chloride Type II 75°F-150°F	Polytetra-fluoro-ethylene 75°F-250°F
Neutral Salts:						
Calcium chloride, nitrate, sulfate	E E	E E	E E	E E	E E	E E
Magnesium chloride, nitrate, sulfate	E E	E E	E E	E E	E E	E E
Potassium chloride, nitrate, sulfate	E E	E E	E E	E E	E E	E E
Sodium chloride, nitrate, sulfate	E E	E E	E E	E E	E E	E E
Gases:						
Chlorine, dry	P N	E F	G P	E E	E G	E E
Chlorine, wet	N N	E P	P N	E G	G F	E E
Sulfur dioxide, dry	E E	E E	E E	E E	E E	E E
Sulfur dioxide, wet	E E	E E	E E	E E	E E	E E
Organic Materials:						
Acetone	P N	N N	N N	N N	N N	E E
Alcohol, methyl, ethyl	E P	E P	N N	E G	E F	E E
Aniline	N N	N N	N N	N N	N N	E E
Benzene	N N	N N	N N	P N	N N	E E
Carbon tetrachloride	N N	N N	N N	F N	N N	E E
Chloroform	N N	N N	N N	N N	N N	E E
Ethyl acetate	N N	N N	N N	N N	N N	E E
Ethylene chloride	N N	N N	N N	N N	N N	E E
Formaldehyde, 37%	E E	E E	E G	E E	E E	E E
Phenol, 5%	E G	G F	N N	E G	E F	E E
Trichloroethylene	N N	N N	N N	N N	N N	E E
Papermill Applications:						
Kraft liquor	E E	E F	E F	E E	E E	E E
Black liquor	E E	E F	E F	E E	E E	E E
Green liquor	E E	E F	E F	E E	E E	E E
White liquor	E E	E F	E F	E E	E E	E E
Sulfite liquor	E E	E F	E G	E E	E E	E E
Chlorite bleach	E P	E P	F P	E G	G F	E E
Alum	E E	E E	E E	E E	E E	E E
Chlorine dioxide	F N	G F	N N	E E	G F	E E
Photographic Industry:						
Developers	E E	E E	E E	E E	E E	E E
General use	E E	E E	E E	E E	E E	E E
Silver nitrate	E E	E E	E E	E E	E E	E E

TABLE 15-4 (Continued)

	Polyethylene 75°F-125°F		Styrene Copolymer Rubber-Resin Blends 75°F-160°F		Polymethyl Methacrylate 75°F-150°F		Polyvinyl Chloride Type I 75°F-160°F		Polyvinyl Chloride Type II 75°F-150°F		Polytetrafluoroethylene 75°F-250°F	
Fertilizer Industry:												
General use	E	E	E	F	E	E	E	E	E	E	E	E
Steel Industry:												
Sulfuric acid pickling	E	G	E	E	E	G	E	E	E	E	E	E
Hydrochloric acid pickling	E	G	E	E	G	F	E	E	E	E	E	E
H_2SO_4-HNO_3 acid pickling	E	F	N	N	N	N	E	E	E	F	E	E
Textile Industry:												
General use	E	E	E	E	E	E	E	E	E	E	E	E
Food Industry:												
General use	E	E	E	E	E	E	E	E	E	E	E	E
Breweries	E	E	E	E	E	E	E	E	E	E	E	E
Dairies	E	E	E	E	E	E	E	E	E	E	E	E
Miscellaneous Industries:												
Plating	E	F	E	G	E	F	E	E	E	G	E	E
Petroleum	P	N	E	E	N	N	E	E	E	E	E	E
Tanning	E	E	E	E	E	E	E	E	E	E	E	E
Oil and soap	F	N	E	F	G	F	E	E	E	G	E	E
Water and sewer	E	E	E	E	E	E	E	E	E	E	E	E

Ratings: E – No attack
G – Appreciably no attack
F – Some attack but usable in some instances
P – Attacked–not recommended
N – Badly attacked

The physical properties of structural thermoplastics are compared in Table 15-2. Relative practical properties are shown graphically in Table 15-3. Chemical resistance data for these plastics are given in Table 15-4.

Additional information on these plastics can be obtained from the references cited at the end of this chapter. A description of fabrication techniques and specific applications of structural thermoplastics is given in Chapter 16 and 17.

Suggested References

"Mechanical Properties of Polyethylene," R. H. Carey, E. F. Schulz, and G. J. Diener, Ind. Eng. Chem., 42, 842 (1950).

"Materials of Construction in the Chemical Industry," (Birmingham, England Symposium) Society of Chemical Industry (1950).

"Plastic Progress," G. Haim and H. P. Zade, Dorset House, London (1951).

"High Impact Styrene Copolymers," R. B. Seymour and R. H. Steiner, Chem. Eng., 60, No. 1, 264 (1951).

"Plastics Equipment Reference Sheet No. 15—High Impact Styrene Copolymers," R. B. Seymour and R. H. Steiner, Chem. Eng. Prog., 48, No. 11, 596 (1952).

"Plastic Processing Equipment Today," R. B. Seymour and J. H. Fry, Chem. Eng., 59, No. 3, 136 (1952).

"Industrial Applications of Resistant Plastics and Rubbers," F. F. Jaray, Corrosion Prevention and Control, 1, No. 5, 282 (1954).

"Plastic Components for Mechanical Equipment," J. R. Boyer and W. R. Myers, Symposium on Plastics as Materials of Construction, American Chemical Society, Division of Paint, Plastics and Printing Ink Chemistry, New York, Sept. 1954.

"Plastics in Plants Manufacturing Heavy Chemicals," G. A. Griess, Symposium on Plastics as Materials of Construction, American Chemical Society, Division of Paint, Plastics and Printing Ink Chemistry, New York, Sept. 1954.

"Engineering Aspects of Modified Styrene Plastics," R. H. Steiner, Symposium on Plastics as Materials of Construction, American Chemical Society, Division of Paint, Plastics and Printing Ink Chemistry, New York, Sept. 1954.

"Thermoplastics In Service with Particular Reference to the Application of Unplasticized Polyvinyl Chloride," J. D. D. Morgan, Plastics Prog., Papers and Discussion at the British Plastics Convention, 1951.

"Fabrication and Use of Rigid Polyvinyl Chloride Plastics," J. L. Huscher, Materials & Methods, 39, No. 6, 119 (1954).

"Plastics for Chemical Engineering Construction—Polyvinyl Chloride," George S. Laaff, Chem. Eng. Progr., 50, No. 6, 275 (1954).

"Plastics," R. B. Seymour, Ind. Eng. Chem., 46, No. 10, 2135-2148 (1954).

"Corrosion Keys--Plastics," R. B. Seymour and R. H. Steiner, Chem. Processing, 17, No. 12, 92 (1954).

16. THERMOPLASTIC STRUCTURES

The availability of thermoplastic sheets of varying thickness as discussed in Chapter 15 has made possible an entirely new industry. These sheets may be sawed, drilled, machined, routed and welded using adhesive or thermal techniques. Thus, it is now possible to produce tanks, hoods, duct systems, fans, fan housings, fume stacks, tank covers, sinks, trays, siphons, pumps, scoops, buckets, funnels, filters and racks. The variety of structures already in service and planned for the future is limited only by the imagination of the design engineer and the skill of the fabricator.

Manufacture of Unplasticized Thermoplastic Sheet

The processes used in the production of unplasticized thermoplastic sheet are essentially the same as those developed for plasticized thermoplastics. However, the lower plasticity and the critical heat stability of the stock requires careful control of processing temperature and considerable skill.

The base plastic is usually compounded with stabilizers, lubricants and pigments on a mill or in a Banbury mixer. The latter is more economical and less tedious but usually requires large-scale production.

It is important that the processing temperature on the mill or in the Banbury mixer be kept as low as possible since it is usually necessary to increase the temperature in each subsequent processing step. Even when the most efficient stabilizers are used, the decomposition point for some unplasticized thermoplastics is not much greater than the normal processing temperature.

It is customary to calender or extrude the compounded material to produce sheets approximately 20 mils thick. Regardless of whether the sheets are extruded or calendered they may be processed further to produce thick sheets using a Rotocure or a flat bed compression press. In either case, several sheets are placed together and heated with a pressure in the order of 100 psi.

Sheets produced in presses are as large as 50 inches wide and 120 inches long. The sheets produced from the Rotocure may be of similar width and of unlimited length. The maximum thickness of sheet produced on a Rotocure is 1/4 inch but sheet of any thickness may be produced on a press. At present, it is standard practice to produce sheet in thickness up to 2 inches on flat bed presses.

One of the most difficult materials to process is Type I unplasticized polyvinyl chloride. Type II unplasticized polyvinyl chloride may be processed at slightly lower temperatures. Styrene copolymer rubber resin blend and polyethylene are readily processed. Heavy sheets of these materials may be produced directly by extrusion techniques.

Molding Unplasticized Thermoplastics

Polyethylene, styrene copolymer rubber resin blends and polymethyl methacrylate can be injection molded readily, but the flow characteristics of unplasticized polyvinyl chloride are not suitable for standard injection molding procedures.

Unplasticized polyvinyl chloride has been molded successfully by a recently developed extrusion-molding process. Threaded pipe fittings in sizes up to 4 inches can be produced successfully by this process.

Heat Drawing of Unplasticized Thermoplastics

Sheets of polyethylene, polymethyl methacrylate, styrene copolymer rubber resin blends and unplasticized polyvinyl chloride become soft when heated and can be formed over suitable molds. For example, after being heated in an oven at 260 to 300°F, unplasticized polyvinyl chloride sheets can be formed using suitable unheated male and female dies at pressures as low as 10 psi.

These sheets may also be formed by vacuum-drawing techniques. In this process, the heated sheet is clamped in place over the mold and drawn by means of vacuum or pressure.

Fabrication of Thermoplastic Sheet

All thermoplastic materials under discussion except polyethylene and polyfluorocarbons may be solvent-welded. In this process, a suitable solvent is applied to the joining surfaces in order to soften the plastic. When sufficient tack is developed, the close fitting surfaces are clamped and the structure held in place until the bond has developed sufficient strength.

Thermal Welding

Thermal welding is preferred when heavy sections are used and if the sheet is subjected to hot-forming techniques. Polyethylene, polymethyl methacrylate, polyvinyl chloride and polyfluorocarbons can be heat welded through the use of specialized techniques which are specific for each material.

The edges of sheets to be welded are usually beveled at a 60° angle with a router or sander. Any loose ground plastic must be removed mechanically from the beveled edge, but solvent cleaning is usually discouraged as any excess solvent will soften the beveled edge and make quality welding impossible.

In the welding of unplasticized polyvinyl chloride, the beveled edges to be joined should be mated in position with the adjacent sections properly aligned but not touching each other. Round welding rod of 3/32 to 3/16 inch diameter is fed into the groove at right angles while being heated with gas from a welding gun at temperatures of 500 to 550°F. It is important that only sufficient pressure be applied to the rod to permit it to flow into the root of the weld. Excessive pressure will result in an unsatisfactory, highly strained weld. The welding of plastic sheet and structures is shown in Figures 16-1 and 16-2.

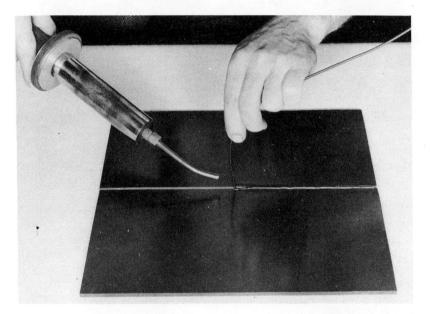

Figure 16-1. Welding of unplasticized polyvinyl chloride sheet.

The highest weld strengths are obtained by welding from both sides of the sheet. However, this method is seldom practical for industrial construction since it is customary to weld from one side only except in special cases.

The plastic welding process is much slower than metal welding. The speed varies from 2 to 12 inches per minute depending upon the thickness and the plastic material being welded.

Recently developed semiautomatic welding devices which can double these rates on straight-line welds are encouraging but they have not been used on any large commercial installations as yet. Higher speed can also be secured through the use of slightly plasticized polyvinyl chloride welding rod, but this practice is not condoned because of the lower heat resistance of the welds.

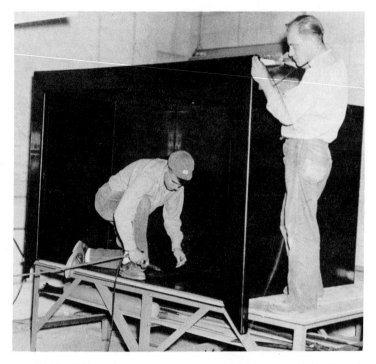

Figure 16-2. Welding of a self-supporting unplasticized polyvinyl chloride tank.

It is advantageous to use the largest welding rod that can be contained within the beveled groove formed by the mated sections. Unlike metal, the plastic welding rod does not melt completely but merely softens. However, care must be taken to ascertain that continuous contact with all edges of the plastic sheet and the softened rod is secured.

Triangular and elliptical rod have been used experimentally, but circular rod is preferred for most commercial plastic welding. Care should be exercised to prevent stretching of the rod during the welding operation. It is also essential that the plastic material not be overheated or charred during the welding operation.

Some background information can be secured by a review of the preceding precautions and observing the accompanying drawings describing the plastic welding process. However, like metal welding, the welding of plastics is an art and can be learned only through practice under the guidance of experts. A training period of at least eight weeks is required by most fabricating shops before new welders are allowed to work on production items.

Guns for plastics welding are available commercially in this country and abroad. Some differ in design but all provide a hot gas stream at a temperature of 500 to 600°F. The source of heat may be a gas flame or an electric heating cartridge. An inert gas such as nitrogen or carbon dioxide must be used for welding polyethylene but dry compressed air is satisfactory for unplasticized polyvinyl chloride.

Welding Procedures

The following tentative methods of test for the evaluation of welding performance of unplasticized polyvinyl chloride structures have been proposed by the Thermoplastic Structures Division of the Society of the Plastics Industry to determine comparative welding performance of individual welders. To insure maintenance of proper welding values, each thermoplastic structures welder must be subjected to periodic performance tests.

The mechanical performance of welded thermoplastic structures is dependent largely upon the quality of the welding operation. Each fabricator should determine that the proper welding procedures are followed and that the welders maintain their proficiency providing proper safeguards against deviation from the recommended procedures. Such deviations may be due to individualistic modifications or unconscious error resulting from fatigue or misunderstanding of the basic rules of thermoplastic welding.

The apparatus for testing welding strength should consist of a tension testing machine and its accessory equipment which should conform to the requirements specified in the tentative Method of Test for Tensile Properties of Plastics (ASTM Designation D638-52T).

The following accessories should be provided:

A hot-air welding gun for plastics, a thermometer to measure air temperature at nozzle (up to 600°F), a band saw to cut tensile strips, a sander to sand edges of specimens and a micrometer for measuring the width and thickness of specimens. These should be placed in a conditioning chamber with a constant temperature of 23°C + 2°C and 50 + 2 per cent relative humidity. Suitable clamps should be provided to hold samples while welding.

The base material should be prepared as follows:

Unplasticized polyvinyl chloride sheet approximately 8 x 6 x 3/16 inches should be provided. Control samples should be cut from the same sheet to determine tensile strength of the sheet according to ASTM D-638-52T. Specimen should be cut in halves to obtain two pieces 4 x 6 inches. Two pieces should be beveled by sanding one 6 inch side of each. The best bevel angle should be approximately 60° (30° for each piece). The sheet should be sanded approximately 1/64 cleaned thoroughly without the use of any solvent. Test specimen should be clamped securely on the test bench leaving a space of approximately 1/64 inch between the flattened apexes in accordance with the diagram in Figure 16-3.

The air temperature at the nozzle of the welding gun should be

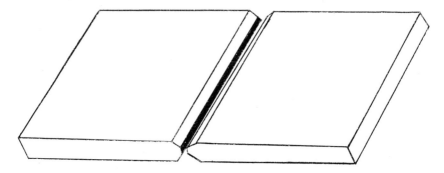

Figure 16-3. Unplasticized thermoplastic just before welding.

set to approximately 550°F as measured at a distance of 1/4 inch from the nozzle.

The specimen should be welded by applying three beads on each side using 1/8 inch rod for root welding and two 5/32-inch rods to complete the weld. Caution must be exercised that root is filled and bonded. No notch or groove should be noticeable along the weld line.

The following precautions should be noted:

Both surfaces must be heated uniformly to the flow point. Uniform pressure must be provided and excess stretching of rod must be avoided.

The following sketches in Figure 16-4 illustrate correct and incorrect methods of welding:

It is important to note that fusing must be homogeneous with the weld line, uniform in diameter and welds must be free of blisters and other defects.

The weld quality may be determined as follows:

Five tensile specimens of uniform width approximately 0.5 inch wide should be cut and their edges should be carefully sanded.

The test specimens should be conditioned for 24 hours at 23°C $\pm$ 2° @ 50 $\pm$ 2 per cent relative humidity before testing and tested under these conditions of temperature and humidity.

The width and thickness of the specimen should be measured to the nearest .001 inch at several points along its length (not on the bead).

Tensile tests to determine break strength should then be conducted in accordance with ASTM D-638-52T.

The welding value may be calculated using the following formula:

$$\frac{\text{Break strength of weld} \times 100}{\text{Break strength of sheet}} = \text{Welding value}$$

The welded specimen may also be evaluated qualitatively by the use of free-hand bend tests as illustrated in Figure 16-5. In this test, specimens should not break readily on a 180° bend. When a

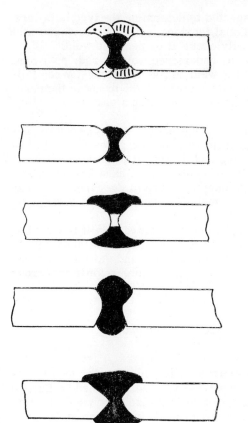

Good Weld (three rods)

Improper Size Rod

Core Not Welded

Rod Not Hot Enough

Sheet Not Hot Enough

Figure 16-4. Diagram of various types of thermoplastic welds.

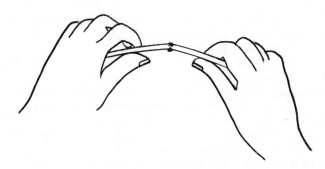

Figure 16-5. Free hand bend test

break occurs it should be inspected to determine the type of failure. Because of thickness, multiaxial tensions and rough surface finish of the weld, a break will usually occur at or near the weld. Most weld failures are due to undersized welding rod, poor bond or insufficient penetration of the welding rod in the core. When failure is associated with undersized welding rod, the break in the hand-bend test occurs at the beginning of the notch along the weld line. sheet and rod.

A poor bond between welding rod and the sheet may be due to surface contamination resulting from oil, wax or grease, insufficient heating, overheating or charring and the use of unsatisfactory plastic sheet. If the welding rod is not visible in the hand-broken specimen, the rod did not penetrate deeply enough in the core. This may be due to insufficient space between the openings of the test specimen.

Welded thermoplastic sheet should be accepted only if the welding value is at least 75 per cent and the acetone test is satisfactory. In the latter test, no separation between the weld and the sheet nor delamination should be noted after a 30-minute immersion in anhydrous acetone.

Formation of Circular Unplasticized Thermoplastic Structures

Thermoplastic pipe in sizes up to 8 inches in diameter may be extruded economically. Some success has been attained in Europe with the extrusion of larger sizes of unplasticized polyvinyl chloride pipe but most of the large-sized duct work in the United States is formed on standard sized mandrels with heated sheet. Short sections of circular duct work have also been produced by wrapping calendered sheet over a collapsible mandrel and heating the complete unit in an oven.

Duct work is manufactured in lengths up to 8 1/2 feet in standard ID sizes. The sheet is cut and beveled after allowances have been made for shrinkage during heating. It is then heated in an oven for approximately 10 minutes at a temperature above the softening point and formed around a mandrel.

This sheet is held in place until it cools to a temperature below 100°F. It is important that the size of the unwelded duct be essentially that of the finished piece; otherwise, excess stress will be placed on the weld under service conditions. The seam is welded by standard techniques and the ends are squared.

The formed circular duct may be flanged or welded with another section to form longer sections. A 50-foot length of 24-inch plastic duct work is shown in Figure 16-6. Actual installation of a fume system is shown in Figure 16-7.

Figure 16-6. Unplasticized rigid polyvinyl chloride duct system
(50 ft. long, 24-in. diameter).

Rectangular Duct Work

In contrast to circular structures in which the entire sheet must be heated, rectangular shapes may be fabricated using a modified metal bending brake. While metal is bent by force only, unplasticized thermoplastic sheets are formed by heating both sides of the sheet before bending.

Obviously, less force is required for the heated plastic sheet than for metal. However, precautions must be taken with plastics to prevent setting up stresses. A heated section must be at least 2 inches in width and the bend must be circular rather than at right angles.

Rectangular-shaped duct is produced by welding together two channel sections. Two right-angle sections may also be joined, but the required corner welds are usually less satisfactory than butt welds.

Fabrication of Flanges

It is permissible to flare one end of circular thermoplastic duct work in order to form an accurately mated bell and spigot joint for light-duty service. In this type of construction, two sections may be cemented in place by use of appropriate solvents or cements.

Figure 16-7. Two 24-in. fume systems (on right) serving a pickling area. Note leakage of new coated sheet metal duct on left.

When flange connections are specified, it is standard practice to cut the flange from a single sheet of plastic at least 25 per cent thicker than the duct work. The cut flanges are then welded to each end of the duct sections.

Another technique used for the fabrication of flanges is particularly well adapted for rectangular duct work. In this economical modification, the ends of the sheet are turned at right angles so that a flange with open corners is formed when the sheet is converted into a rectangular duct. When this type of duct is assembled, four separate extruded cap pieces are placed over adjacent flanged sections and the four thicknesses of plastic are joined by welding.

Fabrication of Odd Shapes

Odd shapes such as transformation pieces for joining of circular and rectangular duct work are formed by the same technique described for making circular duct sections. The pieces are cut to size after making allowances for shrinkage during heating and forming of the plastic sheet.

The fabrication of transformation pieces and elbows is an adaptation of the sheet metal art. Patterns for elbows should be cut in advance and tracings made on the flat plastic sheet.

General Design Information

Construction based on conservative design is expensive but under-designed structures are certainly not economical. It should not be forgotten that plastic structures have given approximately twenty years of satisfactory service in Germany. The German engineers emphasized correct design and used high factors of safety.

A safety factor of at least 4 based on tensile or flexural strength at the maximum operating temperature should be used in all standard design work. Allowance for expansion with temperature must be provided for. European practice allows for a movement of 6 inches for every 15-foot section. American practice is less conservative, particularly for duct work not subject to large temperature variations.

Thermal expansion must be taken into account in all systems through the use of compressible gaskets or expansion joints. Expansion joints have been fabricated from sleeves of plasticized polyvinyl chloride sheet which are used to connect sections of unplasticized polyvinyl chloride. Draw bands of unplasticized polyvinyl chloride or metal are drawn around the sleeves and positioned on the duct.

Methods of support for duct work are as important as correct design. Unplasticized polyvinyl chloride and styrene copolymer rubber resin blend duct work should be supported horizontally at least every 25 feet. Vertical sections of polyethylene should be supported at least every 5 feet and preferably supported continuously. Exterior supported duct work is shown in Figure 16-8.

Consideration should be given to the design of structures that will provide for smooth fluid flow. Transition and transformation pieces should be at least 12 inches in length for every 1 inch change in inside diameter. Whenever possible, 90° and 45° elbows should be used with a throat radius equal to the diameter of the duct.

Bolts at least 3/8 inch in diameter should be used to join all flanges, the number of bolts for each flange being equal to the number of inches of inside diameter of the duct work. Care should be taken to prevent excessive stress from the bolts in these flanges. Insofar as possible, the use of guy wires for vertical structures should follow standard practices for steel.

It is recommended that free-fitting plasticized polyvinyl chloride rings at least 4 inches in width be placed around unplasticized polyvinyl chloride duct work before fastening the split metal clamps for attaching guy wires. It should be remembered that plastic structures are much lighter than comparable steel structures and hence, less support is needed.

For example, a 12-inch unplasticized polyvinyl chloride duct 100 feet tall will weight approximately 300 pounds compared to one ton for a steel duct of comparable size. It is considered good practice to support vertical stacks every 35 feet. However, 100 foot tall plastic stacks in Germany have operated successfully for many years with only top and center guy supports.

Figure 16-8. Installation of a 36-in. diameter unplasticized polyvinyl chloride exhaust stack. Scaffolding is for erection purposes only and was removed.

The information in Table 16-1 may be used as a guide for thicknesses of plastic sheet for round and square duct of various sizes.

Horizontal unplasticized polyvinyl chloride duct work should be supported continuously by a "V" groove or a 1 inch wide rod whenever possible. When it is not possible to provide such support, the length of section from flange to flange should not exceed 8 1/2 feet and ring supports should be placed 6 inches from each side of all meeting flanges. A plasticized polyvinyl chloride sleeve should be placed between the supporting ring and the duct work.

Plastic duct work should be installed as a free member throughout its entire length and should not be held rigid at any point. Some

TABLE 16-1. RECOMMENDED MINIMUM THICKNESS
(IN INCHES) FOR DUCT OF VARIOUS SIZES

I.D.	Round Duct	Square Duct
8	1/8 or 1/16 webbed	1/8
12	1/8	1/8
16	1/8	1/8
20	1/8	3/16
24	3/16	3/16
30	3/16	1/4
36	1/4	1/4
above 40	1/4	1/4

Figure 16-9. Large fume system fabricated from Type I unplasticized
polyvinyl chloride.

Figure 16-10. Large photographic developing tanks fabricated of Type I unplasticized polyvinyl chloride. Note stainless steel girth bands.

of the precautions previously cited may be modified somewhat for cold temperature service but best performance of most systems will be secured if the foregoing recommendations are followed.

The diameter of discharge stacks should be enlarged gradually in order to produce a slight increase in resistance pressure proportional to the decrease in velocity pressure. Complete information on design of exhaust systems is beyond the scope of this chapter. However, it should be pointed out that since smooth flow is secured much more readily in plastic duct work, there are fewer problems with plastic than with exhaust systems made from other materials of construction.

Plastic duct work must be insulated from fan vibration, preferably through the use of plasticized polyvinyl chloride sleeves. Bellowing of flexible vibration insulating sections can be minimized by supporting the sleeve at 6 inch intervals.

Unplasticized polyvinyl chloride centrifugal blowers have been manufactured in Europe for several years and are now available commercially in this country. These units, which weigh less than 60 lbs. without motor shaft, have a rotor diameter of 32 inches, a

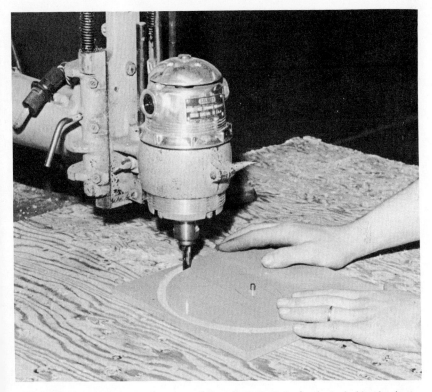

Figure 16-11. Routing a circular piece of Type II unplasticized polyvinyl chloride sheet.

speed of 1,000 rpm. and are rated at 875 cu. ft. per min. of air. The thickness of the sheet used varies from 0.200 inch for flanges and varies to 0.333 inch for rotor flanges and the stator.

Unplasticized polyvinyl chloride bifurcators ranging in sizes from 12 inches to 30 inches in diameter have been fabricated in this country. Most of these units contain an "L" type wheel and operate with 1/8 to 3 horse power motors at 1750 rpm. Since these units are driven directly and the motor is not in the path of the exhaust fumes, fans of this type have given excellent service in acid exhaust systems.

A large exhaust system is shown in Figure 16-9. Two large motion picture film development tanks are shown in Figure 16-10.

The routing technique used for unplasticized thermoplastic sheet is shown in Figure 16-11.

The following service data on industrial installations of various thermoplastic structures should be of considerable interest to corrosion engineers:

	No. Years of Satisfactory Service
Polyethylene	
Environment:	
Hydrochloric acid	
Polyethylene ware, 1- and 2-gallon bottles	6
Safety jugs, 12 in. dia., 15 in. high	6
Tank liner	5
Valves, 1 in. and 2 in.	4
6 in piping, welded flanges	5
Exhaust system at 90°F	4
Sulfuric acid	
5-gallon buckets	6
Exhaust duct line	5
Welded polyethylene bucket	5
Exhaust system 45% acid at 140°F	4
Nitric acid	
Removable tank liner	5
Tank liner	5
Tank liner	4
Textile industry	
Reinforced tank	5
Piping and valves	5
Float guide	5
Glass industry	
Washing machine for television picture tubes	4
Television tube washing tub for etching and cleaning TV tubes	4
Plating industry	
6 in. piping	3
2 in. valves	3
Styrene Copolymer Rubber-Resin Blends:	
Hydrochloric acid	
Piping 35% HCl, 100°F	2
Sulfuric acid	
Piping 45% H_2SO_4, 140°F	2
Chlorine	
Exhaust system, 100°F	1
Exhaust system, 195°F	1
Sodium chloride	
Piping, 60°F	1
Unplasticized Polyvinyl Chloride	
Hydrochloric acid	
6 in. piping handling HCl gas – outdoors	6
2½ in. pipeline, conc. HCl – outdoors, HCl production unit	18
20 in duct, 300 ft. long, HCl gas – outdoors, HCl production unit	11
3 in. piping and valves, HCl production unit – outdoors	11
3 in. piping, 1/8 in. wall valves – 200 ft. – HCl production unit outdoors – 22° Bé at 140°F (gas & aqueous)	4
4 in. piping, 3/16 in. wall, 500 ft., HCl production unit all outdoors, temp. @ 140°F	4

	No. Years of Satisfactory Service
Unplasticized Polyvinyl Chloride (Cont.)	
Hydrochloric acid (Cont.)	
500 cu. ft. tank handling 10% HCl	3
Exhaust system 35% HCl, 200°F	3
2 in. pipe handling hydrochloric acid outdoors	3
Hydrochloric acid pipeline	2½
Sulfuric acid	
6½ in. dia. x ¾ in. thick bubble plate in washing tower	2
Exhaust ventilators for gas – 12,000 cu. meters/min.	8
60 ft. high cooling tower – outdoors	6
Piping – all sizes, H_2SO_4 production unit.	5
Storage tank, 15% H_2SO_4	14
Piping and duct work in H_2SO_4 production unit	14
2 in. dia. piping and valves in H_2SO_4 production unit	3
Piping, duct work and ventilator fans – H_2SO_4 production plant	14
Exhaust system 30% H_2SO_4	4
Sulfuric acid test at 160°F	2½
24 in duct work	3
Exhaust system for strip pickling at 160°F	3
Exhaust system for piping operation at 180°F	3
2 in. pipeline dilute sulfuric acid	3
2 in. pipeline dilute hydrochloric acid	2½
Exhaust hood and duct system sulfuric acid, 160°F	3½
Nitric acid	
Exhaust ventilators for gas, 12,000 cu. meters/min.	7
Piping for 100% HNO_3 – outdoors	13 (70% disintegrated)
Storage tank – pickling acid – HNO_3, H_2SO_4 and HF	14
260 ft. stack, 20 in. dia. for gas	2½
100 ft, 3 ft. dia. duct work – HNO_3 production plant	2½
100 ft, 2 in. x 4 in. piping and valves – production plant	2½
Tank 10 ft. high handling fuming HNO_3	6
Exhaust system	2
Exhaust system aqua regia	3
Valves and piping system 10% acid at 120°F	2½
Phosphoric acid	
Pipeline 75% acid	2½
Chlorine	
Gas at 158°F – 2 in. pipe, 3/16 in. wall	5 (sl. attack 20% destroyed)
20 ft. high x 20 in. dia. chlorination column (¼ in. thick sheet)	2
12 ft. high chlorination column	3
Exhaust system	3
2 in. line outdoors	2
Chlorine dioxide	
Reaction vessel	3
Lids for towers	2½
Pumps	1
Pipeline outdoors	1½

	No. Years of Satisfactory Service
Unplasticized Polyvinyl Chloride (Cont.)	
Aluminum chloride	
Duct work, 1 ft. fia., 120 ft. high – outdoors	11
Hydrogen peroxide	
Rotary filter 6 ft x 8 ft.	5
350 cu. ft. tank, 50% H_2O_2	2½
Hydrofluoric acid	
3 ft. dia. duct work, 3/8 in. thick, 100 ft. long	1
24 in. dia. exhaust system 150 ft. long	1½
Acid etching systems	3
Television tube manufacturing exhaust systems	2½
Hydrochloric – sulfuric acid	
4 in. pipeline and fittings inside	2
1½ in. pipeline and fittings outside	2½
Hydrofluoric – nitric acid	
23 ft. hood and 24 in. duct work	3
Sulfur dioxide	
Piping and valves, 3 in. dia.	6
Sodium hydroxide	
Piping and valves	3
Phthalic and maleic anhydride	
Piping, ventilator fans in production plant	3
General – in chemical plant atmosphere	
Drain pipes and gutters	8
Chemical plant	
2 in. Ammonium sulfate pipeline	2½
1½ in. cuprous chloride pipeline	2
Caustic scrubber line 1.5% sodium hydroxide,	
3% hydrochloric acid 130°F	2½
Air washer tank – various acids 100°F	3
1 in. pipeline 50% caustic	2½
4 in dilute acid pipeline	2
Exhaust fans	2
Textile industry	
Rayon spinning boxes, tanks, duct work	3
1½ in. piping and valves	2½
10,000 ft. pipeline	3
300 ft. duct work (dilute sulfuric acid)	2
1000 ft. piping (dilute sulfuric acid)	2
Duct work	5
Pulleys – 6 in dia., 1/8 in. cover (dilute sulfuric acid)	4
(6 of 60,000 failed)	
Duct work and piping	4
100 ft. x 9 ft. x 5 ft. tanks – dilute sulfuric acid @ 140°F	5
Piping and valves	3
Steel industry	
Duct work for pickling and plating process	4
Hoods and 16 in. duct work for pickling process	3

No. Years of
Satisfactory
Service

Unplasticized Polyvinyl Chloride (Cont.)

Steel industry (Cont.)

Pickling tank covers, 15% sulfuric, nitric acid	5
Pickling tank covers, nitric, hydrofluoric acid	3

Electroplating industry

Hoods and exhaust systems for 84 plating tanks	2½
Various sized pipelines in radio tube plant	3
Fume exhaust system anodizing process	3
Hood and exhaust system	6
Anodizing tanks (small metal parts)	4
Anodizing tanks (watch factories)	5
Galvanic, tanks and piping	7
Galvanic, tank and piping	6

Photographic industry

5000 ft. pipeline	2
Large development tanks and piping	2½
Dipping baskets	2
6 in. Waste line	1½
Development tanks and trays	6
Wash basins and drainboards	6
Shovels and stirrers	6
Perforated containers, strainers	6
Work tables	6
Piping and valves	6
Tanks	2

Food industry

Wine – piping	7
Brewery – piping	5
Vinegar – piping	11
Milk – piping	7
Sugar factories – containers for ion exchange resins	4

Leather tanning industry

Piping	4
Piping and containers	5
Piping and valves	2

Paper industry

1½ in. Piping	2
Tanks and piping	5
Tanks and piping	4
Tanks and piping	3

Water treatment

Chlorination tanks and piping	4
Containers for ion exchange resins	4

Soap industry

Soap storage tank	5

Pharmaceutical industry

Piping, duct work	7

	No. Years of Satisfactory Service
Unplasticized Polyvinyl Chloride (Cont.)	
Organic color manufacture	
Piping, duct work	7
Piping and valves	5
Agricultural chemicals	
Piping, ventilator fans	7
Oil Refineries	
Piping	7
PVC Production	
Piping and duct work	7
Chemical Laboratories	
Sinks, piping, hoods, duct work	11
Utensils for Handling Chemicals	
Siphons, pumps, valves, strainers, cans, bottles, flasks, scoops, ladles, buckets, funnels, trays, and racks	11
Miscellaneous	
3 in. salt brine line	2½
1¼ in. water line	2
1½ in. vinegar line	2

The data in these case histories are far from complete. At best, they should be considered as a guide for other applications. Committee T-5D of the National Association of Corrosion Engineers has concluded from questionnaires that when properly selected, designed and fabricated, thermoplastics perform outstanding service in chemical industry.

These data will never be completely up-to-date because history is being recorded almost daily in this new and important phase of plastics application. Additional information on past performance can be found in the references cited at the end of this chapter.

No attempt has been made to separate service data for exhaust systems and piping in the previous tables. However, the subject of plastic pipe is sufficiently complex to merit separate treatment. Hence, Chapter 17 is devoted entirely to the subject of plastic pipe, fittings and valves.

Suggested References

"Compounding and Processing of Rigid Polyvinyl Chloride," R. J. Ettinger, SPE Journal, Feb. 1953.

"Applications for Hard PVC in Europe," P. J. Weaver, Discussion—Thermoplastic Structures Division, Society of the Plastics Industry, Spring Lake, N. J., Aug. 27-28, 1953.

THERMOPLASTIC STRUCTURES 265

"Welding of Plastics," G. Haim and H. B. Zade, Crosby-Lockwood & Sons, Ltd, London, England (1947).

"Unplasticized Polyvinyl Chloride," Joseph L. Huscher, Chem. Eng., Nov. 1952.

"Proper Fabrication of Unplasticized PVC Equipment," George S. Laaff, Chem. Eng., June 1953.

"Plastic Processing Equipment Today," R. B. Seymour and J. H. Fry, Chem. Eng., March 1952.

"Polyethylene," J. L. Huscher, Chem. Eng., 59, No. 10, 260 (1953).

"Hot Gas Welding of Plastics," J. A. Neumann, Modern Plastics, 28, No. 3, 97 (1950).

"Manual for Plastic Welding," G. Haim and J. A. Neumann, Industrial Publishing Co., Cleveland, Ohio, 1954.

"Plastics in Piping, Valves and Ducts," Raymond B. Seymour, Symposium on Plastics as Materials of Construction, American Chemical Society, Division of Paint, Plastics and Printing Ink Chemistry, New York, Sept. 1954.

"Plastics for Vessels," J. A. Neumann and F. H. Bockhoff, Symposium on Plastics as Materials of Construction, American Chemical Society, Division of Paint, Plastics and Printing Ink Chemistry, New York, Sept. 1954.

"Plastics for Containers," Robert F. Uncles, Symposium on Plastics as Materials of Construction, American Chemical Society, Division of Paint, Plastics and Printing Ink Chemistry, New York, Sept. 1954.

"Plastics in Plants Manufacturing Textile Fibers," W. A. Haldeman and E. F. Wesp, Symposium on Plastics as Materials of Construction, American Chemical Society, Division of Paint, Plastics and Printing Ink Chemistry, New York, Sept. 1954.

"Plastics in Plants Manufacturing Fine Chemicals," John R. Yost, Jr., and A. J. Sargent, Symposium on Plastics as Materials of Construction, American Chemical Society, Division of Paint, Plastics and Printing Ink Chemistry, New York, Sept. 1954.

"Plastics in Food Processing Plants," Lawrence J. Turney, Symposium on Plastics as Materials of Construction, American Chemical Society, Division of Paint, Plastics and Printing Ink Chemistry, New York, Sept. 1954.

"Creep and Relaxation of Polyvinyl Chloride Rigid Resins," M. L. Dannis, Symposium on Plastics as Materials of Construction, American Chemical Society, Division of Paint, Plastics and Printing Ink Chemistry, New York, Sept. 1954.

"Plastic Pipe for Underground Structures," Raymond B. Seymour, Presented to the Niagara Frontier Section of the N.A.C.E., University of Buffalo, New York, Oct. 27, 1954.

"Plastic Ducts and Conduits," Raymond B. Seymour, Presented to the Conference on "Plastics in Building," Building Research Institute, Washington, D. C., Oct. 28, 1954.

"Results of Survey are Discussed at Meeting of T-5D," Corrosion, 10, No, 11 (1954).

17· PLASTIC PIPE, VALVES AND FITTINGS

Pipe may be made from either thermoplastic or thermosetting plastics. Each type of product is produced by different techniques and each fulfills a specific function in the chemical process industry.

This application of plastics is much too new to permit the making of realistic appraisals of the relative values of different types of pipe. It is estimated that 150 million pounds of plastic pipe will be produced in 1960 as compared with 35 million pounds in 1953. Obviously, any prediction on the future use of any specific plastic pipe is apt to be inaccurate.

Hence, the data in Table 17-1 showing relative use of plastic pipe should be considered as a guide only. Obviously, too little is known about the role to be played by reinforced thermosetting plastic pipe. It is safe to assume, however, that polyethylene pipe will account for over 50 per cent of all pipe produced for many years.

Production Methods

Reinforced thermosetting pipe can be produced by extrusion, centrifugal casting and mandrel wrapping methods. All these methods are practical but each is most readily adaptable for production of different sized pipe. Obviously, the real growth in use of this type of pipe will be hampered until some sort of size standardization is established.

The Pipe Committee of the Reinforced Plastics Division of the Society of The Plastics Industry has attempted to establish standard sizes but unfortunately only the extrusion process can be readily adapted to iron pipe sizes. There is a tendency to use standard iron pipe as forms for centrifugal casting and mandrel forming. Hence, the outside diameter of the former corresponds to the inside diameter of the latter.

In the centrifugal casting technique, glass fibers and catalyzed resins are distributed inside a spinning pipe. The pipe may then be heated to convert the liquid resin to a solid before removal. Woven fiberglas or glass mat can also be used to produce stronger pipe. Pipe produced by this method usually has a smooth resin-rich interior surface.

In an alternate method, a mixture of fibers and resins is extruded through an orifice. As previously mentioned, it is essential to design dies for the process and, hence, it is not dependent upon the size of iron pipe for its production.

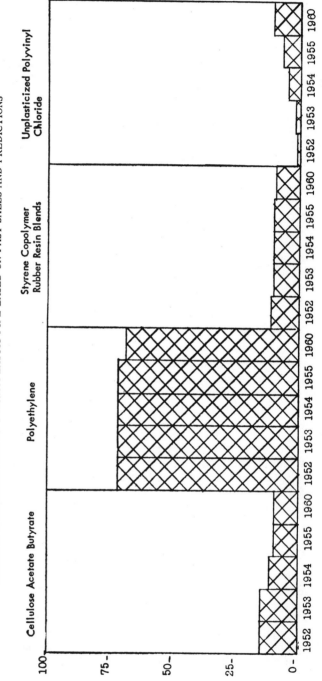

TABLE 17-1. RELATIVE USE OF THERMOPLASTIC PIPE BASED ON PAST SALES AND PREDICTIONS

In the most popular method, glass fabric wrapped around a mandrel is impregnated with catalyzed resin. The assembly is heated to cure the resin and the pipe is then removed from the mandrel. Regardless of the outside diameter of the reinforced plastic pipe, it may be built up to standard iron pipe sizes by adding additional thickness at the ends. This may be accomplished by cementing a molded ring or wrapping with a strip of glass fabric and impregnating with catalyzed resin. The built-up ring may be threaded or grooved to permit joining of the pipe.

Thermosetting plastic pipe may also be produced by the impregnation of graphite, as discussed in Chapter 12. This pipe is expensive but can be used at temperatures far above those recommended for most other plastic pipe.

Most thermoplastic pipe is manufactured by the extrusion process. As indicated by the data in Table 17-1, the principal types of commercial thermoplastic pipe are based on polyethylene, cellulose acetate butyrate, styrene copolymer rubber resin blends, saran and unplasticized polyvinyl chloride.

Prior to extrusion, the base resin is blended with lubricants and pigments and compounded on a mill or in a Banbury mixer. In some instances, the plastic is compounded by a quick preliminary pass through the extruder. The compounded material is fed to the extruder and forced under heat and pressure through a die to form pipes of various sizes. The rate of production varies from 50 to 250 lbs/hour depending on the specific plastic and the equipment used. This process is shown in Figure 3-1 (page 26).

Properties of Plastic Pipe

It must be recognized that practically all commercial plastic pipe available will give good performance at ordinary pressures or at temperatures below 125°F. The continued performance of plastic pipe after twenty years of service in corrosive environment cannot be discounted. However, it must be emphasized that in spite of such records of successful performance even the best plastic pipe has many disadvantages which must be recognized and understood.

Many improvements are now being made to overcome such shortcomings. Hence, it seems logical to assume that the most widely used plastic pipe in 1960 will resemble present pipe in the same manner that the 1955 automobiles resemble the Model T Ford. This statement should not be interpreted as a condemnation of the Model T. Some models are still giving service but there have been tremendous improvements in design and performance.

Some interesting innovations in plastic pipe design have already been observed. Thermoplastic pipe has been wrapped with glass cloth reinforced epoxy resins. A thin tubing of aluminum has been extruded over the thermoplastic pipe and it has also been reinforced with both fiberglas mat, steel wire and metal tubing. Also, the interior of glass reinforced pipe has been coated with a thermosetting or thermoplastic product.

In general, thermosetting pipe has excellent resistance to pressure while thermoplastic pipe has superior resistance to corrosives.

Flow Characteristics

One of the principal advantages of plastic pipe over other types of pipe is its low coefficient of friction. This property often permits the use of smaller sized pipe and prevents the accumulation of deposits in the line.

Flow characteristics for all types of plastic pipe can be obtained from the formula

$$P = \frac{.065 \times 1.75G}{4.75D}$$

where
P — pressure loss in psi/100 ft of pipe
G — flow, gals./min.
D — I.D. in inches

Creep Properties

As discussed in Chapter 4, the creep tendency of plastic under stress, the property that the Germans call "dauerstandsfestigkeit," must be taken into consideration in the design of pipelines. The maximum permissible working pressure at any temperature must be calculated from long term data.

Allowable stress values for all plastic pipe can be calculated from Barlow's formula

$$P = \frac{2T \times S}{D}$$

where
P — maximum working pressure (psi gage)
T — minimum effective wall thickness (inches)
S — allowable stress (psi)
D — outside diameter (inches)

This formula has been used to calculate maximum working pressures for various sized pipe at normal temperatures. Obviously, "T" for threaded pipe is less than the wall thickness of the unthreaded pipe.

Bursting Pressure

Because of the previously mentioned creep, attempts have been made to extrapolate values for long-term service using instantaneous burst values. While no conclusive statements can be made at present, the relation of the logarithm of per cent instantaneous burst to the logarithm of time has shown promise.

Thus, when these data are plotted for unplasticized polyvinyl chloride in Figure 17-1, bursting pressures for long periods of time may be estimated. These data indicate that after 1 million hours, (approximately 100 years) the bursting strength would still be approximately 50 per cent of the original instantaneous burst strength value.

Information available at present shows that the instantaneous burst values decrease as the temperature is raised. Indications are that the relation between short and long time bursting pressures is similar at all useful temperatures. However, the relation between short and long time burst values is characteristically different for each type of plastic pipe.

As shown in Figure 17-2, the hoop-stress of rigid thermoplastic pipe such as unplasticized polyvinyl chloride is much greater than that of semirigid materials such as polyethylene. These values appear to decrease at a constant rate within the useful temperature range as the temperature increases.

The Thermoplastic Pipe Division of the Society of the Plastics Industry in cooperation with the American Gas Association has recommended maximum stress values for different types of plastic pipe for transporting gas at temperatures up to 100° F. The recommended

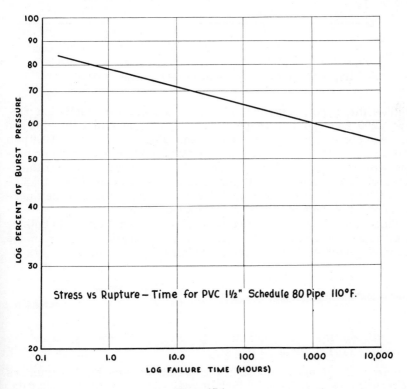

Figure 17-1.

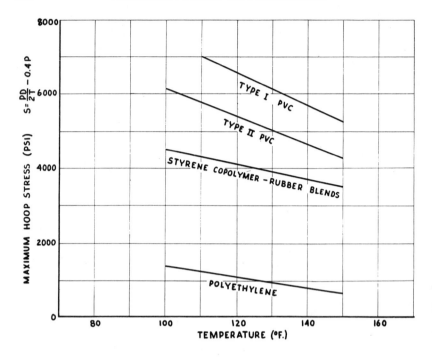

Figure 17-2. Effect of temperature on burst pressure — ½ in. pipe.

values for Type I polyvinyl chloride and cellulose acetate butyrate are 1200 and 700 psi, respectively. Type II polyvinyl chloride and styrene copolymer rubber resin blend pipe are rated at 1000 psi.

For installations in which the plastic pipe is pulled through existing gas distribution lines, this division recommends a wall thickness of 0.062 inches for all services having pressures less than 60 psi and temperatures below 100°F. It is recommended that the thickness of 1 3/4-inch butyrate pipe be 0.080 inches.

Since pipe of this type must be inserted in metal pipe, its outside dimension must obviously be less than the inside diameter of the existing pipeline. The recommended sizes are as follows:

Nominal size (inches)	½	¾	1	1¼	1¾
O.D. (inches)	0.625	0.875	1.125	1.375	1.875

Activities of the Thermoplastic Pipe Division of the Society of The Plastics Industry

Three of the most important complaints by industrial consumers of plastic pipe have been (1) lack of realistic bursting strength data,

(2) lack of reliable chemical resistance data, and (3) lack of standardization on outside diameters. Fortunately, many of these shortcomings are being overcome primarily through the efforts of the Thermoplastic Pipe Division of the Society of the Plastics Industry which was established in 1953.

The objectives of this group are to establish standards on plastic pipe for various applications, to conduct essential research projects in order to establish suitable test methods and to secure accurate physical data, to coordinate plastic pipe activities with other interested agencies, and to resolve pertinent problems affecting the manufacture of high quality plastic pipe.

This group has established an extensive engineering research program at Battelle Memorial Institute to investigate bursting strengths, safe working pressures and long-range serviceability under static pressure and dynamic loading. A previously sponsored project at the National Sanitation Foundation showed that properly compounded polyethylene, cellulose acetate butyrate, styrene rubber blends and unplasticized polyvinyl chloride pipe were suitable for the transmission of potable water.

Joining Methods

Thermoplastic pipe may be joined using threaded fittings, solvent-welded slip fittings, insert fittings, bell sections and mechanical couplings. The first method is recommended primarily for heavy wall (Schedule 80) pipe. As shown in Table 17-2 the thickness of the remaining wall after threading thin wall (Schedule 40) pipe will be less than 50 per cent of the original thickness for 1-inch pipe.

Solvent-welding techniques are applicable to thin wall pipe and standard sizes have been designated as "SWP" for pipe of this type. Joints are made by applying solvent or cement to the pipe end and to a closely matched slip fitting. The solvent-softened plastic surfaces are mated, turned approximately one half a full turn and then held in place until a secure adhesive bond is obtained.

Polyethylene cannot be solvent welded and is not satisfactory with threaded joints except in very thick sections. The inserts may be cast from metal or molded from styrene copolymer rubber resin blend. Obviously the latter is required for corrosion resistant application.

One of the simplest methods for joining pipe utilizes a simple bell and spigot technique. The bell is formed by heating and flaring one end over a suitable form. This bell is then joined with a standard pipe end through the use of a cement based on the same material.

Schedule 80 pipe may also be joined by the use of metal couplings. One type is shown in Figures 17-3 and 17-4. These consist of half-circle metal clamps placed over continuous rings of elastomeric materials.

Much of the cellulose acetate butyrate pipe and some unplasticized

TABLE 17-2. DATA ON WALL THICKNESS OF SCHEDULE 40 AND 80 THERMOPLASTIC THREADED PIPE

Nominal Size (In.)	SCHEDULE 40				SCHEDULE 80			
	Wall Thickness (In.)	Max. Depth of Thread (In.)	Remaining Wall Thickness(T) (In.)	Remaining Wall Thickness (%)	Wall Thickness (In.)	Max. Depth of Thread (In.)	Remaining Wall Thickness(T) (In.)	Remaining Wall Thickness (%)
½	0.109	0.057	0.052	47.7	0.147	0.057	0.090	61.2
¾	.113	.057	.056	49.5	.154	.057	.097	63.0
1	.133	.069	.064	48.2	.179	.069	.110	61.5
1¼	.140	.069	.071	50.7	.191	.069	.122	64.0
1½	.145	.069	.076	52.4	.200	.069	.131	65.5
2	.154	.069	.085	55.2	.218	.069	.149	68.5
2½	.203	.100	.103	50.8	.276	.100	.176	63.8
3	.216	.100	.116	53.7	.300	.100	.200	66.7
3½	.226	.100	.126	55.8	.318	.100	.218	68.5
4	.237	.100	.137	57.9	.337	.100	.237	70.4
6	.280	.100	.180	64.4	.432	.100	.332	76.8

Figure 17-3. View of mechanical joint for plastic pipe before assembling.

Figure 17-4. Plastic pipe joined with Victaulic coupling.

polyvinyl chloride and styrene copolymer rubber resin blend pipe is manufactured in SWP sizes. As can be observed from the data in Table 17-3, the inside diameter corresponds to the nominal size for the pipe while the inside of the slip-on fitting is tapered to correspond with the outside diameter of the pipe.

Figure 17-5 shows the applications of solvent to clear 3 inch SWP cellulose acetate butyrate pipe. The installation shown in this photograph is a quarter of a mile pipeline carrying water to a power plant in Wilmington, North Carolina.

(Courtesy of Eastman Chemical Products, Inc.)

Figure 17-5. Assembling SWP pipe. Applying solvent to the end of the pipe.

Iron pipe sizes (IPS) have been accepted as standard by the Thermoplastic Pipe Division for threaded fitting pipe. Schedule 40 is sometimes used for light-duty service but as previously mentioned, the "T" value for threaded Schedule 40 pipe is less than 50 per cent of the thickness of the unthreaded pipe for sizes less than 1 inch. Even for 4-inch pipe the remaining wall is less than 60 per cent of the original thickness.

Properly threaded Schedule 80 IPS pipe allows sufficient effective thickness for normal working pressures. The wall thicknesses of

TABLE 17-3. TECHNICAL DATA FOR SWP PIPE AND FITTINGS

Nominal Size (In.)	PIPE				FITTINGS		
	Outside Diameter (In.)	Inside Diameter (In.)	Wall Thick. (In.)	Tolerance (O.D. In.) ±	Entrance (I.D. In.)	End of Taper (I.D. In.)	Length of Taper (In.)
½	0.600	0.500	0.050	0.005	0.600	0.595	0.625
¾	0.855	0.750	0.053	0.005	0.855	0.850	0.720
1	1.140	1.000	0.070	0.005	1.140	1.135	0.875
1¼	1.420	1.250	0.085	0.005	1.420	1.145	0.943
1½	1.730	1.500	0.115	0.006	1.730	1.725	1.062
2	2.250	2.000	0.125	0.008	2.250	2.245	1.375
2½	2.570	2.320	0.125	0.009			
3	3.250	3.000	0.125	0.010	3.250	3.240	1.943
3½	3.660	3.360	0.150	0.011			
4	4.100	3.800	0.150	0.012	4.100	4.090	2.500
5	5.110	4.750	0.180	0.014	5.110	5.095	2.812
6	6.220	5.760	0.230	0.016	6.220	6.205	3.125

both Schedule 40 and 80 IPS are given in Table 17-2. These data also include the depth of the thread and show the amount of wall ("T") remaining after the pipe has been threaded. This value for "T" rather than the original wall thickness should be used in calculating working pressures for pipe.

As shown in Table 17-4, a different set of standard dimensions has been established by the Thermoplastic Pipe Division of the Society of the Plastics Industry for transporting natural gas in new services and mains.

Schedule 80 pipe of all types can be threaded quite readily without cutting compounds through the use of sharp cutting tools, preferably with a front rake angle of approximately 5°. It is customary to insert a tapered brass or wooden plug into the pipe during the threading operation to minimize distortion.

Plastic pipe dopes based on aqueous dispersions of polyfluorocarbons are recommended for joining all types of threaded plastic pipe to minimize chattering, galling and leaking. Although this type

TABLE 17-4. DATA ON WALL THICKNESS OF PLASTIC PIPE FOR GAS SERVICE

Nominal Size (In.)	O. D. (In.)	Thickness (In.)		
		Cellulose Acetate Butyrate	Type I PVC	Type II PVC or Styrene Copolymer Rubber Resin Blend
½	0.840	0.90	0.90	0.90
2½	2.875	0.135	0.100	0.110
3	3.500	0.160	0.120	0.125
4	4,500	0.205	0.145	0.155
5	5.563	0.250	0.170	0.190
6	6.625	0.300	0.200	0.220

of dope is expensive, it is far superior to standard pipe dope used for iron pipe. Unfortunately, many commercial dopes contain oils which may produce permanently bonded joints.

Assembly of threaded plastic pipe joints should be made with strap wrenches rather than with pipe wrenches which tend to bite into the pipe. Figure 17-6 illustrates the use of a strap wrench on a 1 1/2 inch pipe.

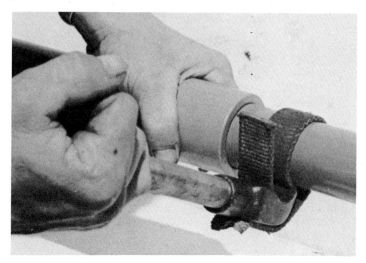

Figure 17-6. Tightening a threaded pipe joint with a strap wrench.

Injection molded fittings for pipe sizes up to 2 in. are available commercially, but, at present, fabricated fittings or flanged joints must be used for larger sizes. Flanged fittings are usually employed when joining to existing metal pipelines. Bolts on flanged joints should be tightened enough to compress the gasket material slightly to produce a good seal but should not be made tight enough to deform the flange. Figure 17-7 shows the preferred method for flanged joints as used on a 9-mile oil pipeline in Poplar, Montana.

Hanging of Plastic Pipe

All thermoplastic pipe should be hung so that it can move independently of the supporting members. Whenever possible, overhead lines should be supported continuously by angle irons. If hangers are used, they should be placed at maximum intervals of 4 feet.

Precautions should be taken in storage of plastic pipe to ascertain that it is properly supported and not allowed to sag. This is particularly true of flanged pipe which must be stored so that none of its weight is supported by the flanged ends. Because plastic pipe has a high coefficient of expansion, suitable provision to accommo-

(Courtesy of Eastman Chemical Products, Inc.)
Figure 17-7. Joining a 4-in. plastic pipeline to
a metal line by means of metal flanges.

date change in length with temperature must be made in all long
lines restricted at both ends.

Provisions for Expansion of Plastic Pipe

Two commonly used methods for fabricating expansion pieces for
thermoplastic pipe are depicted in Figures 17-8 and 17-9. The latter is used more frequently with rigid unplasticized polyvinyl chloride. A third method used is a continuous overlapping loop where the
diameter of the loop is five times the outside diameter of the pipe.

While plastic pipe should be selected on the basis of anticipated
performance rather than cost, comparative cost data are of interest.
Polyethylene and cellulose acetate butyrate are in the same price
range as steel and galvanized iron pipe. Styrene copolymer rubber
resin blend and unplasticized polyvinyl chloride pipe are in the same
price range as aluminum and are less expensive than copper, brass
or stainless steel.

In this chapter, each specific type of plastic will be discussed
separately using the same order of presentation as that in Chapter 5.

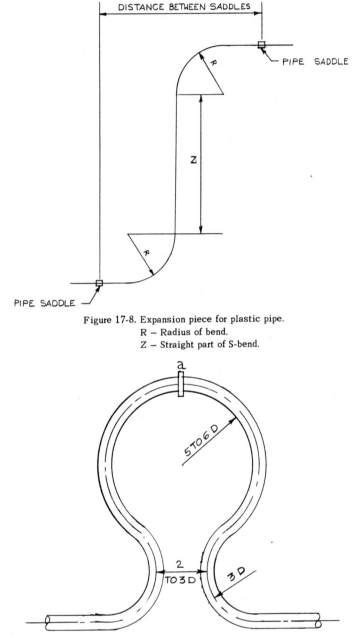

Figure 17-8. Expansion piece for plastic pipe.
R — Radius of bend.
Z — Straight part of S-bend.

Figure 17-9. Expansion piece for plastic pipe.
a — Fixed point
D — External or outside pipe diameter

THERMOPLASTICS

Polyethylene

As outlined in Chapter 5, polyethylene has excellent resistance to acids, salts and alkalies. It can be extruded readily, possesses permanent flexibility, is economical and potentially available in large quantities. Therefore, there is every reason to expect that its use as extruded pipe will continue to grow for many years.

Approximately 32 million pounds of polyethylene pipe was extruded in 1954 compared to almost 5 million pounds in 1950. It has been estimated that 74 million pounds of polyethylene pipe will be produced in 1958 and that there will be a market for approximately 100 million pounds in 1960. At present, almost 20 per cent of the polyethylene produced is extruded as pipe.

Because of its low water absorption and excellent electrical properties, almost all the polyethylene produced during World War II was consumed in electronic applications by the military. As production increased in the post-war years, considerable quantities of polyethylene were made available for film and pipe. In spite of its potentials in the chemical process industry, much of the output of polyethylene pipe is now used for private well systems. A small quantity is used for mine water pipe for natural gas lines and small water systems such as those on golf courses.

One of the advantages of polyethylene pipe is that it may be snaked inside of old metal pipelines where its smooth interior surface reduces the rate of liquid or gas flow much less than metal pipe. Many miles of polyethylene pipe have been installed for water service lines on farms and for carrying natural gas.

As unpigmented polyethylene pipe is affected adversely by sunlight and weather, most pipe that is used above ground should be extruded from black pigmented virgin polyethylene resin.

As shown by the data in Figure 17-2, the hoop stress of polyethylene pipe is extremely low at elevated temperatures. This property can be improved somewhat by irradiation but this process has not been used commercially on polyethylene pipe as yet.

It has been estimated that over a million molded fittings were used for joining polyethylene pipe in 1953 and that over 5 million of this type of fitting will be used in 1960. Polyethylene may also be flared to form flanges which may be clamped in place using a split ring metal clamp.

The Commodity Standards Division of the U. S. Department oof Commerce has already established dimensional standards CS197-54 for flexible polyethylene pipe. Data for these standards are given in Table 17-5.

Several firms are extruding so-called heavy wall polyethylene pipe and the data given in Table 17-6 have been proposed by the Thermoplastic Pipe Division of the Society of the Plastics Industry as a commercial standard.

TABLE 17-5. DIMENSION AND SIZE FOR SCHEDULE 40 IPS POLYETHYLENE PIPE

Commodity Standard CS197-54

Nominal Size (In.)	Inside Diameter (In.)	Tolerances (In.) +	Tolerances (In.) −	Outside Diameter (In.)	Wall Thickness (In.)	Tolerances (In.) ±	Weight Lbs/100 ft Minimum	Weight Lbs/100 ft Nominal
½	0.622	0.010	0.010	0.840	0.109	0.006	9	10
¾	0.824	0.010	0.015	1.050	0.113	0.006	12.2	13
1	1.049	0.010	0.020	1.315	0.133	0.007	18	20
1¼	1.380	0.010	0.020	1.660	0.140	0.007	24.6	27
1½	1.610	0.015	0.020	1.900	0.145	0.008	29.3	32
2	2.067	0.015	0.020	2.375	0.154	0.008	39.7	43
2½	2.469	0.015	0.025	2.875	0.203	0.009	63.4	68
3	3.068	0.015	0.030	3.500	0.216	0.010	82.8	89
4	4.026	0.015	0.035	4.500	0.237	0.012	117.5	127
6	6.065	0.020	0.035	6.625	0.280	0.015	206.7	223

Dimensions have also been proposed for an extra heavy wall polyethylene pipe. Data given for this pipe in Table 17-7 is presented for guidance only since no standards have been set for this weight pipe.

While most plastic pipe is supplied in 10 and 20 foot sections, Schedule 40 and lighter wall polyethylene pipe is supplied in coils. While no standards on coils have been established as yet, the data given in 17-8 on coil sizes are of interest. These data are based on the average obtained from eleven different firms manufacturing Schedule 40 polyethylene pipe.

A small quantity of polyethylene pipe is extruded as Schedule 80 pipe in 10 and 20 foot lengths. Data for this pipe are given in Table 17-9

Asphalt

Asphalt, coal-tar pitch, and coumarone-indene resins are not suitable for the production of pipe. Coal-tar pitch impregnated paper

TABLE 17-6. DIMENSIONS AND TOLERANCES
FOR HEAVY-WALL POLYETHYLENE PIPE

Nominal Pipe Size (In.)	Outside Diameter (In.)	Inside Diameter (In.)	Tolerance Inside Diameter +	Tolerance Inside Diameter −	Tolerance Wall Thickness ±	Nominal Weight Lbs/100 ft
½	0.731	0.622	0.010	0.010	0.006	10.0
¾	0.967	0.824	0.010	0.015	0.008	17.6
1	1.229	1.049	0.010	0.020	0.010	27.7
1¼	1.620	1.380	0.010	0.020	0.011	48.7
1½	1.890	1.610	0.015	0.020	0.013	66.2
2	2.422	2.067	0.015	0.020	0.015	107.7

TABLE 17-7. DIMENSION AND SIZES
FOR EXTRA HEAVY WALL POLYETHYLENE PIPE

Nominal Pipe Size (In.)	Inside Diameter (In.)	Outside Diameter (In.)	Weight Lbs/100 ft
½	.916	.622	14.2
¾	1.132	.824	18.9
1	1.407	1.049	27.5
1¼	1.762	1.380	37.5
1½	2.010	1.610	45.7
2	2.500	2.067	61.7
2½	2.950	2.469	82.0
3	3.670	3.068	127.0
4	4.700	4.026	185.0
6	6.930	6.065	352.0

TABLE 17-8. DATA ON COIL DIAMETERS
OF SCHEDULE 40 POLYETHYLENE PIPE

Pipe Size (In.)	Average I. D.	Average O. D.	Approx. Thickness (In.)	Per Cent Stretch	Lbs/ cu ft	Max. I.D. Reported	Min. I.D. Reported
½	24	36	6	3.0	9.34	38	15
¾	24	38	8½	3.8	7.45	38	18
1	25	41	9	5	6.73	38	20
1¼	31	49	9	4.8	6.38	48	24
1½	36	54	10	4.9	4.75	48	28
2	52	74	9	4.3	3.05	63	40

TABLE 17-9. DATA ON SIZE AND MAXIMUM WORKING
PRESSURES FOR SCHEDULE 80 IPS POLYETHYLENE PIPE

Nominal Size (In.)	Inside Diameter (In.)	Outside Diameter (In.)	Wall Thickness (In.)	Lbs/ft	Maximum Working Pressures (psi - gage at 73.4°F)
½	0.546	0.840	0.294	0.14	240
¾	0.742	1.050	0.308	0.20	190
1	0.957	1.315	0.358	0.28	170
1¼	1.278	1.660	0.382	0.36	140
1½	1.500	1.900	0.400	0.39	130
2	1.939	2.375	0.436	0.54	100

tubing has been available for many years under specific trade names. This pipe, which is available in 5-foot lengths in sizes ranging from 3 to 8 inches in diameter, is supplied with a factory-machined taper on each end. A female mating taper sleeve is used as a coupling. This product has been used for nonpressure, noncorrosive waste disposal services and as a protective jacket for underground metal pipe or electric wiring.

Styrene Copolymer Rubber Resin Blends

Styrene butadiene copolymer resins can be extruded as pipe but most of the interest to date in styrene-based pipe has been in the so-called styrene copolymer rubber resin blends. Approximately 2 million pounds of this pipe was produced in 1953. It has been predicted that approximately 4 million and 10 million pounds will be produced in 1955 and 1960, respectively.

It is available in 10 and 20 foot threaded and unthreaded sections in SWP, as well as Schedule 40 and 80 IPS. Short sections of styrene copolymer rubber resin blend pipe with fittings in sizes from 1/2 to 2 inches are shown in Figure 17-10, and data are given in Tables 17-10 and 17-11.

When properly supported and installed, styrene copolymer rubber resin blend pipe is suitable for service with most non-oxidizing acids, salts and alkalies at temperatures of −20 to 160° F. Like most other thermoplastic pipe materials, styrene copolymer rubber resin blend pipe can be bent and shaped when heated above 260° F.

The weight of molded fittings for this type pipe is given in Table 17-12

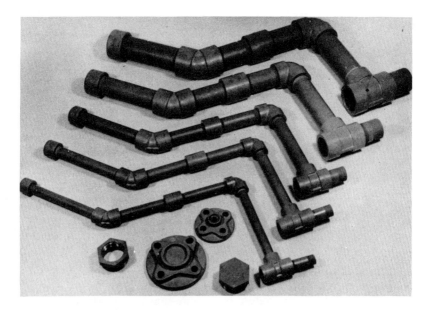

Figure 17-10. Styrene copolymer rubber-resin blend pipe and fittings from ½ in. through 2 in.

TABLE 17-10. TECHNICAL DATA FOR STYRENE COPOLYMER RUBBER RESIN BLEND PLASTIC PIPE.

Nominal Sizes (In.)	SCHEDULE 40					SCHEDULE 80				
	Outside Diameter (In.)	Inside Diameter (In.)	Wt. Lbs/Ft	Recommended Working Pressure (psi-gage) at 75°F	Recommended Working Pressure (psi-gage) at 150°F	Outside Diamater (In.)	Inside Diameter (In.)	Wt. Lbs/Ft	Recommended Working Pressure (psi-gage) at 75°F	Recommended Working Pressure (psi-gage) at 150°F
½	0.840	0.546	0.12	75	50	0.840	0.546	0.15	150	100
¾	1.050	0.742	0.16	75	50	1.050	0.742	0.20	150	100
1	1.315	0.957	0.23	60	40	1.315	0.957	0.30	125	80
1¼	1.660	1.278	0.31	50	35	1.660	1.278	0.41	100	75
1½	1.900	1.500	0.37	45	30	1.900	1.500	0.50	90	60
2	2.375	1.939	0.50	40	25	2.375	1.939	0.70	75	50
3	3.500	2.842	1.04	30	20	3.500	2.842	1.40	60	40
4	4.500	3.749	1.50	30	20	4.500	3.749	2.00	60	40
6	6.625	5.761	2.62	25	15	6.625	5.761	3.85	50	35

TABLE 17-11. TECHNICAL DATA FOR SWP STYRENE COPOLYMER RUBBER RESIN BLEND PIPE AND FITTINGS.

Nominal Size (In.)	PIPE					FITTINGS		
	Outside Diameter (In.)	Inside Diameter (In.)	Wall Thickness (In.)	Tolerances (O.D. In.) ±	Max. Working Pressure (psi-gage) at 73.4°F	Entrance (I.D. In.)	End of Taper (I.D. In.)	Length of Taper (In.)
½	0.600	0.500	0.050	0.005	200	0.600	0.595	0.625
¾	0.855	0.750	0.053	0.005	150	0.855	0.850	0.720
1	1.140	1.000	0.070	0.005	150	1.140	1.135	0.875
1¼	1.420	1.250	0.085	0.005	150	1.420	1.145	0.943
1½	1.730	1.500	0.115	0.006	150	1.730	1.725	1.062
2	2.250	2.000	0.125	0.008	140	2.250	2.245	1.375
2½	2.570	2.230	0.125	0.008	125	2.570	2.565	1.625
3	3.250	3.000	0.125	0.010	100	3.250	3.240	1.943
3½	3.660	3.360	0.150	0.015	100	3.660	3.650	2.250
4	4.100	3.800	0.150	0.012	90	4.100	4.090	2.500
5	5.110	4.750	0.180	0.014	90	5.110	5.095	2.812
6	6.220	5.760	0.230	0.016	90	6.220	6.205	3.125

TABLE 17-12. WEIGHT IN POUNDS FOR MOLDED THREADED
STYRENE COPOLYMER RUBBER RESIN BLEND FITTINGS

Type	½ In.	¾ In.	1 In.	1¼ In.	2 In.
90° Elbow	0.09	0.11	0.19	0.36	0.53
45° Elbow	0.09	0.11	0.19	0.34	0.48
Tee	0.12	0.17	0.27	0.54	0.75
Coupling	0.06	0.09	0.14	0.25	0.34
Cap	0.05	0.06	0.09	0.17	0.23
Flange Companion	0.16	0.22	0.31	0.47	0.72
Flange Blind	0.19	0.25	0.34	0.56	0.84
Flange Reducing	0.16	0.22	0.31	0.47	0.72
Reducer Bushing	–	0.03	0.05	0.09	0.13
Plug	0.05	0.07	0.09	0.13	0.20

Acrylates

Transparent pipe and tubing in standard 52 inch lengths is extruded from polymethyl methacrylate. As indicated in Chapter 5, its resistance to acids and alkalies is somewhat limited, but it is suitable for service with fruit acids, milk, vegetable extracts, sugar and salt solutions at temperatures up to 150°F.

Technical data for polymethyl methacrylate tubing are given in Table 17-13.

Vinyls

While flexible vinyl tubing has been produced by extruding plasticized polyvinyl chloride, plasticized copolymers of vinyl chloride and vinyl acetate, polyvinyl alcohol and polyvinyl butyral, this discussion will be limited to rigid Type I and Type II unplasticized polyvinyl chloride. Both products are available commercially as extruded pipe in sizes up to 8 inches in Schedules 40 and 80 IPS in 10 and 20 foot lengths. Schedule 80 is preferred for threaded pipe in industrial applications.

The definitions, specifications and physical properties of these two types of materials were discussed in Chapter 15.

Based on almost twenty years European experience and approximately five years service in American industry, it may be predicted that more unplasticized polyvinyl chloride pipe will be used in chemical industry in the future than any other type of plastic pipe. This pipe is already out-performing almost all other materials for corrosion resistant services particularly for drain and discharge lines.

Although 2 million pounds were used in Germany and almost a million pounds in France in 1953, less than a million pounds of unplasticized polyvinyl chloride pipe had been used by American industry prior to 1953. It has been estimated that there will be a market for over 2 million and 12 million of unplasticized polyvinyl chloride pipe in 1955 and 1960, respectively.

TABLE 17-13. TECHNICAL DATA FOR
POLYMETHYL METHACRYLATE TUBING

Nominal Size (In.)	Wall Thickness(T) (In.)	Inside Diameter (In.)	Lbs/Ft
1.5	1/8	1 1/4	0.28
	3/16	1 1/8	0.40
1.75	1/8	1 1/2	0.33
	1/4	1 1/4	0.60
2.0	3/16	1 5/8	0.55
	3/8	1 1/4	0.98
2.5	3/16	2 1/8	0.71
	3/8	1 3/4	1.28
3.0	3/16	2 5/8	0.85
	3/8	2 1/4	1.58
3.5	3/16	3 1/8	1.00
	3/8	2 3/4	1.88
4.0	3/16	3 5/8	1.20
	3/8	3 1/4	2.18
4.5	3/16	4 1/8	1.31
	3/8	3 3/4	2.50
5.0	3/16	4 5/8	1.45
	3/8	4 1/4	2.80
5.5	3/16	5 1/8	1.60
	3/8	4 3/4	3.08
6.0	3/16	5 5/8	1.77
	3/8	5 1/4	3.43

In spite of its newness in the United States, industrial installations consisting of several thousand feet of rigid unplasticized polyvinyl chloride pipe are not uncommon. It is expected that many miles of 2-inch and 4-inch unplasticized polyvinyl chloride pipe will be installed in mid-western oilfields within the next few years. This prediction is based on satisfactory performance of many miles of a solvent-welded Type II unplasticized polyvinyl chloride pipeline in Kansas. One line alone used to transport salt water from petroleum separators is over three miles in length.

Type I and II unplasticized polyvinyl chloride pipe are now being extruded in Schedule 40 and Schedule 80 IPS in sizes up to 6 inches in this country. In addition 8 and 12 inch Schedule 80 IPS pipe is being extruded commercially from Type II unplasticized polyvinyl chloride in the United States. It has been reported that larger sizes are being extruded experimentally on the European continent but in some cases, it is known that a plasticizer is being added in order to facilitate processing.

Type I unplasticized polyvinyl chloride pipe is one of the few materials that is satisfactory for chlorine dioxide, chlorine and nitric acid service. Type II unplasticized polyvinyl chloride pipe has exceptional resistance to impact and should be considered for service with non-oxidizing acids, salts and alkalies at temperatures up to 150°F.

Figure 17-11 shows a section of a spray-type fume scrubber made from Type I polyvinyl chloride pipe. Figure 17-12 shows the laying of a 4-inch Type II polyvinyl chloride pipeline for handling corrosive water in an oilfield.

Both Types I and II may be used at somewhat higher temperatures when they are armored with fiberglas reinforced polyester plastics. The armor may be applied in the shop or in the field. In any case, it is necessary to field-wrap any molded fittings that are used.

Technical data for Type I and II unplasticized polyvinyl chloride pipe are given in Tables 17-14 and 17-15. Data for fittings are given in Tables 17-16 and 17-17. Data on the weight of unplasticized polyvinyl chloride fittings are given in Table 17-18.

Saran

Extruded saran pipe introduced prior to World War II was the first commercially available corrosion-resistant thermoplastic pipe in the United States. It is suitable for service with most acids and salts at temperatures up to 150°F but is not recommended for service

Figure 17-11. Spray-type fume scrubber fabricated of Type I unplasticized polyvinyl chloride.

(Courtesy of B. F. Goodrich Chemical Company)

Figure 17-12. Laying a 4-inch Type II polyvinyl chloride pipeline in an oil field.

with ammonium hydroxide, nonpolar solvents and some oxidizing agents. It is available in sizes of 1/2 to 6 inches, Schedule 80 IPS. It can be threaded and corresponding molded fittings are available as in the case of other rigid thermoplastics. Technical data for saran pipe and tubing are given in Table 17-19.

Saran-lined pipe is available for services at temperatures as high as 180 °F. It is produced by inserting the saran pipe directly into a steel pipe having an inside diameter corresponding with the outside diameter of the plastic pipe. Technical data for saran-lined pipe are given in Table 17-20. Cross-sections of 4-inch pipe of this type are shown in Figure 17-13.

Polyfluorocarbons

Pipe and tubing based on polytetrafluoroethylene and polytrifluorochloroethylene are now available in sizes from 1/8 to 3 1/2 inches in Schedule 40 and 80 IPS in standard 12 foot lengths. Molded fittings

TABLE 17-14. TECHNICAL DATA FOR TYPE I UNPLASTICIZED POLYVINYL CHLORIDE PIPE

Nominal Sizes (In.)	SCHEDULE 40				SCHEDULE 80			
	Outside Diameter (In.)	Wall Thickness (In.)	Wt. Lbs/Ft	Recommended Working Pressure (psi-gage at 75°F)	Outside Diameter (In.)	Wall Thickness (In.)	Wt. Lbs/Ft	Recommended Working Pressure (psi-gage at 75°F)
½	0.840	0.109	0.157	120	0.840	0.147	0.201	250
¾	1.050	0.113	0.209	120	1.050	0.154	0.270	215
1	1.315	0.133	0.310	120	1.315	0.179	0.401	190
1¼	1.660	0.140	0.420	95	1.660	0.191	0.544	165
1½	1.900	0.145	0.503	95	1.900	0.200	0.671	160
2	2.375	0.154	0.675	75	2.375	0.218	0.928	140
2½	2.875	0.203	1.071	75	2.875	0.276	1.417	135
3	3.500	0.216	1.401	75	3.500	0.300	1.896	130
3½	4.000	0.226	1.684	60	4.000	0.318	2.312	130
4	4.500	0.237	1.995	60	4.500	0.337	2.770	125
6	6.625	0.280	3.640	60	6.625	0.432	6.730	120

TABLE 17-15. TECHNICAL DATA FOR TYPE II UNPLASTICIZED POLYVINYL CHLORIDE PIPE

Nominal Sizes (In.)	SCHEDULE 40				SCHEDULE 80			
	Outside Diameter (In.)	Wall Thickness (In.)	Wt. Lbs/Ft	Recommended Working Pressure (psi-gage at 75°F)	Outside Diameter (In.)	Wall Thickness (In.)	Wt. Lbs/Ft	Recommended Working Pressure (psi-gage at 75°F)
½	0.840	0.109	0.157	100	0.840	0.147	0.185	215
¾	1.050	0.113	0.209	100	1.050	0.154	0.251	175
1	1.315	0.133	0.310	100	1.315	0.179	0.371	150
1¼	1.660	0.140	0.420	75	1.660	0.191	0.518	120
1½	1.900	0.145	0.503	75	1.900	0.200	0.618	110
2	2.375	0.154	0.675	60	2.375	0.218	0.858	90
2½	2.875	0.203	1.071	60	2.875	0.276	1.336	90
3	3.500	0.216	1.401	60	3.500	0.300	1.750	80
3½	4.000	0.226	1.684	50	4.000	0.318	2.180	75
4	4.500	0.237	1.995	50	4.500	0.337	2.560	70
6	6.625	0.280	3.640	50	6.625	0.432	5.780	60

TABLE 17-16. SIZE DATA FOR SLIP SLEEVE FITTINGS
FOR SCHEDULE 40 IPS UNPLASTICIZED POLYVINYL CHLORIDE PIPE

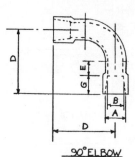
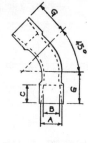
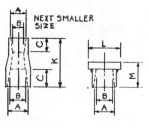

90° ELBOW   45° ELBOW   TEE

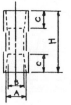
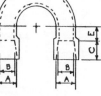

COUPLING   180° BEND   REDUCER   CAP

NOTE: ALL RADII ARE 1.5 × PIPE SIZE

NOM. PIPE SIZE	A (DIA)	B (DIA)	C	D	E	F	G	H	J	K	L (DIA)	M
1/2	.845	.825	1/2	1 7/8	5/8	3	1 1/8	1 1/2	1 1/2	1 5/8	1 1/16	3/4
3/4	1.055	1.035	3/4	2 1/2	5/8	3 3/4	1 3/8	2 1/4	1 7/8	2 1/8	1 9/16	1
1	1.320	1.295	1	3 1/8	5/8	4 1/2	1 5/8	3	2 1/4	2 5/8	1 5/8	1 1/4
1 1/4	1.665	1.640	1 1/4	3 3/4	5/8	5 1/4	1 7/8	3 3/4	2 5/8	3 1/8	2	1 1/2
1 1/2	1.905	1.880	1 1/2	4 3/8	5/8	6	2 1/8	4 1/2	3	3 5/8	2 1/4	1 3/4
2	2.385	2.350	2	5 5/8	5/8	7 1/2	2 5/8	6	3 3/4	4 5/8	2 11/16	2 1/4

In spite of its expense, polyfluorocarbon pipe is often the only material suitable for use at high temperatures with specific corrosives. As shown in Chapter 5, it is not attacked by acids, alkalies or solvents and will withstand temperatures as high as 400°F. Technical data for polyfluorocarbon pipe are given in Table 17-21.

Some success has been attained in the production of glass fiber reinforced polyfluorocarbon pipe. It has been proposed that this pipe be flared and joined by inserting a ring of the same material and bringing the ends together with metal flanged fittings.

TABLE 17-17. SIZE DATA FOR SLIP SLEEVE FITTINGS
FOR SCHEDULE 40 IPS UNPLASTICIZED POLYVINYL CHLORIDE PIPE

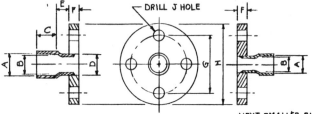

REDUCING FLANGES

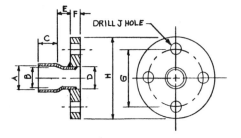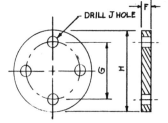

COMPANION FLANGE   BLIND FLANGE

NOM. PIPE SIZE	A(DIA)	B(DIA)	C	D(DIA)	E	F	G(DIA)	H(DIA)	J(DIA)
$\frac{1}{2}$	.845	.825	$\frac{1}{2}$	.840	$\frac{5}{8}$	$\frac{7}{16}$	$2\frac{3}{8}$	$3\frac{1}{2}$	$\frac{9}{16}$
$\frac{3}{4}$	1.055	1.035	$\frac{3}{4}$	1.050	$\frac{5}{8}$	$\frac{1}{2}$	$2\frac{7}{8}$	$3\frac{7}{8}$	$\frac{9}{16}$
1	1.320	1.295	1	1.315	$\frac{5}{8}$	$\frac{9}{16}$	$3\frac{5}{32}$	$4\frac{5}{16}$	$\frac{9}{16}$
$1\frac{1}{4}$	1.665	1.640	$1\frac{1}{4}$	1.660	$\frac{5}{8}$	$\frac{5}{8}$	$3\frac{1}{2}$	$4\frac{5}{8}$	$\frac{9}{16}$
$1\frac{1}{2}$	1.905	1.880	$1\frac{1}{2}$	1.900	$\frac{5}{8}$	$\frac{5}{8}$	$3\frac{7}{8}$	5	$\frac{9}{16}$
2	2.385	2.350	2	2.375	$\frac{5}{8}$	$\frac{11}{16}$	$4\frac{3}{4}$	6	$\frac{11}{16}$

Polyfluorocarbons are also used to produce stainless steel wire braid reinforced tubing. Technical data on this tubing are given in Table 17-22. This tubing, threaded pipe, molded parts and the previously discussed flanged assembly of polyfluorocarbons are shown in Figure 17-15.

Polyamides

Nylon pipe is available commercially in small sizes but because of its lack of resistance to acids, is not used to any great extent in

(Courtesy of Dow Chemical Company)

Figure 17-13. Gross section of 4-in. Saran-lined steel pipe.

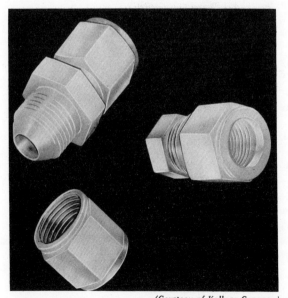

(Courtesy of Kellogg Company)

Figure 17-14. Machined pipe fittings of polychlorotrifluoro-ethylene.

TABLE 17-18. WEIGHT IN POUNDS OF MOLDED THREADED
UNPLASTICIZED POLYVINYL CHLORIDE FITTINGS

Type	½ In.	¾ In.	1 In.	1¼ In.	2 In.
90° Elbow	0.14	0.17	0.30	0.54	0.80
45° Elbow	0.14	0.17	0.30	0.51	0.72
Tee	0.18	0.26	0.40	0.81	1.12
Coupling	0.09	0.14	0.21	0.38	0.51
Cap	0.09	0.09	0.14	0.26	0.35
Flange, companion	0.24	0.33	0.47	0.71	1.08
Flange, blind	0.29	0.38	0.51	0.84	1.26
Flange, reducing	0.24	0.33	0.47	0.71	1.08
Reducer bushing	–	0.05	0.09	0.14	0.20
Plug	0.09	0.11	0.14	0.20	0.30

TABLE 17-19. TECHNICAL DATA FOR
SARAN PIPE AND TUBING

Nominal Size (In.)	Outside Diameter (In.)	Inside Diameter (In.)	Wt. Lbs/Ft	Minumum Bursting Pressure (Psi-gage at 77°F)	Maximum Working Pressure (psi-gage at 77°F)
Pipe					
½	0.840	0.546	0.236	1300	260
¾	1.050	0.742	0.320	1060	210
1	1.315	0.957	0.475	970	190
1¼	1.660	1.278	0.650	820	160
1½	1.900	1.500	0.790	740	150
2	2.375	1.939	1.090	620	125
2½	2.875	2.277	1.805	570	115
3	3.500	2.842	2.480	510	105
3½	4.000	3.307	3.010	470	95
4	4.500	3.749	3.760	460	90
6	6.625	5.767	7.140	370	75
Tubing	Wall Thickness (In.)				
1/8	0.031		0.0095	1850	370
3/16	0.045		0.0149	1850	370
1/4	0.045		0.0212	1350	270
5/16	0.031		0.0204	570	115
3/8	0.062		0.0445	1225	245
1/2	0.062		0.0690	875	175
5/8	0.062		0.0800	700	140
3/4	0.062		0.0950	575	115

PLASTIC PIPE, VALVES AND FITTINGS 295

TABLE 17-20. TECHNICAL DATA
FOR SARAN-LINED PIPE

Nominal Pipe Size (In.)	Inside Diameter (In.)	Thickness Lining (In.)	Wt. Lbs/ft
1	0.6875	0.180	2.4
1¼	1.0625	0.160	2.8
1½	1.3438	0.135	3.2
2	1.6875	0.190	4.9
2½	2.1563	0.155	6.7
3	2.750	0.160	9.4
4	3.6250	0.200	12.0

TABLE 17-21. TECHNICAL DATA FOR POLYFLUOROCARBON PIPE

Nominal Size (In.)	SCHEDULE 40			SCHEDULE 80		
	Outside Diameter (In.)	Inside Diameter (In.)	Max. Working Pressure (gage-psi)	Outside Diameter (In.)	Inside Diameter (In.)	Max. Working Pressure (gage-psi)
1/8	0.405	0.269	387	0.405	0.215	560
1/4	0.540	0.364	375	0.540	0.302	523
3/8	0.675	0.493	304	0.675	0.423	436
1/2	0.840	0.622	292	0.840	0.546	406
3/4	1.050	0.824	238	1.050	0.742	334
1	1.315	1.049	222	1.315	0.957	308
1¼	1.660	1.380	183	1.660	1.278	256
1½	1.900	1.610	164	1.900	1.500	232
2	2.375	2.067	151	2.375	1.939	217
2½	2.875	2.469	138	2.875	2.323	200
3	3.500	3.068	131	3.500	2.900	186

TABLE 17-22. TECHNICAL DATA ON POLYFLUOROCARBON
WIRE BRAID REINFORCED RUBING

Nominal Size (In.)	Outside Diameter (In.)	Inside Diameter (In.)	Wt. Lbs/Ft	Minimum Bursting Pressure (psi 77°F)	Working Pressure (psi)	Minimum Bending Radius (In.)
3/16	5/16	3/16	0.065	12,000	1000	2
1/4	3/8	1/4	0.085	10,000	1000	3
5/16	7/16	5/16	0.114	9,000	1000	4
13/32	9/16	13/32	0.150	8,000	1000	4 5/8
1/2	21/32	1/2	0.188	7,000	1000	5 1/2
5/8	25/32	5/8	0.216	6,000	1000	6 1/2
7/8	1	7/8	0.305	3,200	1000	7 3/8
1 1/8	1 1/4	1 1/8	0.386	3,000	1000	9
1 3/8	1 1/2	1 3/8	0.434	3,000	1000	11

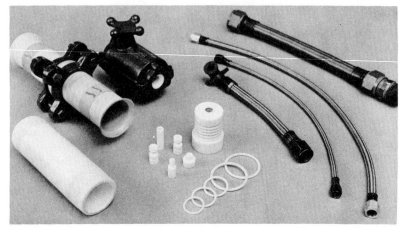

(Courtesy of Resistoflex Corporation)

Figure 17-15. Representative polyfluorocarbon products.

the chemical process industry. It has shown promise for transporting solvents at temperatures above 150°F.

NATURAL AND SYNTHETIC RUBBERS AND DERIVATIVES

Rubber

Rigid hard rubber pipe has been available for many years. It has good resistance to non-oxidizing acids, alkalies and salts at temperatures up to 220°F but should not be used in the presence of solvents. It should be noted that hard acrylonitrile rubber has good solvent resistance. Hard rubber has a coefficient of linear expansion of 3.5×10^{-5} in./in./°F and as in the case of other plastic pipe, provisions should be made for expansion. It is available in 10 foot lengths in Schedule 80 IPS from 1/4 to 8 inches. The weights per foot for 1, 1 1/2, 3, 4, 6, and 8 inches are 0.344, 0.641, 0.883, 1.985, 2.875 and 4.800 pounds, respectively.

As discussed in Chapter 8, rubber-lined pipe is also available commercially in 1/8 or 1/4 inch thicknesses in 20-foot lengths. These standard sizes and weights are shown in Table 17-23.

Flexible rubber hose reinforced with fabric or metal is available commercially with inside diameters ranging from 1/2 to 12 inches.

Cellulose Acetate Butyrate

In spite of its limited chemical resistance, more cellulose acetate butyrate extruded pipe was produced in 1953 than any other plastic pipe except polyethylene. Almost 1 1/2 million pounds was produced in 1951 and about 4 million pounds in 1953. It has been estimated

TABLE 17-23. TECHNICAL DATA
FOR RUBBER AND NEOPRENE LINED STEEL PIPE

Nominal Size (In.)	Outside Diameter (In.)	Inside Diameter (In.)	Lbs/Ft
1½	1.900	1.225	3.047
2	2.375	1.695	4.095
2½	2.875	2.095	6.336
3	3.500	2.695	8.275
3½	4.000	3.175	9.950
4	4.500	3.665	11.756
5	5.563	4.625	15.854
6	6.625	5.695	19.398
8	8.625	7.695	30.566
10	10.750	9.815	33.804

that 7 million and 20 million pounds will be produced in 1955 and 1960, respectively.

Solvent-welded butyrate pipe has been used successfully for eight years in California for the transportation of natural gas but is not recommended for use with artificial gas or in rocky ground. Like polyethylene, butyrate pipe has also been used for water service.

Considerable quantities of butyrate pipe have been used in oilfields. It has given satisfactory performance in the presence of sour crudes, oil and brine. Much of the pipe is unpigmented which permits visual inspection of the line. Paraffin deposits do not adhere to this pipe or other types of thermoplastic pipe. Also, as in the case of other thermoplastic pipe, the flow of liquid through butyrate pipe is as much as 40 per cent greater than that in steel pipe.

The Thermoplastic Pipe Division of the Society of the Plastics Industry has established tentative standards for SWP Schedules A and B butyrate pipe. Schedule A is rated at 75 psi and Schedule B at 100 psi bursting pressure at 73.4°F. Technical data on this pipe are given in Table 17-24.

Figure 17-16 shows one man lowering part of a 9-mile length of a black pigmented SWP 3 inch cellulose acetate butyrate line in Poplar, Montana. This pipe laid in a ditch 5 feet 4 inches deep, was snaked so that it touched the opposite side of the ditch every 200 feet to provide for expansion and contraction. This line was installed by a three man crew at the rate of 10,000 feet per day.

THERMOSETTING RESINS

Polyesters

The problems of thermal expansion, creep and realistic bursting

TABLE 17-24. TECHNICAL DATA FOR
SWP CELLULOSE ACETATE BUTYRATE PIPE

Nominal Size (In.)	Outside Diameter (In.)	Schedule A Maximum Working Pressure 75 psi at 73.4°F		Schedule B Maximum Working Pressure 100 psi at 73.4°F	
		Wall Thickness (In.)	Nominal Weight lbs/100 ft	Wall Thickness (In.)	Nominal Weight lbs/100 ft
½	0.600	0.050 ± 0.003	4.50	0.050 ± 0.003	4.5
¾	0.855	0.053 ± 0.003	6.95	0.060 ± 0.004	7.8
1	1.140	0.060 ± 0.004	10.60	0.080 ± 0.004	13.9
1¼	1.420	0.075 ± 0.004	16.44	0.100 ± 0.006	21.5
1½	1.730	0.092 ± 0.005	24.50	0.125 ± 0.007	32.8
2	2.250	0.120 ± 0.006	41.75	0.160 ± 0.009	54.8
2½	2.570	0.135 ± 0.007	53.66	0.185 ± 0.011	72.0
3	3.250	0.175 ± 0.010	87.7	0.235 ± 0.015	115.5
3½	3.660	0.195 ± 0.012	110.4	0.260 ± 0.017	144.3
4	4.100	0.220 ± 0.014	139.5	0.295 ± 0.020	183.2
5	5.110	0.275 ± 0.018	217.0	0.365 ± 0.025	282.7
6	6.220	0.335 ± 0.022	321.9	0.445 ± 0.030	419.4

(Courtesy of Eastman Chemical Products, Inc.)
Figure 17-16. Laying of a SWP 3-in. cellulose acetate pipeline over 9 miles in length.

pressures for thermoplastic pipe are dwarfed by the unsolved problems existent in the glass reinforced polyester pipe industry. Millions of dollars have been invested in research in an attempt to develop a glass fiber finish that would produce a homogeneous laminate with polyester resins. Admittedly, considerable progress has been made; however, while reinforced polyester sport car bodies, airplane parts and boats are suitable applications, polyester pipe is still not a perfect solution for the chemical processing industry.

Unfortunately, the resin and its reinforcing member often fail to act in unison in pipe construction. Doubtlessly, this type of pipe is suitable for low pressure and low temperature service, but available field reports on commercial polyester pipe indicate that leaks develop occasionally at high pressure and temperatures. Obviously some of the difficulties are associated with improper selection, design, fabrication, and installation but a discussion of these problems with proprietary reinforced plastic pipe is beyond the scope of this chapter.

As previously stated, reinforced polyester pipe is produced commercially by extrusion, wrapping around mandrels and spinning within tubing. Unfortunately, since the dimensions of the tubing used correspond to standard iron pipe sizes, the pipe made by the last two methods differ considerably in size.

Commercial standards for reinforced plastic pipe have not been established as yet. The most reliable data available on sizes of reinforced polyester pipe are given in Table 17-25.

Duct sections based on glass fiber reinforced polyester resins are available in nominal sizes ranging from 2 to 36 inches. While structural glass reinforcing duct work made from general-purpose polyester resins is sometimes suitable for mild corrosive environments, the slightly higher cost of chemical or flame-resistant structures is usually justified for use in corrosive environments.

General-purpose polyester resins are resistant to salts but are attacked by alkalies, solvents and some acids at ordinary temperatures. Pipe produced by the impregnation of chemical-resistant glass fibers with chemical resistant polyester resin is suitable for service with non-oxidizing acids at 170°F. However, this pipe is not recommended for alkaline service at any temperature nor for service with non-oxidizing acids such as hydrochloric acid at temperatures above 200°F.

Cross-sections of a polyester pipe (in center) as contrasted to steel and cement lined steel after 14 months in oil field service are shown in Figure 17-7.

Attempts to use unfilled cast phenolic piping have not been successful. Commercial paper laminated phenolic resin pipe is manufactured by heat curing of a wrapped mandrel. This process is tedious and expensive and at present limited to small diameter pipe.

Some attempts have been made to produce glass-laminated phe-

TABLE 17-25. DATA ON SIZES AND
DIMENSIONS OF REINFORCED PLASTIC PIPE
(Tentative SPI Standard)

Nominal Pipe Size (In.)	Centrifugally Cast Pipe Outside Diameter (In.)	Wrapped Mandrel Process Pipe Inside Diameter (In.)
1/8	0.405	0.125
1/4	0.504	0.250
3/8	0.675	0.375
1/2	0.840	0.500
3/4	1.050	0.750
1	1.315	1.000
1¼	1.660	1.250
1½	1.900	1.500
2	2.375	2.000
2½	2.875	2.500
3	3.500	3.000
3½	4.000	3.500
4	4.500	4.000
4½	5.000	4.500
5	5.563	5.000
5½	6.000	5.500
6	6.625	6.000
7	8.000	–
8	8.625	8.000
9	10.000	–
10	10.750	–
12	–	12.000
16	16.000	–
20	20.000	–

nolic resin pipe but this product has not been used as widely as fiber-glas polyester resin pipe. As discussed in Chapter 10, the most successful commercial phenolic pipe has been cast from acid washed asbestos-liquid phenolic mixtures. This type of pipe is also produced with carbon fillers and from furan resins.

Cast asbestos-phenolic pipe is available in 4 and 10 foot lengths in sizes up to 12 inches. This type of pipe is recommended for service at temperatures up to 265°F at pressures as high as 65 psi for sizes up to 4 inches, 50 psi for pipe up to 5 and 8 inches and 30 psi for 10 and 12 inch pipe.

Carbon-filled phenolic pipe is resistant to all non-oxidizing acids, most salts and some solvents. It should not be used with aniline, acetone, ethyl acetate, acetic anhydride, pyridine, bromine or iodine. Furan carbon-filled pipe is resistant to non-oxidizing acids, salts, alkalies and most solvents.

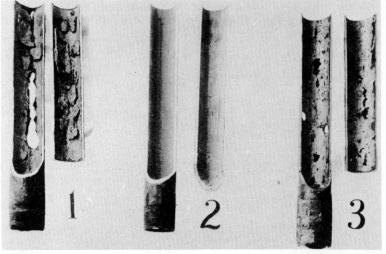

(Courtesy of Bakelite Corp.)

Figure 17-17. Three types of pipe after 14 months oil field service. (1) cement-lined steel tubing, (2) glass reinforced polyester, (3) plastic coated steel tubing.

This type of pipe may be threaded using American National coarse thread, Class I, with six threads per inch of the loose fit type. It is also available as bell and spigot type pipe. However, most asbestos-resin pipe is joined with split metal flanges set in tapered grooves machined near the pipe ends. A 1/8-inch thick soft rubber sheet is used as a gasket. Obviously, all flange bolts must be tightened evenly in order to distribute the pressure uniformly.

A minimum of three hangers is recommended for each 10-foot length of pipe. These hangers should permit horizontal movement. Expansion joints must be used to minimize the development of stress resulting from vibration.

If both ends of a pipeline are free to expand, expansion joints are required only when the length exceeds 100 feet. When both ends are fixed expansion joints are required even for short lines. In such cases, at least one expansion joint for each 100 foot length of pipe is recommended. If the temperature differential exceeds 150°F., additional expansion joints must be provided.

Technical data for asbestos-phenolic and furan pipe and duct are given in Tables 17-26 and 17-27.

Epoxy Resins

Pipe produced from epoxy resin-glass fiber laminates has shown promise. It is more expensive than resin-asbestos compositions but has greater resistance to impact.

TABLE 17-26. TECHNICAL DATA FOR
ASBESTOS-PHENOLIC AND FURAN PIPE

Nominal Size (In.)	Outside Diameter (In.)	Wall Thickness (In.)
½	1¼	3/8
¾	1½	3/8
1	1¾	3/8
1¼	2	3/8
1½	2½	1/2
2	3	1/2
2½	3½	1/2
3	4¼	5/8
3½	4¾	5/8
4	5¼	5/8
5	6½	3/4
6	7½	3/4
8	9¾	7/8
10	12	1
12	14	1

TABLE 17-27. TECHNICAL DATA FOR
ASBESTOS-PHENOLIC OR FURAN DUCT

Nominal Size (In.)	Outside Diameter (In.)	Wall Thickness (In.)
2	2¾	3/8
3	3¾	3/8
4	4¾	3/8
5	6	1/2
6	7	1/2
8	9	1/2
10	11	1/2
12	13	1/2
14	15½	1/2
16	17½	1/2
18	19¼	1/2
20	21½	1/2
24	25¼	5/8
30	31½	5/8
36	37¼	5/8

Furan Resins

In addition to the previously mentioned asbestos-filled furan product, plastic pipe has also been produced by the "Fiberglas" reinforcement of furan resins. This product, which is usually produced on a
removable mandrel, may be joined by the use of a sleeve of larger

pipe which is cemented in place with a furan mortar cement. This pipe is also manufactured with bell and spigot joints. Pipe may also be produced by the extrusion of furan resin cements. Such pipe has the characteristic excellent chemical resistance previously described for furan cements.

As discussed in Chapter 12, impervious graphite has been produced by impregnating graphite with furfuryl alcohol or furfural and polymerizing in situ. This pipe is available in 6-foot lengths in sizes up to 10 inches. Impervious graphite pipe may be joined by threaded joints or flanges. Technical data for this type pipe are given in Table 17-28.

TABLE 17-28. TECHNICAL DATA FOR
IMPERVIOUS GRAPHITE PIPE

Nominal Size (In.)	Outside Diameter (In.)	Inside Diameter (In.)	Wall Thickness (In.)	Weight Lbs/Ft
1	1.5	1	0.25	0.74
1½	2	1.5	0.25	1.1
2	2.75	2	0.37	1.7
2½	3	1.37	0.31	2.0
3	4	3	0.5	5.4
4	5.25	4	0.62	8.1
5	6.25	5	0.62	10.3
6	7.5	6	0.75	15.6
8	9.75	7.5	1.1	24.3
10	13	10	1.5	45.1

Plastic Valves

Since at least one valve is used for every 100 feet of pipe in a chemical plant, it is important that suitable valves be available. While the development of plastic valves has lagged behind that of pipe and fittings, many types of valves based on standard design are now available commercially.

While a description of the mechanism of the various valves is beyond the scope of this discussion, it should be noted that plastic plug, globe and diaphragm valves are available commercially. Exploded views of polyethylene and saran plug valves are shown in Figure 17-18.

Two different types of globe valves machined from Type I unplasticized polyvinyl chloride are shown in Figures 17-19 and 17-20. A 4 inch fabricated "Y" valve and its component parts are shown in Figures 17-21 and 17-22.

The component parts of a metal armored polytetrafluoroethylene valve are shown in Figure 17-23. Part of the plastic section on the right has been cut away in order to show structural details.

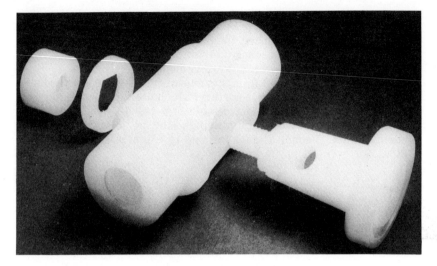

Figure 17-18. Polyethylene plug valves.

Figure 17-19. One-inch Type I polyvinyl chloride globe valves.

As shown in Figure 17-24, metal and porcelain valves now utilize polytetrafluoroethylene component parts. The metal alloy valve utilizes a polytetrafluoroethylene chevron packing and disc ring. The porcelain valve shown not only contains a polytetrafluoroethylene packing and seat but is also protected from thermal and mechanical shock by a glass fabric reinforced epoxy resin armor.

The most widely used all-plastic valve is the diaphragm valve, the component parts of which are shown in Figure 17-25. The bonnet and body of such valves may be polyethylene, unplasticized polyvinyl chloride or a styrene copolymer rubber resin blends. The diaphragm is usually made from polytetrafluoroethylene.

(Courtesy of H. N. Hartwell & Sons)

Figure 17-20. Globe valve fabricated from Type I unplasticized polyvinyl chloride pipe.

(Courtesy of Bolta Division, General Tire & Rubber Co.)

Figure 17-21. German 4-in. "Y" valve of Type I unplasticized polyvinyl chloride.

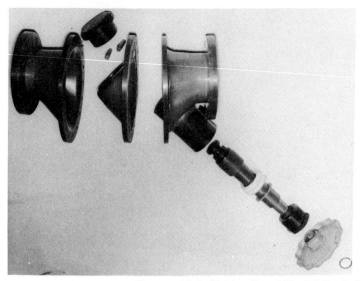

(Courtesy of Bolta Division, General Tire & Rubber Co.)
Figure 17-22. Component parts of valve shown in Figure 17-21.

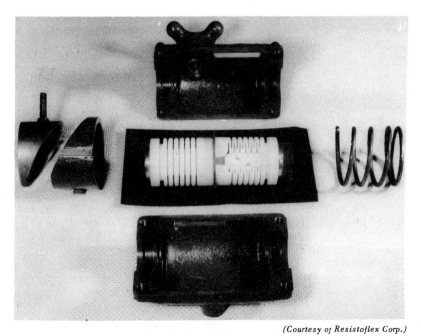

(Courtesy of Resistoflex Corp.)
Figure 17-23. Polytetrafluoroethylene valve with metal casing which has been cut away and disassembled to show construction details.

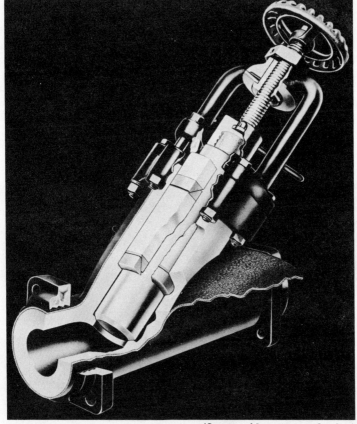

(Courtesy of Lapp Insulator Co., Inc.)
Figure 17-24. Porcelain valve reinforced with epoxy resin and glass cloth.

The most widely used valves of this type have a metal bonnet and a plastic body as shown in Figure 17-26.

Nonplastic bodies for diaphragm valves have been cast from iron, stainless steel, Monel, nickle, "Hastelloy" B and C, lead, aluminum, tin and many alloys. Cast iron bodies have been lined with soft rubber, neoprene, glass, vitreous enamel, porcelain, zinc, baked phenolic coatings, saran rubber, saran, polyethylene, polyfluorocarbon polymers and various protective coatings. Bodies have also been cast from asbestos-filled phenolics and furan plastics and molded from saran, styrene copolymer rubber resin blend and unplasticized polyvinyl chloride.

Diaphragms have been constructed from natural rubber, neoprene, butyl rubber, acrylonitrile rubber, saran rubber, styrene rubber, plasticized polyvinyl chloride, polyethylene, polyvinyl alcohol, and polyfluorocarbon polymers. A diaphragm valve is shown in Figure 17-27 and the corresponding dimensions are given in Table 17-29. The physical properties of plastic pipe are compared in Tables 17-30 and 17-31. The practical values are given in 17-33. Table 17-32 and comparative chemical resistance in Table 17-33. Obviously, the generalizations may lead to misunderstandings in specific applications. While the information is invaluable for screening purposes it is based on conservative experience data and, hence, may not be appropriate for plastic pipe formulated for specific end uses. As in the case of similar tabulations in previous chapters, the information is not intended to discredit any specific type of plastic

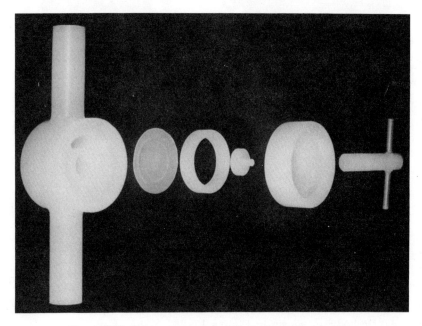

Figure 17-25. Component parts of an all plastic diaphragm valve.

TABLE 17-29. DIMENSIONS OF DIAPHRAGM VALVES
WITH METAL BONNET AND PLASTIC BODY

			(In inches)				Approx. Weight (Lbs)
Size	A	B	C	D	E	F	
1/2	2 7/8	1 5/16	3 21/32	3	21/32	2 1/4	1.6
3/4	3 1/8	1 9/16	4 5/16	3 17/32	25/32	2 3/4	2.0
1	5	2 1/8	5 1/32	3 31/32	1 1/16	3	3.5
1 1/4	5	2 1/8	5 5/32	4 3/32	1 1/16	3	3.2
1 1/2	5 7/8	2 3/8	6	4 13/16	1 3/16	5	5.7
2	7	3	7 5/16	5 13/16	1 1/2	6	9.3

(Courtesy of Hills-McCanna Co.)

Figure 17-26. Component parts of a diaphragm valve with plastic body and metal bonnet.

pipe nor to be considered a substitute for on-stream testing under actual service conditions.

More complete data on chemical resistance may be found in Table 15-4 (p. 240). Additional information on this subject may be found in the references listed at the end of this chapter. Because of the newness of this application, more complete information may be anticipated in the future.

It should be remembered that the plastic pipe industry is still relatively small. Fortunately, most producers of plastic pipe are sincere in their attempts to develop standards and supply a real service to American industry. The major producers are confident that through proper selection, adequate design and correct application, plastic pipe will become one of the most important segments of the plastics industry.

However, plastics will never displace standard pipe materials completely. Cast iron will continue to be used for many water mains and vitrified clay pipe will be used for a large number of sewer lines. Since both types of pipe may be joined with plastics, they are discussed in Chapter 18 and 19.

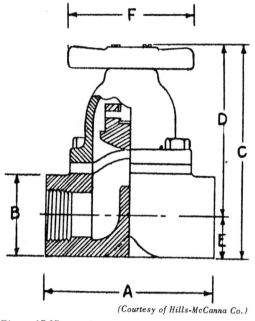

(Courtesy of Hills-McCanna Co.)

Figure 17-27. Diaphragm valve. See Table 17-29 for dimensions.

TABLE 17-30. COMPARATIVE PHYSICAL PROPERTIES
OF PLASTIC PIPE MATERIALS

	Specific Gravity	Strength Tensile (psi)	Flexural Strength (psi)	Thermal Expansion (in./in./°F x 10⁻⁵)	Impact (ft lbs/in. notch)	Maximum Useful Service Temp.(°F)
Polyethylene	0.92	1400	1700	10	high	125
Styrene copolymer rubber resin blend	1.04	4000	6500	5	9	170
Polyvinyl chloride—Type I	1.45	8500	14000	4	0.8	160
Polyvinyl chloride—Type II	1.45	5800	11000	6	8-16	150
Saran	1.7	5000	16000	11	1.0	150
Polytetrafluoroethylene	2.2	1800	–	5.5	4	400
Hard rubber	1.21	7500	11130	4.0	0.9	170
Cellulose acetate butyrate	1.2	5000	5800	7	1.5	140
Glass polyester	1.7	20000	40000	1	1.5	200
Phenolic-asbestos	1.7	4000	6500	1.5	0.4	250
Furan-asbestos	1.75	4000	7500	1.5	0.5	250
Impervious graphite	1.9	2600	5000	2.2	0.5	340

TABLE 17-31. COMPARATIVE PHYSICAL
PROPERTIES OF PLASTIC PIPE

Specific Gravity	0 0.5 1.0 1.5 2.0
Epoxy-Glass	
Polyester-Glass	
Cellulose Acetate Butyrate	
Polyethylene	
Styrene Copolymer Rubber Blend	
Polyvinyl Chloride, Type I	
Polyvinyl Chloride, Type II	

Tensile Strength (Psi)	0 10,000 20,000
Epoxy-Glass	
Polyester-Glass	
Cellulose Acetate Butyrate	
Polyethylene	
Styrene Copolymer Rubber Blend	
Polyvinyl Chloride, Type I	
Polyvinyl Chloride, Type II	

Flexural Strength (Psi)	0 10,000 20,000 30,000 40,000
Epoxy-Glass	
Polyester-Glass	
Cellulose Acetate Butyrate	
Polyethylene	
Styrene Copolymer Rubber Blend	
Polyvinyl Chloride, Type I	
Polyvinyl Chloride, Type II	

Thermal Expansion (in./in./° F. x10⁻⁵)	0 5 10
Epoxy-Glass	
Polyester-Glass	
Cellulose Acetate Butyrate	
Polyethylene	
Styrene Copolymer Rubber Blend	
Polyvinyl Chloride, Type I	
Polyvinyl Chloride, Type II	

Impact (notch) Ft. lb./in.	0 10 20
Epoxy-Glass	
Polyester-Glass	
Cellulose Acetate Butyrate	
Polyethylene	
Styrene Copolymer Rubber Blend	
Polyvinyl Chloride, Type I	
Polyvinyl Chloride, Type II	

Maximum Useful Service Temp.(°F.)	100 200 300
Epoxy-Glass	
Polyester-Glass	
Cellulose Acetate Butyrate	
Polyethylene	
Styrene Copolymer Rubber Blend	
Polyvinyl Chloride, Type I	
Polyvinyl Chloride, Type II	

TABLE 17-32. COMPARISON OF
PRACTICAL VALUES FOR PLASTIC PIPE

Epoxy Glass Laminate — scale 0 to 10 — TOTAL **87**

Relative Resistance to External and Internal Environment:
- Relative Cost
- Temperature
- Impact
- Soil
- Natural Gas
- Artificial Gas
- Salts
- Caustic
- Petroleum Crudes
- Hydrochloric Acid

Cellulose Acetate Butyrate — scale 0 to 10 — TOTAL **59**

Relative Resistance to External and Internal Environment:
- Relative Cost
- Temperature
- Impact
- Soil
- Natural Gas
- Artificial Gas
- Salts
- Caustic
- Petroleum Crudes
- Hydrochloric Acid

Styrene Copolymer Rubber Resin Blend — scale 0 to 10 — TOTAL **87**

Relative Resistance to External and Internal Environment:
- Relative Cost
- Temperature
- Impact
- Soil
- Natural Gas
- Artificial Gas
- Salts
- Caustic
- Petroleum Crudes
- Hydrochloric Acid

Polyvinyl Chloride Type I — scale 0 to 10 — TOTAL **87**

Relative Resistance to External and Internal Environment:
- Relative Cost
- Temperature
- Impact
- Soil
- Natural Gas
- Artificial Gas
- Salts
- Caustic
- Petroleum Crudes
- Hydrochloric Acid

TABLE 17-32 (Continued).

Polyester Glass Laminate	0	1	2	3	4	5	6	7	8	9	10	TOTAL
Relative Cost												**83**
Temperature												
Impact												
Soil												
Natural Gas												
Artificial Gas												
Salts												
Caustic												
Petroleum Crudes												
Hydrochloric Acid												

Relative Resistance to External and Internal Environment

Polyethylene	0	1	2	3	4	5	6	7	8	9	10	TOTAL
Relative Cost												**84**
Temperature												
Impact												
Soil												
Natural Gas												
Artificial Gas												
Salts												
Caustic												
Petroleum Crudes												
Hydrochloric Acid												

Relative Resistance to External and Internal Environment

Polyvinyl Chloride Type II	0	1	2	3	4	5	6	7	8	9	10	TOTAL
Relative Cost												**91**
Temperature												
Impact												
Soil												
Natural Gas												
Artificial Gas												
Salts												
Caustic												
Petroleum Crudes												
Hydrochloric Acid												

Relative Resistance to External and Internal Environment

Cast Iron	0	1	2	3	4	5	6	7	8	9	10	TOTAL
Relative Cost												**71**
Temperature												
Impact												
Soil												
Natural Gas												
Artificial Gas												
Salts												
Caustic												
Petroleum Crudes												
Hydrochloric Acid												

Relative Resistance to External and Internal Environment

TABLE 17-33. COMPARATIVE CHEMICAL RESISTANCE OF PLASTIC PIPE (77°F)

	Water	10% NaOH	10% Sulfuric	70% Sulfuric	10% Nitric	Sea Water	5% Chlorite Bleach	Gasoline	Benzene	Trichloro-ethylene
Polyethylene	E	E	E	E	E	E	E	E	N	N
Styrene copolymer rubber resin blend	E	E	E	F	F	E	E	E	N	N
Polyvinyl chloride—Type I	E	E	E	E	E	E	E	E	P	N
Polyvinyl chloride—Type II	E	G	E	G	E	E	G	G	N	N
Saran	E	G	E	E	E	E	G	E	F	N
Polytetrafluoroethylene	E	E	E	E	E	E	E	E	E	E
Hard rubber	E	E	E	E	G	E	G	N	N	N
Cellulose acetate butyrate	E	N	N	N	N	E	N	G	N	N
Glass - polyester	E	N	E	F	F	E	G	E	N	N
Phenolic - asbestos	E	N	E	E	F	E	N	E	E	E
Furan - asbestos	E	G	E	E	P	E	N	E	E	E
Impervious graphite	E	E	E	E	E	E	G	E	E	E

Ratings: E – Excellent
           G – Good
           F – Fair
           P – Poor
           N – Not recommended

Suggested References

"Plastic Pipe Selection--Application Data," Raymond B. Seymour and Earl A. Erich, Southern Power & Industry, June 1953.

"Experience with Plastic Tubing for Water Service Installations," J. G. Carns, and M. E. Flentje, Water & Sewage Works, 99, No. 11, 446-47 (1952).

"Polyethylene," J. L. Huscher, Chem. Eng., 59, No. 10, 260 (1953).

"Plastic Processing Equipment Today," R. B. Seymour and J. H. Fry, Chem. Eng., 59, No. 3, 136 (1952).

"Futures for Plastic Pipe," Modern Plastics, 31, No. 7, 73 (1954).

"Industrial Piping," C. T. Littleton, McGraw-Hill Publishing Co., New York, 1951.

"Chemical Engineering Handbook," Section 5, John P. Perry, T. B. Drew, H. H. Dunkle and P. P. Genereaux, McGraw-Hill Publishing Co., New York, 1950.

"Plastic Pipe: What's Its Future?", Eng. News-Record, 150, No. 19, 37-38 (1953).

"Studies on Plastic Pipe for Potable Water Supplies," Walter D. Tiedeman, Am. Water Works J., 46, 775 (1954).

"Plastic in Piping, Valves and Ducts," Raymond B. Seymour, Symposium on Plastics as Materials of Construction, American Chemical Society, Division of Paint, Plastics and Printing Ink Chemistry, New York, Sept. 1954.

"Plastics in Petroleum Production," Bryant W. Bradley, Symposium on Plastics as Materials of Construction, American Chemical Society, Division of Paint, Plastics and Printing Ink Chemistry, New York, Sept. 1954.

"Plastics in Plants Manufacturing Textile Fibers," W. A. Haldeman and E. F. Wesp, Symposium on Plastics as Materials of Construction, American Chemical Society, Division of Paint, Plastics and Printing Ink Chemistry, New York, Sept. 1954.

"Plastics in Plants Manufacturing Heavy Chemicals," G. A. Griess, Symposium on Plastics as Materials of Construction, American Chemical Society, Division of Paint, Plastics and Printing Ink Chemistry, New York, Sept. 1954.

"Plastics in Food Processing Plants," Lawrence J. Turney, Symposium on Plastics as Materials of Construction, American Chemical Society, Division of Paint, Plastics and Printing Ink Chemistry, New York, Sept. 1954.

"The Future Outlook for Plastic Valves," R. B. Seymour, Chem. Eng., June 1955, p. 280.

"Plastic Pipe for Underground Structures," R. B. Seymour, Corrosion (in press).

"Facts About Plastic Pipe," W. E. Jacobson, Air Conditioning, Heating & Ventilating, 52, No. 1, 87 (1955).

18. WATER JOINTING MATERIALS

Cast iron, steel, hydraulic cement and plastics are the materials usually considered for water pipe construction. Cast iron mains are generally used for water distribution systems since centuries of satisfactory service attest to the durability of such pipe.

Until recent years, cast iron pipe with bell and spigot joints was standard for practically all water line installations. Today, however, approximately 50 per cent of the cast iron pipe produced uses bolted connections and is known as mechanical jointed pipe. The favorable reception given to mechanical jointed pipe in the water field has resulted primarily from high labor costs of standard installation methods.

Steel is stronger and more expensive than cast iron. Thin walled steel pipe is used for economic reasons but such pipelines are not able to withstand high external pressures. Steel may be attacked by corrosive soils and by the water being transported.

Reinforced concrete pressure pipe is used chiefly for large diameter mains. This pipe finds ready acceptance for long conduits and aqueducts. Asbestos-cement pipe developed in Italy about thirty five years ago, and currently manufactured under several different trade names, is used widely for water mains.

Asphalt-impregnated fiberboard has been used successfully in water lines in outlying districts. Related structures based on asbestos or "Fiberglas"-reinforced phenolic, furan, or polyester plastic have shown promise in such applications. "Fiberglas"-reinforced polyester pipe has been used in several water distribution lines in the Los Angeles area.

As stated in Chapter 17, the most widely used plastic pipes are extruded from polyethylene, cellulose acetate butyrate, unplasticized polyvinyl chloride and styrene copolymer rubber resin blends. The use of these materials for transporting potable water in this country is relatively new and it is difficult to predict future preference.

It should be noted that unplasticized polyvinyl chloride pipe has been used successfully for water service lines in Europe for almost twenty years. However, European engineers were not able to choose from the wide variety of plastic pipe materials that are now available in this country.

As might be expected in an embryonic industry, inferior quality plastic pipe has been sold occasionally. There has been a lack of understanding of tolerances, standards and physical properties such as creep. On one hand, extravagant unsubstantiated claims have been made by newcomers to the industry. On the other, questions which have never been answered for any other type of pipe have been asked about plastic pipe.

Fortunately for the consumer, more information is now available on plastic pipe than on almost any other material used for transporting potable water. As the result of a project at the National Sanitation Foundation at the University of Michigan, questions on toxicity have been answered. Properly formulated plastic pipe is completely satisfactory for transporting potable water.

As discussed in Chapter 17, dimensional standards have already been established for polyethylene pipe and these efforts of the Thermoplastic Pipe Division of the Society of the Plastics Industry are being continued. Data from the project sponsored by this division at Battelle Memorial Institute supply reliable information on bursting pressures under conditions of service. It is now possible to use instantaneous bursting pressure data to predict long-term performance providing the maximum temperature anticipated is known.

Methods of Joining Pipe for Water Mains

Perhaps the simplest joint construction is based on bell and spigot pipe. In this design, a molten product is used to fill the annular space remaining after the spigot has been inserted in the bell. As mentioned previously, the bell and spigot joint is being replaced to some extent by several different types of mechanical joint constructions.

Lead Joints

Up until about fifty years ago, lead was practically the only jointing material used for joining cast iron bell and spigot water pipe. Today, in spite of the trend toward more economical jointing compounds, lead is still utilized to a certain extent as a hot poured jointing material. Lead joints must be caulked in order to secure a tight seal.

Regardless of whether lead or a lead substitute is used, tight joints will depend to a large extent upon the operations which precede the actual placement of the material in the annular space. The spigot and bell ends of the pipe should be clean, dry and free from foreign matter before being joined.

Hot poured joints are usually constructed by butting the spigot end against the base of the bell and yarning to a depth of 1 to 2 inches with materials such as rubber, paper, asbestos or jute. Care should be taken to force the yarning material solidly around the entire circumference since the effectiveness of the joint depends to a large extent upon this operation. The purpose of the yarning material is to dam off the end of the pipe and thus prevent the fluid jointing material from running into the pipe itself. At the same time the ring of

Material helps to center the pipe prior to application of the jointing compound. Rubber rings are preferred by many waterworks engineers. They do not contribute to corrosion, provide a completely dry annular space, cannot harbor bacteria, and are easy to assemble. When rubber strips or other types of linear yarning material are used, the product is usually cut slightly longer than the circumference of the pipe to insure a tight joint when the material is driven home with the yarning iron.

Following the yarning operation, an asbestos runner is clamped around the spigot and in contact with the circumference of the bell. A pouring gate is inserted at the top and the annular space is filled with molten jointing material. Because of the high shrinkage factor, lead must be caulked as it cools. The lead is poured in small quantities so as not to fill the joint all at once. Great care must be taken to have the joint perfectly dry before pouring the lead, otherwise steam that is generated can blow the lead from the joint.

Most engineers insist on the use of virgin lead which is furnished as 60 and 100 pound pigs and 3 and 6 pound ingots. Before pouring, lead is melted until a spectrum or "rainbow colors" appear, then it is skimmed and used. Lead has a specific gravity of 11.3 (708 lbs/cu ft) and a melting point of 327 °C (620 °F).

Plasticized Sulfur Cement Joints

Over 10 million pounds of proprietary sulfur compounds are used annually for joining bell and spigot cast iron pipe in the United States and Canada. The first recorded use of sulfur compounds in cast iron pipe joints was less than a century ago.

A terra cotta pipeline joined with a sulfur-sand mixture and used for carrying water from a spring to a residence was unearthed some years ago at Wilmington, N. C. It was thought to be at least 200 years old and laid with pipe imported from England. Both the pipe and sulfur compound were in excellent condition after this long time of service.

Some of the early proprietary sulfur compounds were apparently mixtures of sulfur, pyrites, copper sulfide, silica and carbon. Another proprietary composition which was introduced about fifty years ago, was made up of sulfur and clay, whereas a competitive product consisted of sulfur and ground slag. There are at least four sulfur compounds manufactured in the United States today. Three of these have been available commercially for over twenty years.

The chemical composition, physical properties, and test methods for sulfur cements have been discussed in Chapter 9 on Chemical Resistant Mortar Cements. It should be emphasized again that sulfur cements for use in jointing cast iron pipes are more highly plasticized than those designed for joining acid-proof brick because greater ductility is required during the initial settling period in the trench. Also, bactericides such as sodium silicofluoride are frequently added to prevent attack by sulfur bacteria present in many types of soils.

Sulfur cements should meet ASTM Specification C287-52T and Federal Specification SS-C-608 which covers jointing materials for hot and cold water mains.

Sulfur compound joints are poured in much the same manner as lead. The asbestos runner must be mudded with puddled clay to prevent the sulfur compound from adhering and a tall pouring gate must be used. The sulfur compound should be melted with stirring in a pot equipped with a lid, heated to 265 to 290°F and poured at this temperature range, which is readily recognizable by the presence of a mirrored surface.

The sulfur compounds are not sufficiently molten for pouring of joints at temperatures lower than 265°F and some tend to thicken at temperatures above 300°F. While sulfur will not ignite spontaneously even at temperatures above 500°F, it will ignite when heated excessively over an open flame. Therefore, local over-heating should not be permitted. Sulfur fires can be readily extinguished by closing the lid or excluding air by covering the top of the pot with a damp burlap bag.

Sulfur compound joints are less expensive than lead, and have the important advantage of requiring no caulking. Plasticized sulfur cement joints are more resistant to vibration. Sulfur joints leak or "weep" when first placed in service but will become tight in a comparatively short time. If the joints are poured properly, the trench may be back-filled immediately.

The relative ductility of proprietary sulfur cements can be determined by applying loads to a 1/8-inch diameter rod placed on cast 2-inch cubes. Loads of greater than 750 pounds are required to secure a penetration of 3/16-inch in unplasticized specimens. Also, unplasticized sulfur cements crack under this test while plasticized cements remain intact. The laying of an underground water main jointed with plasticized sulfur cement is shown in Figure 18-1.

Portland Cement Joints

These have been used with some success for jointing cast iron pipe, particularly in the Pacific Coast area. The labor costs of cement joints are higher than for hot-poured joints or the mechanical pipe joints, and considerable skill is required to secure a joint that is completely full. In preparing these joints 1 gallon of dry cement is mixed with 1 pint of water and the neat cement obtained is caulked in the joint. It is of great importance to ascertain that the cement joint is well caulked all the way around, and that the joints are not made in freezing weather.

Before joining operations are begun, it is necessary to thoroughly clean the joint ring surfaces and lubricate the rubber gasket with a vegetable soap. The outer annular joint space between the adjacent

Figure 18-1. Laying a 36-in. cast iron water line with plasticized sulfur cement. joints.

pipes is filled with either a cement grout or sulfur cement to protect the steel joint rings. In larger diameter pipe, the inner annular joint space is often filled with mortar to produce a continuously smooth surface within the pipe.

Another type of concrete pipe joint specified occasionally for large diameter pipe is the lead and steel joint. In this type of construction, the tolerance between the spigot and the bell ring is extremely small. The spigot ring is sloped to form a wedge-shaped recess with the bell ring so that a fiber-filled lead gasket can be caulked between the joint rings from within the pipe. This operation is performed after the pipe has been laid and back-filled.

To assemble this joint, the gasket is placed evenly against the inner surface of the bell ring, the spigot is pushed home and the gasket is then caulked tightly between the joint rings from within the pipe. The inner concrete shoulder at the bell end of the pipe is shaped to leave room for caulking. The joint is subsequently back-filled on the inside and out with hydraulic cement mortar. This pipe joint is said to allow a joint deflection of 1/2 inch which makes it desirable for use on long radius curves and for use under wet trench conditions.

Care must be taken to insure that no pressure tests are made on a line joined with portland cement until at least two weeks after installation. Portland cement joints, of course, are not resistant to corrosive soil conditions and are apt to be porous and to develop settlement cracks. They are also rigid and will not withstand vibration or unstable soil conditions. The addition of iron filings to the neat cement is said to reduce the time required for sealing because of the formation of rust.

Mechanical Joints for Cast Iron Pipe

There are several types of mechanical joint constructions. The most common arrangement uses a wedge-shaped rubber gasket which is contained by a cast iron follower ring. This ring is held in place by bolts which fasten to lugs on the end of the adjoining length of pipe, normally considered the bell end. The rubber ring forms a flexible, relatively tight joint.

Since the rubber gasket is in constant compression under conditions considered ideal for the preservation of rubber, long life of the joint has been predicted by those advocating this system. Flanged mechanical joints are frequently used on cast iron water pipe within pumping stations or other locations where working space is limited. The flange-type joint necessarily calls for close tolerances and perfect alignment.

Cast iron pipe incorporating the use of a rubber gasket which is rolled back into the annular space of the pipe under compression is also available. While this joint is not extensively used, it is said to provide a permanent flexible water-tight seal.

Joints for Steel Pipe

Joints in steel pipe can be constructed by riveting or welding. It is also possible to use a proprietary coupling which depends on rubber rings for water tightness. This type of joint provides a degree of flexibility not obtained through riveting or welding. The couplings are prevented from working off the joint by a rib on the inside of the sleeve.

Joints for water service connections cannot be made by tapping unless the steel is 1/4 inch or more in thickness. Pipe saddles with the proper size hole tapped in them may be clamped to the steel pipe. Also, a plate may be welded directly to the steel pipe and then drilled and tapped. Fittings are available for working pressures up to 125 psi.

Joints for Concrete Pipe

Concrete pressure pipe and prestressed concrete cylinder pipe usually utilize a tongue and groove jointing arrangement embracing the use of rubber gaskets and steel plates. The steel rings cast on the joint sections provide a close tolerance between the rings which center the pipe and fully compress the rubber ring gasket previously placed on the steel spigot ring.

Joints for Cement Asbestos Pipe

The plain ends of cement asbestos pipe are machined to accomodate two circular rubber rings which are rolled over the pipe under pressure of a cement asbestos collar. The collar is rolled on by use of a friction-type puller with two operating handles connected to rods on each side of the pipe. Coupling hooks are employed to apply pressure to the coupling.

Joints for Plastic Pipe

As described in Chapter 17, plastic pipe may be joined by threaded, flanged, solvent-welded or Victaulic fittings. Threaded plastic pipe is satisfactory for small pipelines but is not considered practical for large water mains. Likewise, while flanged joints are desirable for chemical plant use they will probably not be used for water mains.

Victaulic fittings produce a tight joint but since they are usually made from metal, they are apt to corrode when buried underground. At present, the solvent-welded type construction appears to hold the greatest promise for joining plastic water distribution lines.

In a modification of this process, glass fiber-reinforced thermosetting plastic pipe is joined by a sleeve of the same material. The sleeve may be formed on the job by resin impregnating glass cloth or mat wrapped around butted straight end pipe. Since the resin used is compounded with a catalyst and promoter, curing of the resin takes place at ordinary temperatures.

Preformed sleeves may also be cemented over the butted ends of straight end pipe. Both techniques produce strong joints with physical and chemical properties comparable to the pipe itself.

Molded insert fittings are available for joining flexible sections such as thin wall polyethylene pipe. However, the use of such techniques is not practical for large diameter pipe.

Molded solvent-welded fittings are also available for cellulose acetate butyrate, styrene copolymer rubber resin blend and unplasticized polyvinyl chloride pipe. These fittings may be fabricated from sections of pipe. It is also possible to form bells in plastic pipe by forcing the heated end over a machined form.

Fittings on the bell and spigot ends are cemented by the use of solvent adhesives or cements depending upon the closeness of the fit between the sections. Providing the surfaces to be joined are held in place for several hours, joints as strong as the pipe itself can be secured. Because of economics and relative ease of use, solvent-welding techniques show the greatest promise for joining plastic pipe in water service lines.

In addition to requiring a knowledge of water service lines, corrosion engineers are often called upon to make recommendations
for joining sewer pipe. Much of the information required on this
subject will be found in the next chapter.

Suggested References

"Jointing Materials for Cast Iron Pipe," R. B. Seymour and D. F.
Deakin, Public Works, 27, 50 (July 1952).

"Performance Studies on Sulfur Jointing Compounds," R. B. Seymour, W. R. Pascoe, W. J. Eney, A. C. Loewer, R. H. Steiner and
R. D. Stoudt, Journal AWWA, 43, No. 12, 1001-14 (1951).

"Results of Research on Sulfur Jointing Compounds," R. B. Seymour, W. R. Pascoe, and R. H. Steiner, Journal AWWA, 46, No. 3, 237-
245 (1954).

"Bell and Spigot Pipe Joints with Sulfur Cement Caulking Material,"
M. Kootz, Gesundh-Ing., 62, 36-40 (1939).

"Physical Properties of Plasticized Sulfur Cement," A. C. Loewer,
W. J. Eney, R. B. Seymour and W. R. Pascoe, ASTM Proc., Vol. 51
(1951).

"Plastic Pipe Selection--Application Data," R. B. Seymour and E.
A. Erich, Southern Power & Industry, June 1953.

19. SEWER JOINTING MATERIALS

While water and wastes must be transported in completely separate lines, the problems encountered with sewerage and industrial wastes are somewhat similar to those discussed in Chapter 18. Most wastes are more corrosive than potable water, hence, more resistant materials of construction such as vitrified clay pipe are used. Sewerage is generally transported by gravity or at low pressures in contrast to the high pressures used in water mains. Hence, less attention is sometimes given to joints in sewer lines. However, leaks in sewer lines will result in infiltration or exfiltration. Both are expensive and the latter is extremely hazardous and unsanitary.

While most waste lines consist of short sections of vitrified clay pipe, many other types of pipe may be used if the material of construction is resistant to the soil and the waste. Portland cement pipe has been used satisfactorily with noncorrosive wastes. Cement-asbestos pipe is denser and slightly more resistant than hydraulic cement but not adequate for most domestic or industrial waste lines.

The resistance of both types of pipe has been improved somewhat by coating with vinyl or epoxy coatings. Better success has been noted when the pipe was lined with natural rubber or sheet plastic.

In many instances, large pipe has been constructed of vitrified clay liner plates which are joined by chemical-resistant mortar cements. A hydraulic cement pipe is then cast around the inner pipe formed from liner plates. This type construction is expensive but essential for very large size pipelines. A similar type construction has been proposed using plasticized polyvinyl chloride liner plates, which are welded on the job in the form of a tube.

Both types of liner plate construction when properly installed are suitable for transportation of cold domestic and industrial wastes. Poor joints in either method may result in failure and external hydrostatic pressure may cause collapse of flexible liners.

Since coatings, linings and chemical-resistant cements were previously discussed in Chapters 7, 8, and 9, respectively, no attempt will be made in this chapter to describe these products or their application. However, the reader who is interested in modifications of hydraulic cement pipe through the application of coatings, linings or chemical-resistant cements should refer to the appropriate chapter.

Cast iron, silicon-iron alloys, fiber-filled asphalt or coal tar and plastics have also been used successfully for waste lines. Because of their newness, plastics have not been used extensively for this application. However, both glass-reinforced thermosetting plastics and unfilled thermoplastics have been used to a limited extent.

It may be predicted that more plastic pipe will be used in this application in the future. Since plastic pipe was discussed quite completely in Chapter 17, the reader should refer to it for additional information.

While vitrified clay and concrete pipe are brittle, they are generally considered adequate for waste lines. Vitrified clay is completely resistant to all materials normally found in sewerage. It is attacked by fluorides and alkalies but these are seldom found in normal sewerage.

Although many attempts have been made to use specially designed precast joints and trowelable jointing compositions, most vitrified clay pipe sewer lines consist of short sections of bell and spigot pipe joined with hot-poured materials. There are more than a hundred patents on various methods for joining pipe, but this discussion is restricted to a description of the most widely used types of jointing materials.

Pipe Joint Specifications

The ideal pipe joint should have the following properties:

1. Simplified directions for use.
2. Foolproof and rapid installation procedures to permit early use of the line.
3. Freedom from toxic or soluble components, porosity, or other imperfections.
4. Permanent bond to the pipe under all normal service conditions.
5. High resistance to infiltration and exfiltration.
6. Complete resistance to normal household wastes, cleaners, detergents, greases, and normal soil conditions.
7. Sufficient flexibility to permit normal movement of the pipeline resulting from settling, etc.
8. Sufficient strength to resist breaking of the joint in the trench.
9. Retention of the original properties during long periods of service.
10. Resistance to slumping.
11. Resistance to cracking under normal underground service conditions.
12. Resistance to penetration by roots.
13. Economic advantages.

A completely foolproof pipe joint has yet to be perfected. Nevertheless, as will be evident from the subsequent description, several satisfactory sewer jointing materials are available commercially.

Hot-Poured Filled Asphalt Joints

The oldest and best known hot-poured joint is a filled asphaltic compound developed about fifty years ago. Compounds of this type are usually composed of equal parts by weight of properly graded fillers and specially prepared asphalts. These products have a specific gravity of about 1.5, an ASTM penetration of about 12 throughout the entire temperature range expected in actual service (32 to 115°F), and a ball and ring softening point of about 225°F. Federal Specification SS-S-169, Type I describes this type of product.

Priming of bells and spigots with an asphalt cutback prior to the pouring of any hot-poured sewer jointing material is advisable and is essential if the joints are constructed under wet conditions. In all cases, it is important that the bell and spigot surfaces be clean and dry and that the annular space be yarned with clean dry jute.

Two or more pipes may be joined while in a vertical position; in this case, the hot compound is poured without the necessity of using an asbestos runner. A rubber or asbestos runner, of course, must be used for all joints poured in the trench.

When hot-poured asphaltic compositions are heated with stirring at 400 to 450°F, they flow freely. The material should be ladled out when the recommended temperature within this range has been attained and the joint should be filled in one pouring. The shortest possible distance between melting pot and pouring site should be maintained at all times. The quantities of both jute and compound will vary with the type and size of pipe used.

An estimate of quantities required can be secured by multiplying the volume of the annular space in cubic inches by 0.056 to determine the weight in pounds of the compound required for each joint. Slide charts and tables are available for determining quantities required for various standard-size pipes.

A properly poured bituminous joint has good adhesion, is strong, dense, and chemically inert, has some flexibility, solidifies quickly, will deflect without breaking the joint or the pipe, and is economical and easy to use. Properly poured filled asphaltic-type joints have displaced hydraulic cement mortar joints almost completely and have proved to be satisfactory over a period of years in many different geographical locations.

Filled Plasticized Sulfur Compositions

Sulfur compound joints similar to those discussed in Chapter 18 have been widely used for joining of vitrified clay pipe. These materials are more root resistant and less flexible than asphaltic types. Improved sulfur compounds contain a bactericide in sufficient quantities to prevent attack by sulfur bacteria.

Filled Coal-Tar Pitch Joints

A hot-poured jointing material based on filled coal-tar pitch is also produced. This product is reported to have superior root resistance but adhesion to the pipe surfaces is sometimes poor. This deficiency permits roots to penetrate at the interface between the compound and the pipe. Even in the absence of root growth, infiltration can take place at this interface.

A typical filled coal-tar pitch composition will have a tensile strength of approximately 250 psi and ASTM penetration of less than 1 throughout the entire anticipated temperature range, a ball and ring melting point of 195 °F, and a specific gravity of 1.5. The coal-tar pitch content is usually greater than 70 per cent of the entire composition. This type jointing material is described in Federal Specification SS-S-169, Type 2.

Hot-Poured Filled Plastic Joints

Another widely used jointing material based on a hydrocarbon plastic has outstanding root resistance and excellent adhesion to ceramic surfaces. This produce does not lose adhesion, even when soaked in water for long periods of time. A large number of long-term tests made in various parts of the country have shown this product to be completely resistant to a wide variety of plant roots.

Unlike asphalt and coal tar products, the hot plastic melt is not affected adversely by long-term heating in the melting pot. The filler in this product does not tend to settle in the melting pot. However, intermittent stirring is advocated to minimize coking. Also, the pot must be emptied whenever heating is discontinued such as at the close of each day's work. The melt is not readily ignited when heated under field conditions. This product has low shrinkage and outstanding chemical resistance.

A typical hot-melt plastic jointing material contains approximately 40 per cent hydrocarbon plastic and 60 per cent graded filler. The specific gravity is approximately 1.7 and the softening point (ball and ring) is about 225 °F.

The ASTM penetration of this material is usually less than 1 through the entire range expected under service conditions. The adhesion to primed unglazed vitrified clay pipe is greater than 200 psi, even after the joint has been soaked in water for long periods of time. This product is described by Federal Specifications SS-S-169, Type 3.

As in the case of filled asphalt and coal-tar compositions, priming of the bell and spigot surfaces is recommended for all installations and is essential when the joints are made under wet trench conditions. This plastic product is slightly more expensive than filled asphalt or coal-tar pitch, but its properties are closer to the specifications for a perfect pipe joint than any other known commercial material.

Figure 19-1 shows the pouring of a molten plastic based compound in a vitrified clay pipeline.

Precast Asphaltic Joints

High-melting asphalt-type joints are also precast and used as rings on both the bell and the spigot. The asphaltic surfaces to be

Figure 19-1. Pouring a joint in a vitrified clay pipe waste line with a molten root-resistant plastic based jointing cement.

joined are painted with a solvent just before the pipe is placed in position in order to secure a monolithic joint.

This joint can be laid faster than many other types and can be installed under the most adverse conditions. In spite of the simplicity of the operation, it is sometimes difficult to secure good joints due to the irregularities in the pipe and damage of the collars on the spigot end during storage and transportation.

A slip-joint type of asphaltic composition is most satisfactory on large jobs when the shape and size of the pipe is fairly uniform. The filled asphaltic compositions used usually have a ball and ring softening point of at least 240°F, a penetration of between 5 and 10, and a specific gravity of 1.5. This product is described by Federal Specification SS-S-169, Type I, Class 2.

Neat Cement Joints

Other commonly used jointing materials consist of neat cement and other trowelable compositions. These are used with vitrified clay pipe and require expert workmanship. Infiltration and root penetration of the rigid neat cement joints can be prevented through the use of a metal collar, such as a Weston gasket. The metal form is left on the pipe permanently when cement joints are constructed in this manner.

Ready-Mixed Trowelable Compositions

Trowelable compositions based on asphalt and synthetic rubber have been used, particularly with tongue and groove concrete pipe. These products set by evaporation of solvents, hence, they do not harden under water.

Good joints with trowelable compositions are obtained only through the use of top-quality workmanship. The tendency to leave the bottom section of the annular space unfilled can be overcome in part by troweling in a bead of the material on the bottom two-thirds of the bell interior before shoving the pipe home.

A typical trowelable asphaltic material contains approximately 50 per cent filler, of which at least 35 per cent is asbestos fiber. It has a specific gravity of 1.3 and is completely resistant to normal sewage wastes. It should harden uniformly and not form a surface skin.

A typical filled synthetic rubber composition contains at least 50 per cent filler, of which at least 5 per cent is asbestos. It has a specific gravity of 1.1 and is completely resistant to normal sewage. It should contain at least 10 per cent synthetic rubber and have outstanding adhesion and flexibility.

On-The-Job Mixed Troweling Compositions

These compositions possess the previously cited shortcomings of all troweling compounds and, in addition, require exceptionally good field supervision of the mixing and installation operations. Usually, about three parts of powder are added to one part by weight of liquid with thorough stirring in order to secure an intimate uniform mixture. Slight variations in the ratio of powder to liquid may be made, but large variations will produce unsatisfactory joints.

A typical troweling composition of this type has a specific gravity of 1.4. It should not be gritty but should yield a cohesive mass that will set even under water to form a joint that is completely resistant to normal sewage.

Chemical-Resistant Joints

None of the joints described previously is recommended for service in the presence of solvents or elevated temperatures. Joints based on a combination of furan and sulfur cements, however, are satisfactory for most industrial waste lines, even at elevated temperatures.

In this construction, the more economical sulfur cement is used essentially in the same manner described previously for other hot-poured jointing materials. It fills the main portion of the annular space, but the effectiveness of the joint depends primarily on the presence of a continuous fillet of the more expensive furan cement which is in contact with the effluent.

The furan cement mortar, prepared by the methods described in Chapter 9, is troweled in the portion of the annular space coming in contact with the industrial wastes. As shown in Chapter 9, furan cements are unaffected by alkalies, salts, solvents and most acids, even at temperatures of 350°F. They are attacked by nitric, chromic and concentrated sulfuric acids.

There are several modifications of this joint, but all successful variations consist of an infusible resin cement in contact with the effluent, with the major portion of the annular space filled with a less expensive hot-poured material.

Tubular Joint

One of the recent novel joint developments consists of a deflated rubber tube having essentially the same dimensions as the annular space between the bell and spigot. This tube is inserted in the annular space and then filled with a quick-setting hydraulic cement. Although this joint is somewhat expensive, it can be constructed readily even under adverse conditions.

Vinyl Plastisol Joint

Another recently developed joint makes use of a vinyl plastisol, which is hot-molded in place as a threaded ring on clay pipe. The flexible threaded sections are then joined with a corresponding hard molded phenolic plastic threaded ring. Recent improvements utilize cast vinyl plastisol male and female threaded joints on bell and spigot pipe.

Specialty Socket-Type Joints

Because of the inherent sound design of bell and spigot type joints, most new joint concepts are adaptations of this type of construction. One of the innovations consists of a plain end pipe in which one end is smaller than the other.

In this construction, there is a gradual decrease in diameter in each pipe section rather than an abrupt change as is present in the bell and spigot pipe. The fit between sections of this pipe is sufficiently accurate so that only a troweling composition is required to fill the small void between the two pipe sections.

Other innovations have been dependent upon selection of the more accurately formed bell and spigot pipe which could be joined with a rubber ring gasket. Proposals have been made to utilize the "run of the mill" pipe by grinding the bell and spigot sections to proper size. Pipe that has been ground to a uniform circle can also be joined with a rubber ring.

Plain End Pipe

A large number of the jointing methods that have been patented

TABLE 19-1. A PRACTICAL COMPARISON
OF TYPICAL PROPRIETARY SEWER JOINTS.

Vinyl Plastisol	0 1 2 3 4 5 6 7 8 9 10	TOTAL
Cost		
Ease of Installation		89
Adhesion to pipe		
Ductility		
Resistance to — Roots		
Wet Trench		
Salts		
Alkalies		
Acids		
Slump		

Tubular Joint	0 1 2 3 4 5 6 7 8 9 10	TOTAL
Cost		
Ease of Installation		82
Adhesion to pipe		
Ductility		
Resistance to — Roots		
Wet Trench		
Salts		
Alkalies		
Acids		
Slump		

Sulfur Cement	0 1 2 3 4 5 6 7 8 9 10	TOTAL
Cost		
Ease of Installation		79
Adhesion to pipe		
Ductility		
Resistance to — Roots		
Wet Trench		
Salts		
Alkalies		
Acids		
Slump		

Precast Asphalt	0 1 2 3 4 5 6 7 8 9 10	TOTAL
Cost		
Ease of Installation		72
Adhesion to pipe		
Ductility		
Resistance to — Roots		
Wet Trench		
Salts		
Alkalies		
Acids		
Slump		

Neat Cement	0 1 2 3 4 5 6 7 8 9 10	TOTAL
Cost		
Ease of Installation		55
Adhesion to pipe		
Ductility		
Resistance to — Roots		
Wet Trench		
Salts		
Alkalies		
Acids		
Slump		

TABLE 19-1 (Continued).

Hot Poured Plastic	0 1 2 3 4 5 6 7 8 9 10	TOTAL
Cost		
Ease of Installation		85
Adhesion to pipe		
Ductility		
Resistance to — Roots		
Wet Trench		
Salts		
Alkalies		
Acids		
Slump		

Hot Poured Coal Tar Pitch	0 1 2 3 4 5 6 7 8 9 10	TOTAL
Cost		
Ease of Installation		79
Adhesion to pipe		
Ductility		
Resistance to — Roots		
Wet Trench		
Salts		
Alkalies		
Acids		
Slump		

Sulfur-Furan Cement	0 1 2 3 4 5 6 7 8 9 10	TOTAL
Cost		
Ease of Installation		70
Adhesion to pipe		
Ductility		
Resistance to — Roots		
Wet Trench		
Salts		
Alkalies		
Acids		
Slump		

Filled Asphalt	0 1 2 3 4 5 6 7 8 9 10	TOTAL
Cost		
Ease of Installation		66
Adhesion to pipe		
Ductility		
Resistance to — Roots		
Wet Trench		
Salts		
Alkalies		
Acids		
Slump		

Cold Asphalt Trowelling Cement	0 1 2 3 4 5 6 7 8 9 10	TOTAL
Cost		
Ease of Installation		59
Adhesion to pipe		
Ductility		
Resistance to — Roots		
Wet Trench		
Salts		
Alkalies		
Acids		
Slump		

are based on the use of plain end pipe. However, few of these inventions have been reduced to a large-scale commercial use.

A joint for plain end pipe claimed to be flexible, water right and root proof utilizes rubber couplings as sleeves, clamped in place with adjustable bands. The clamping mechanism is held in place and protected by a subsequently poured cement grout.

Conclusion

Because of the wide variety of pipe materials and jointing methods available, it might be concluded that it is impossible to make recommendations for specific installations. An empirical comparison of sewer pipe joints is given in Table 19-1. The following recommendations are also presented as a guide:

For domestic sewage in dry locations where root resistance is not important, vitrified clay pipe joined by hot-poured filled asphalt joints may be used.

For domestic sewage in wet trench locations or when root resistance is essential and good adhesion to the pipe is imperative, a hot-poured filled plastic joint should be used.

Either of these recommendations is satisfactory for cold industrial wastes in the absence of water-immiscible solvents, but a combination joint consisting of an infusible furan and a plasticized sulfur cement is recommended whenever solvents or warm industrial wastes are present.

In spite of these recommendations, large quantities of other pipe materials and jointing methods will be used. New developments are being announced almost daily: today's recommendations may be subject to revisions a few years from now. In addition, there is no reliable substitute for experience.

If the present methods being used by any specific plant or municipality produce perfect waste lines, it is not recommended that the methods of construction be changed. However, it is suggested that when difficulties relative to the joining of pipe are encountered, the previously cited recommendations be considered.

Because the design of most materials for water and sewer pipe has been standardized, no attempt has been made to supply such information in this or the preceding chapter. However, this is not the case in the design of floors, trenches, sumps, stacks and vessels. Hence, the next four chapters contain design information which is a prerequisite for proper applications of plastic materials of construction.

Suggested References

"A New Plastic Base Sewer Jointing Compound," R. B. Seymour, W. R. Pascoe and R. H. Steiner, Water and Sewage Works, 99, No. 5, 210-16 (1952).

"Jointing Compounds for Sewer Pipe," R. B. Seymour, Public Works, 82, No. 8, 74 (1951).

"Methods of Joining Pipe," J. E. York, Industrial Press, New York, 1949.

"Sewer Pipe Jointing," H. W. House and R. Pomeroy, Sewage Works Journal, 19, No. 2, 191 (1947).

"Plastic Pipe Selection—Application Data," R. B. Seymour and E. A. Erich, Southern Power & Industry, June, 1953.

"Tapered Joint for Sewer Pipe," E. N. McKinstry, Western Construction, pp. 65-66, August 1953.

SECTION IV
PLASTICS IN MASONRY
CONSTRUCTION

20. DESIGN OF CONCRETE FLOORS AND TANKS

Several available plastics are stronger than hydraulic cements. However, since they are also more expensive, they are customarily used as protection of concrete floors and tanks rather than as a basic material of construction.

The use of plastics in floors and tanks is discussed in Chapters 21 and 22. Obviously, the plastic protecting surface will be ineffective unless the basic structure is designed properly. Many floors and tanks are constructed from reinforced concrete.

Concrete is made by mixing a paste of portland cement and water with the proper proportions of inert fine and coarse aggregates. The cement unites with the water chemically and physically to bind the aggregates together to form a hard, solid mass. In order to obtain the durable, strong, dense and water-tight concrete required for sound construction, the proper constituents must be used in correct proportions.

Portland cement, conforming to ASTM Specifications C 150-52 and preferably a Type II portland cement should be used. This cement has a moderate heat-of-hydration and also superior sulfate-resistant properties. It must be stored in a weather-tight building. If the cement has hardened or partially set during storage, it must be replaced. Special or quick-setting cements are not recommended for this type of construction.

Fine and coarse aggregates conforming to ASTM C33-52 should be used. The fine aggregate must be a clean, natural sand consisting of hard, durable grains free from large amounts of dust and dirt and must not contain any alkali or organic matter. Particles of approximately equal dimensions are preferred, since they will produce a denser concrete than elongated grains.

The coarse aggregate should consist of an inert crushed stone such as granite, trap rock, silica, quartzite and gravel or other approved inert materials having hard, strong, clean, durable particles free from harmful amounts of soft, thin or laminated pieces, alkali, organic or other injurious matter. The particles of the coarse aggregate should be cubical or spherical in shape. Flat, thin or long particles will not compact as densely as rounded stones.

The maximum size of aggregate depends upon the type of construction, but it rarely exceeds 2 1/2 inches in diameter. The maximum diameter of the coarse aggregate should not exceed 1/5 the narrowest dimension of the concrete member, and should not be larger than 3/4 of the minimum clear spacing between the reinforcing bars. For example, in heavy reinforced sections 12 inches or more in thickness, coarse aggregate up to 1 1/2 inches may be used. For thinner reinforced sections, such as trenches, beams, slabs, wall, etc., the maximum size of coarse aggregates should be 3/4 inch.

Reinforcing Steel Specifications

Reinforced concrete design is based on a fundamental assumption that the concrete and reinforcement act together as a single unit. To insure good adhesion between the steel and concrete, all reinforcing should be deformed. Round bars are preferable to square ones since they are easier to bend. All reinforcing steel should have physical and chemical properties conforming to the ASTM Specification for billet-steel bars for concrete reinforcement Designation A15-52 and A305-50T.

The concrete should be so proportioned as to secure a minimum compressive strength of 3,000 psi after 28 days of curing. Table 20-1 can be used as a guide in order to determine the proper proportion of water and cement for concrete:

The use of a mechanical mixer is essential in attaining the thorough mixing necessary for a uniform, dense, and a water-tight concrete. The strength of concrete increases with the mixing time, although there is little increase after the first minute. Therefore, concrete should be mixed for no less than 1 minute after all the materials are in the mixer, with slightly additional time depending on the size of the batch. The mixed concrete should be used not later than 45 minutes after the addition of the cement to the mixer.

Proper curing is very important in making so-called "impervious" concrete. Unless provisions are made to prevent initial loss of moisture, concrete will shrink excessively and crack. Concrete must be protected against a loss of moisture from the surface for at least 2 days.

Horizontal surfaces can be cured by continuous wetting burlap, straw, sand, earth, etc. Vertical surfaces can be protected by leaving the forms in place, or by constantly wetting burlap which has been draped over the wall surfaces.

Properties of Concrete

One of the most important properties of concrete, and the primary reason for its great value as a structural material, is its compression strength. The tensile strength of concrete varies from 8 to 15 per cent of its compression strength. Since the tensile and flexural strength are so low they are usually not considered in the design of most concrete structures. The allowable working stresses for concrete are given in Table 20-2.

The uncertain stresses which may be encountered in structures has made it necessary to assume a factor of safety in strength of all materials. For structural steel which has a tensile strength of 66,000 psi and a yield point of 33,000 psi, an allowable design working stress of 20,000 psi is assumed. For chemical-resistant construction a concrete having a compressive strength of at least 3,000 psi is recommended with a 45 per cent safety factor, as listed in Table 20-2 a compressive strength of 1350 psi is assumed.

The coefficient of expansion for concrete varies depending upon the mixture and ingredients used; however, an average value for common mixes is 5.5×10^{-6} in./in./°F. The thermal properties of a 1:2:4 concrete in a temperature range of 72 to 212°F are as follows: Specific heat, 0.190; coefficient of thermal conductivity at 122 and 392°C: 76 to 114 and 146 in Btu/°F/sq ft/in. thickness/24 hours.

TABLE 20-1. TECHNICAL DATA FOR CEMENT
FOUNDATIONS FOR SPECIFIC END USE

End Use	Desired Compressive Strength at 28 days $(lb/in.^2)$	Water-Cement Ratio		
		By Weight	Gallons per Sack	By Volume
High early strength in pavement; strong columns, beams and slabs; or for structures very severely exposed.	5500	0.40	4½	1:1:2
Walls, dams, piers, pavements, and other structures requiring high strength or watertightness; or for structures severely exposed.	4500	0.50	5½	1:1½:2½
Walls, dams, piers, reservoir linings, exposed to weather in northern climate. Water-tight structures, pipes, tanks, sewers, pavements, and thin members exposed to frost action.	3800	0.55	6	1:1½:3 to 1:2¼:4
Walls, dams, piers, reservoir linings, exposed to weather in southern climate. Basement walls of thin structural parts subjected to moderate exposure.	3000	0.60	6¾	1:2:3 to 1:2½:4
Enclosed structural members, piers, retaining walls, foundations, and footings, protected from alternate wetting and drying and from severe weather.	2200	0.65	7½	1:2¼:3½ to 1:3:5
Mass concrete requiring little strength and well protected.	1800	0.75	8½	1:2½:4½ to 1:3½:6

TABLE 20-2. ALLOWABLE WORKING STRESSES FOR CONCRETE

Description	For Any Strength of Concrete $n = \dfrac{30,000}{f'c}$	Maximum Value (psi)	For Strength of Concrete Shown Below f'c			
			2000 n–15	2500 n–12	3000 n–10	3750 n–8
Flexure: fc						
Extreme fiber stress in compression	0.45 f'c		900	1125	1350	1688
Extreme fiber stress in tension in plain concrete footings	0.03 f'c		60	75	90	113
Shear: v (as a measure of diagonal tension)						
Beams with no web reinforcement	0.03 f'c		60	75	90	114
Beams with properly designed web reinforcement	0.12 f'c		240	300	360	450
Flat slabs at distance from edge of column capital or drop panel	0.03 f'c		60	75	90	113
Footings	0.03 f'c	75	60	75	75	75
Bond: u						
Deformed bars						
Top bars	0.07 f'c	245	1140	175	210	245
In 2-way footings (except top bars)	0.08 f'c	280	160	200	240	280
All others	0.10 f'c	350	200	250	300	350
Plain bars (must be hooked)						
Top bars	0.03 f'c	105	60	75	90	105
In 2-way footings (except top bars)	0.036 f'c	126	72	90	108	126
All others	0.045 f'c	158	90	113	135	158
Bearing: fc						
One full area	0.25 f'c		500	625	750	938
One-third area or less	0.375 f'c		750	938	1125	1405

Reinforced Concrete Floor Slabs

Most industrial floors requiring protection against corrosion are constructed of reinforced concrete. These floors, in addition to containing the proper constituents and being sufficiently rigid, must also include features necessary for good chemical resistant design as illustrated in Figure 20-1.

Although the location of construction joints usually depends on physical conditions at the job site, every effort should be made to cast concrete monolithically except, of course, where contraction or expansion joints occur. Construction joints in structural slabs should occur at the center of the span and at right angles to the direction.

There is no definite rule for determining the distance between contraction joints. They may vary anywhere from 15 to 50 feet. When a continuous keyway is being formed and a corrosion-resistant alloy

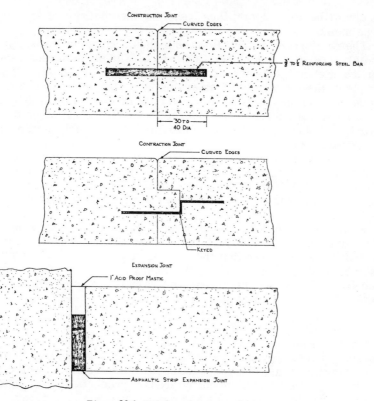

Figure 20-1. Reinforced concrete floors.

sheet inserted, the upper edge of the joints should be finished to a slightly rounded edge on both sides.

Expansion joints are introduced in slabs to relieve side pressures which could cause buckling or other undesirable results. They should normally be installed around all columns and at all points where floor slabs adjoin foundation walls or other walls extending through the floor slab.

The distance between expansion joints varies considerably, depending on many factors, including the location of the plant. The approximate distance should be 90 feet, and the width of the joint approximately 1/2 inch.

The expansion joints should be filled with a poured bituminous mastic or an asphaltic impregnated felt to within 1 inch from the top. The top inch of the expansion joint should consist of an acid-proof, asphaltic, hot-pour compound. The edges of the concrete joint must be rounded.

Floor slabs, which are to receive an acid-proof brick lining, should have a smooth wood-float finish. A slab having a steel-trowel finish is apt to be too smooth, thus lessening the adhesion of an asphaltic type membrane.

The reinforced concrete floor slab should slope to drains approximately 1/8 to 1/4 inch per linear foot. The slope depends entirely on the distance between drains and the type of industry. For example, if the distance between drains is 50 feet, and a 1/4 inch slope is desired on the floor, there would be a 12 inch vertical drop which must be accounted for in the slab, or in a concrete fill over the slab. For this distance, a slope of approximately 1/8 inch per linear foot would be recommended.

A case in the other extreme is possibly a dairy floor where the floors must be kept clean at all times; the drains would be much closer. A 1/4 inch slope would require a concrete fill 2.5 inches thicker at one end than the other, when the distance between drains is 10 feet.

A maximum variation would depend on the slope, but would be in the neighborhood of 1/16 inch for the surface of concrete floor slab. It must be remembered that the contour of an acid-proof brick floor, over an asphaltic membrane, will closely follow that of the concrete sub-base. Therefore, all irregularities must be removed before the application of an impervious membrane.

Reinforced Concrete Vessels

There are no restrictions on the size and shape of concrete structures. Concrete is used as a basic construction material and is well known for buildings, bridges, roads, dams and retaining walls. Concrete is now being used in many precast products such as masonry units, sewer pipe, roof slabs and numerous other structures.

One of the largest, but least known, uses of concrete is for retaining vessels. There is almost no limit to the kind of vessels that can be constructed of concrete, and therefore, classification by usage is quite difficult. A simple method of classification is according to the shape of the unit. Vessels of the same shapes are, essentially, similar in design and construction.

Some examples of reinforced concrete retaining vessels are swimming pools, reservoirs, water towers, storage vessels, bunkers, pickling and plating tanks, sumps and neutralization tanks.

The formwork of any tank is extremely important, because any weakness such as bulging, or sagging may not only disfigure or damage the structure, but cause an eventual failure of a chemical-resistant lined structure. Care must be taken to insure that the inside form does not bow in toward the center of the tank when the concrete is cast.

It is preferable for the form to bow outward, so that the tank is wider at the center than at the ends. In large rectangular vessels, it is often recommended to bow and batter the inside walls in order to place the chemical-resistant, masonry lining in compression upon thermal expansion.

If the formwork is to be constructed of wooden panels, a structural moisture-resistant plywood should be used. A thickness of at least 5/8 inch and not less than five ply, backed up with boards, is suitable for plywood forms. Plywood sheets in widths of 24, 36 and 48 inches and 8 foot lengths are most commonly used for forms.

The common method of using bolts to hold the forms is undesirable, because it is very difficult to repair the depression left by the bolts. Forms braced on the outside are, undoubtedly, the best practice. If bolts or wires are used to hold the forms in position, it is of utmost imporfance that the tie rods in the concrete be removed to a minimum depth of 1 inch, and that the hole should be no greater than 1 inch in diameter. The opening should be free of all loose particles, wetted and then grouted with a portland cement mortar.

The placing of concrete involves many different operations, such as transportation, deposition and final compaction. The type of transportation, depends on the quantity of concrete required, uniformity and cost. In all cases, a batch operation is preferred to a continuous method of mixing.

Concrete should be kept moving into the forms in order to maintain a constant level and to prevent stratification. It should not be allowed to drop freely for more than 5 psi.

As the concrete is deposited in horizontal, even layers, it should be tamped or vibrated until capillary continuity is assured by the glistening of a film of water on the top surface. The top surface should be spaded near the face of the forms and around the reinforcing as the concrete is being poured in, to insure a smooth, non-honeycombed surface and a dense, homogeneous structure.

After approximately a week, the forms must be removed carefully to avoid any damage to the concrete surface. The concrete on the inside of the tank must be smooth and free of depressions or high spots. If high spots are present, they must be removed with a "Carborundum" stone. Honeycomb and porous areas must also be removed by cleaning the concrete, removing loose particles, saturating with water and grouting with a stiff portland cement mortar.

The finished concrete tank should be tested by filling it with water for at least 48 hours, and repairing all leaks that are noted. Tanks which are to be constructed underground should be tested under hydrostatic pressure before the back-fill is placed in position. The walls, in this case, must be designed for water pressure, regardless of the compensating earth pressure.

All concrete tanks, regardless of the shape, should be reinforced with steel. As stated previously, the strength of concrete is much greater in compression than in tension. Since walls of a concrete vessel will fail from the tensile forces on the convex side, they can be greatly strengthened by the addition of steel reinforcing, at least on the convex side.

Steel reinforcing should not be placed closer than 1 1/2 inches from the concrete surface and the minimum center-to-center distance between parallel bars should be three diameters of the bar. Splices should be staggered and approximately 45 diameters in length.

It is almost essential to provide an inner and outer reinforcing ring in large tanks. When the spacing is close and the bars are in one ring, the steel is crowded in the vicinity of each lap. This condition may result in part by the reinforcing not contacting the concrete. The use of two rings of reinforcing will also provide resistance to bending movements which could be caused by exterior forces such as the shifting or settling of the earth.

A common method used in designing cylindrical tanks is to assume that they act as thin cylinders, the walls of which are in pure tension. Usually an assumed quantity (based on experience) of vertical steel bars are inserted at the base to prevent cracks from occuring at the junction of the wall and floor.

Theoretically, hydrostatic pressure would increase the diameter of a tank from top to bottom, and the increase would be the greatest at the bottom if there were no resistance at that point. In chemical proof design, it is recommended that the sidewalls and bottom be cast together and tied in with reinforcing steel.

At the bottom of the wall, therefore, the hoop stress would then be zero and the whole load is resisted in a vertical direction by cantilever strips. Further up the wall, the pressure is resisted more by the hoop in tension and less by cantilever action until a point is reached where the load is almost entirely restricted by the hoop steel.

Rectangular tanks are much more difficult to design, mathematically, than cylindrical units. The side walls of a rectangular tank must resist bending and torque movements, in addition to tension and cantilever forces. Methods for the computation of rectangular vessels have not been standardized.

As might be expected, steel is used even more widely than concrete for construction of tanks and vessels. Design information for steel is given in Chapter 21.

Suggested References

"Kidder Parker Architects' and Builders Handbook," 18th Edition, John Wiley & Sons, Inc., New York, 1948.

"Elements of Strengths of Materials," Timoshenko, MacCullough, D. Van Nostrand & Company, New York, 1949.

"Formulas for Stress and Strain," Roark, 2nd Edition, McGraw Hill Book Company, New York, 1943.

"Chemical Engineers' Handbook," John H. Perry, 3rd Edition, McGraw Hill Book Company, New York, 1950.

"Materials of Construction," John H. Bateman, Pitman Publishing Corporation, 1950.

"C.R.S.I. Design Handbook," R. C. Reese, 1st Edition, Concrete Reinforcing Steel Institute, 1952.

"Simplified Design of Reinforced Concrete," Harry Parker, M.S., John Wiley & Sons, Inc., New York, 1951.

"Reinforced Concrete Water Towers, Bunkers, Silos and Gantries," W. S. Gray, Concrete Publications, Ltd., 1933.

"Standard Specifications for Highway Materials and Methods of Sampling and Testing," 6th Edition, The American Association of State Highway Officials, 1950.

"Johnson's Materials of Construction," M. O. Withey and James Aston, 8th edition, John Wiley & Sons, Inc., New York, 1948.

"Civil Engineering Handbook," Leonard Church Urquhart, 3rd Edition, McGraw Hill Book Company, New York, 1940.

"1952 Book of ASTM Standards," Part 3, American Society for Testing Materials.

"Materials of Construction," M. C. Withey and G. W. Washa, John Wiley & Sons, Inc., New York, 1954.

21. DESIGN OF STEEL VESSELS

As stated in Chapter 20, steel is the most widely used material for the construction of tanks and vessels. Because of its strength, ductility and toughness, it is able to withstand loads, adjust itself to inequalities in stress distribution and resist fracture under impact.

The end uses of steel are so extensive that it is difficult to find a moving or stationary structure without some form of steel. Steel for structural purposes includes a large variety of shapes such as "I" beams, channels, angles, "H" shapes, "T's," "Z's," rivets, bars and plates.

Steel Tanks

Many types of vessels are manufactured by the fabrication and welding of steel plate using proper reinforcement. These vessels may be used for manufacturing, storing or shipping liquids or dry materials. Whenever steel vessels are subject to corrosion, they must be lined with chemical-resistant materials. In such cases, it is necessary for the steel shells to meet certain basic specifications, many of which are outside the realm of this discussion.

Unless otherwise specified, the dimensions for steel tanks are considered as inside capacity of working dimensions. This is quite important since, at times, these inside dimensions, depending on the corrosion-resistant construction, may be inside brick, inside plastic, rubber lining or inside steel.

Confusion sometimes arises on initial sketches or verbal descriptions of any processing vessel when dimensions are defined. Unless otherwise specified, a tolerance of plus or minus 1/8 inch is permissible on all dimensions of 24 inches or less. On dimensions over 24 inches, a tolerance of plus or minus 1/4 inch is permissible. The same tolerance applied to overall dimensions when parts are made up in sections.

Whenever plastic or rubber-type membranes are to be installed in a steel tank, an absolutely smooth steel surface with no obstructions is necessary. In order to attain this requirement, welded construction is preferred over riveted construction.

Welds should be made only by operators who have been qualified previously by tests as prescribed in the "Standard Qualification Procedure" of the American Welding Society. Welding details used on plans or shop drawings, and welding procedures, shall comply with all the requirements for joints as described in the "Code for Arc and Gas Welding in Building Construction" of the American Welding Society.

Steel to be welded must be free from loose scale, slag, rust, grease, paint and any other foreign material while joint surfaces should be free from tears and fins.

All joints over which rubber or plastic membrane is applied must consist of a continuous solid weld. The four general types of continuous welds used are bead, fillet, butt and plug welds as shown in Figure 21-1. The effects of improper welding techniques on lining construction are shown in Figure 21-2.

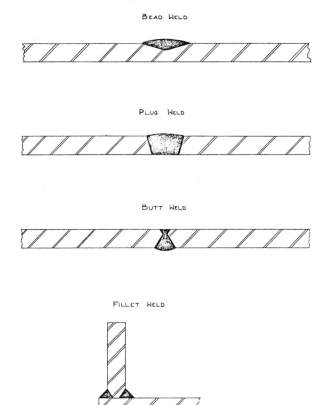

BEAD WELD

PLUG WELD

BUTT WELD

FILLET WELD

Figure 21-1.

All welds must be smooth with no porosity, holes, high spots, lumps or pockets. Peening is required to eliminate porosity, and grinding to remove sharp edges and high spots.

All corners must be ground to a minimum radius of 1/8 inch. As shown in Figure 21-3, concave corners make it possible for rubber lining to form-fit the steel vessel, thus preventing any entrapment

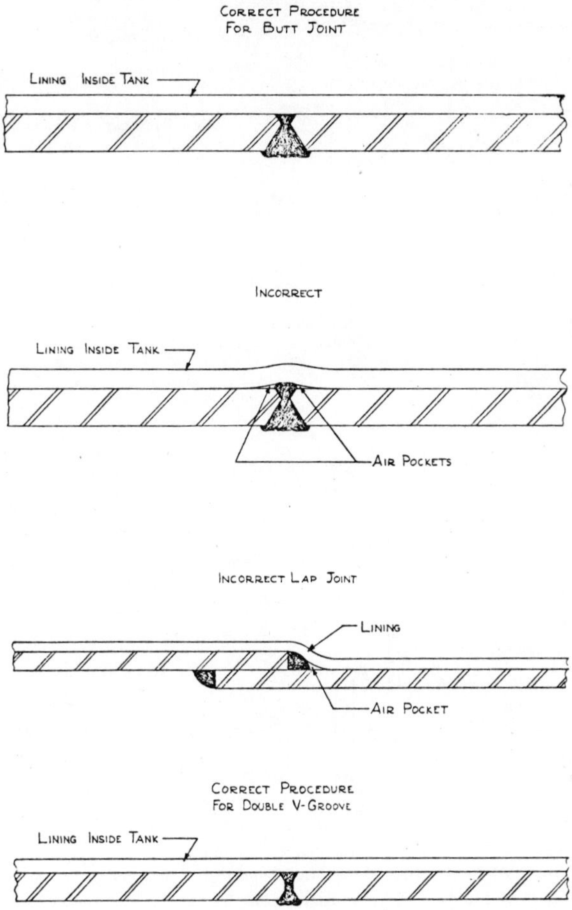

CORRECT PROCEDURE
FOR BUTT JOINT

LINING INSIDE TANK

INCORRECT

LINING INSIDE TANK

AIR POCKETS

INCORRECT LAP JOINT

LINING

AIR POCKET

CORRECT PROCEDURE
FOR DOUBLE V-GROOVE

LINING INSIDE TANK

Figure 21-2.

of air behind the lining. All tanks should be constructed with a minimum number of pieces.

The companion flange of sectional tanks which are bolted together must be square, plumb and smooth, and sections must fit exactly when bolted together. Sectional tanks should be permanently matched and marked on spots that are not to be rubber lined to indicate accurately their position when assembled. All flanges on the outlets should be parallel with the tank, or in other words, the pipeline will leave the tank at right angles to the surface of the same, unless otherwise specified.

Whenever possible, steel tanks should be constructed in a cylindri-

CORRECT PROCEDURE
FOR CORNER WELD

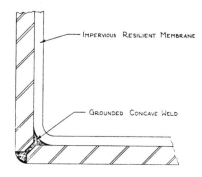

IMPERVIOUS RESILIENT MEMBRANE

GROUNDED CONCAVE WELD

INCORRECT

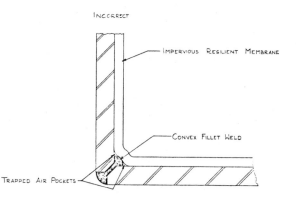

IMPERVIOUS RESILIENT MEMBRANE

CONVEX FILLET WELD

TRAPPED AIR POCKETS

Figure 21-3. Drawing shows the importance of grinding of all corner welds to 1/8-in. radius when the tank is to receive a rubber or plastic membrane.

cal rather than a rectangular shape. Some of the many reasons for the popularity of cylindrical vessels are:
1. Most economical shape.
2. Shape adaptable to many pressures.
3. Pressure vessels almost always require cylindrical shape.
4. Thinner brick linings necessary.
5. Brick lining under compression in cylindrical units provides a denser, more impervious lining.

A manhole at least 18 inch in diameter must be available in all closed tanks to enable men to enter and rubber-line the vessel. This manhole can also be used at a shut-down time for internal inspection. The flange around the manhole and all outlets must be at least 2 inches wide. Rims and grooves on manhole and outlet flanges should be ground smooth for rubber lining. Details on tank outlets are shown in Figure 21-4.

Horizontal tanks shall not exceed the maximum capacities, diameters, or lengths for the corresponding gauges of steel as listed in Table 21-1.

The capacity of horizontal above-ground storage tanks should not be less than 2,500 gallons or greater than 35,000 gallons. These tanks may vary in diameter from 4 to 11 feet, and the length depends on what can be shipped on a single railroad car. In no case should the diameter be greater than the length, or the length greater than six times the diameter.

Vertical above-ground storage tanks vary in size from 2,500 to 25,000 gallon capacities. The height of the tank should never be greater than four times the diameter. A maximum diameter of 11 feet and a maximum height of 35 feet are permissible.

For tanks up to 25 feet in height, the shell should not be less than 3/16 inch thick. For tanks 25 to 30 feet high, the first ring must be at least 1/4 inch thick and not less than 5 feet wide. Tanks 30 to 35 feet high must have the first rings of 5 feet width not less than 1/4 inch thick. The bottom of the subject tanks should be in one or two pieces not less than 3/16 inch thick, while the top could be dished or cone shaped and no less than No. 10 U.S. Gauge.

In cases, where tanks are to be used for the storage of corrosive chemicals where a lining is required, the steel should be at least 1/16 inch thicker. If the storage tanks are to have a brick lining, the vertical tank bottom must be supported by horizontal "I" beams or channel, welded in a perpendicular position underneath the bottom plate. This dunnage stiffens the bottom plate, thus eliminating any possible buckling, and elevates the bottom, preventing the possibility of unseen corrosion taking place.

Rectangular tanks require the heaviest reinforcing to prevent the sidewalls from deforming. Flat plate without reinforcing is a very weak member, and theoretical thicknesses to prevent any bulging are excessive. Thicknesses of steel plate can be reduced considerably by (1) crowning or dishing the plate, (2) rib stiffeners to form a cradle thus dividing the walls into small supported panels. The latter method is most commonly used, although this type of structure is difficult to analyze, and is generally designed by experience rather than by analysis. It is recommended that unduly thin ribs and small fillets at the junction of the plate and the stiffeners be avoided.

The thickness of the sidewall plate of rectangular tanks depends on many factors which are difficult to determine. Normally if the steel tank is sufficiently large to warrant steel reinforcing, the wall and bottom plates should have a minimum thickness of 1/4 inch. Typical design features for rectangular tanks are given in Figure 21-5.

The bottom should be supported by "I" beams or channels and the

FLANGED NIPPLE OUTLET WITH
TAYLOR WELD

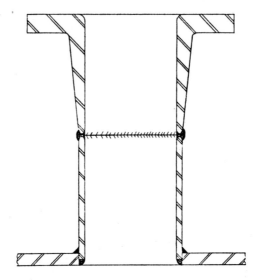

FLANGED NIPPLE OUTLET

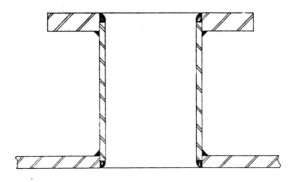

PAD OUTLET

Figure 21-4. Tank outlet details.

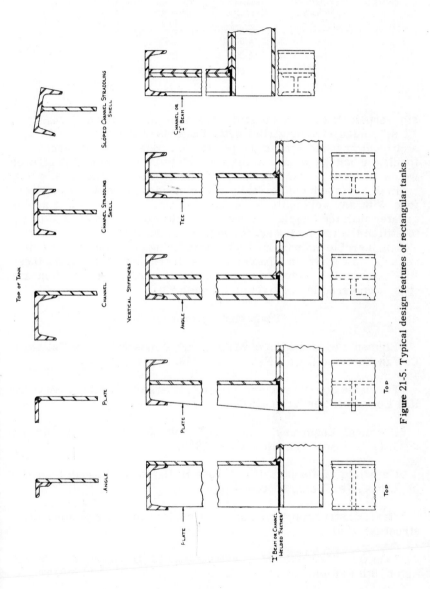

Figure 21-5. Typical design features of rectangular tanks.

TABLE 21-1. TECHNICAL DATA
FOR HORIZONTAL UNDERGROUND TANKS

Approximate Thickness (In.)	Maximum Capacity (Gal.)	Maximum Diameter (In.)	Maximum Length (Ft)
3/16	4,000	84	24
1/4	12,000	126	32
5/16	20,000	132	42
3/8	30,000	132	50

side should have vertical stiffeners such as "I" beams, channels, "T's," angles, etc., or girth bands. The tops of the tanks should have a channel or angle around the perimeter. Basically, the steel reinforcing should be welded to the steel plate in intermittent staggered welds to form a framework or cradle to support the steel shell.

Girth bands are not normally recommended since they can interfere with any acid spillage on the outside. In tanks having depths greater than the length, it is necessary to use a girth band in order to stiffen the vertical panel for structural stability.

Considerable information on organic linings for concrete and steel vessels was given in Chapter 8. As previously mentioned, these linings are often protected by brick sheathings. Information on this type of construction is given in Chapter 22.

Suggested References

"Elements of Strengths of Materials," Timoshenko, MacCullough, D. Van Nostrand & Co., New York, 1949.

"Formulas for Stress and Strain," Roark, 2nd Edition, McGraw Hill Book Co., New York, 1943.

"Chemical Engineers' Handbook," John H. Perry, 3rd Edition, McGraw Hill Book Co., New York, 1950.

"Materials of Construction," John H. Bateman, Pitman Publishing Corp., New York, 1950.

"Steel Construction," 5th Edition, American Institute of Steel Construction, 1951.

"Johnson's Materials of Construction," M. O. Withey and James Aston, 8th Edition, John Wiley & Sons, Inc., New York, 1948.

"Civil Engineering Handbook," Leonard Church Urquhart, 3rd Edition, McGraw Hill Book Co., New York, 1940.

"Simplified Design of Structural Steel," Harry Parker, John Wiley & Sons, Inc., New York, 1951.

"Buffalo Handbook," Buffalo Tank Corporation, 1951.

"1952 Book of ASTM Standards," Part 3, American Society for Testing Materials.

22. CHEMICAL-RESISTANT MASONRY CONSTRUCTION

Since carbon steel or concrete is readily attacked by many corrosives, it must be protected by a coating or lining depending upon the service conditions. As discussed in Chapter 7, a protective coating with a minimum thickness of 5 mils is recommended for protection against splash and fumes.

However, heavy organic linings are required when the equipment will be in contact with liquid corrosives. Thus, as outlined in Chapter 8, vessels, sumps and trenches containing acids or other corrosive chemicals must be protected by an organic lining. These linings are usually at least 60 and preferably 100 or 125 mils thick.

Properly installed organic linings are usually suitable for storage or processing at temperatures below 150°F. However, if there is danger of physical damage, agitation with suspended solids or if the temperature is above 150°F, the organic lining is usually protected by a brick sheathing.

The organic lining is the vital part of this type of construction. Hence, corrosion-resistant brick sheathings are seldom used except for the protection of organic linings. As mentioned previously, organic linings may be used without the protection of brick sheathings. However, it is often economical to install brick sheathings in chemical processing equipment in order to prolong the life of the organic membrane. The type of cement mortars used to join the brickwork were discussed in Chapter 9.

Types of Brick

The three general types of brick available for chemical-proof masonry are hard burned red shale, fireclay and carbon brick. The difference between red shale and a fireclay brick is principally physical rather than chemical. Clays are usually of two types: surface clays, which are upthrusts or extrusions of older deposits, and fireclays, which are usually found and mined at deeper levels and so-called because of their refractory qualities.

The chemical properties of the clay, to a great extent, determine the color and fusibility of the product. Iron oxide in the clay tends to color the finished product in ranges of red, brown and buff, whereas, clay free of this material usually burns to white or cream color.

Lime, if present in sufficient quantity, will produce cream or buff colored brick and tile. Since these materials lower the fusing point of the clay, they are termed fluxes. Other fluxes are oxides of iron, manganese, phosphorous, calcium, magnesium, sodium and potassium.

These oxides are impurities, from a chemical standpoint, but they actually strengthen the burned clay body so that it is suitable for structural purposes. In general, shales and surface clays contain high percentages of oxides, ranging from a minimum of 1.5 per cent to a maximum of 9 per cent.

Carbon brick consists chiefly of granular carbon particles which are compressed with a pitch binder, and then fused and cut into standard structural building units. Graphite bricks have a much higher thermal conductivity and greater resistance to oxidation, but are somewhat softer.

Both carbon and graphite are stable at most commercial temperatures in reducing atmospheres. However, continuous exposure, at temperatures in excess of 650°F for carbon or 750°F for graphite, will cause deterioration if reducing conditions are not maintained.

Carbon and graphite brick resist the corrosive action of all acids, alkalies and solvents except that of strong oxidizing agents. They adhere firmly to bonding materials, are mechanically strong and do not tend to spall excessively.

Bricks which are used in corrosion-proof masonry must be structurally strong in order to take the rough abuse and service which is commonly encountered in the chemical industries. This abuse is particularly severe when the brick are used in floor areas as curbing, piers or tank linings, and, to a lesser degree, when they are used as facing or veneer.

Fireclay and shale brick are inherently resistant to most acids in all concentrations, and most alkalies in moderately weak concentration. Since these brick are chiefly composed of silica they are attacked by solutions of hydrofluoric acid. Fireclay and shale brick are not recommended for alkaline service at concentrations above 20 per cent.

In many cases, even though the brick may be chemically attacked, this attack is not sufficient from the standpoint of economics to justify the use of more expensive carbon brick.

The bond of mortar with ordinary building bricks depends to a great extent upon the rate at which water can be drawn into the capillaries of the brick. In acid-proof construction, surface modifications must be made since this capillary action is not as evident as with less dense brick.

Satisfactory adhesion is often achieved by roughening the surface of the brick to which mortar is to be applied. This roughening may either be accomplished by modifying the texture of the brick or by physically texturing the surface of the unburnt brick by wire cutting or scoring. The adhesion of acid-proof mortar to wire-cut brick varies from 150 psi for silicate cements to 700 psi for furan cements. Hot pour cements such as the sulfur cements may have adhesion values in excess of 450 psi.

Comparable properties for typical types of acid brick are as follows:

	Average Compressive Strength(psi)	Modulus of Rupture (shearing psi)	% Water Absorption 5 hr. Boil Test	Approx. wt.-lbs per cu ft	Burned to Fusion Point(°F)	Thermal Conductivity btu/(hr)(sq ft) (°F/ft)	Tensile Strength (psi)
Red Shale	18,200	2300	2.7	145	1980	9	690
Fireclay	17,600	3807	2.4	138	2250	7	1100
Carbon	8,320	3070	–	100	–	3	1530

The reduction in temperature resulting from red shale brick in a steel vessel are given in Table 22-1.

TABLE 22-1. APPROXIMATE TEMPERATURES OF ORGANIC LININGS BEHIND RED SHALE BRICKWORK

Temperatures of Liquid(°F)	Membrane Temperature (°F)		
	4 Inch Brick	8 Inch Brick	12 Inch Brick
300	210	180	165
275	190	160	140
250	180	150	135
225	170	140	125
210	150	125	110
200	140	120	105
175	130	110	95
150	117.5	92.5	80

Industrial Use of Brick Sheathings

The common sizes of fireclay brick used in vessels are the 9 inch series in straights, arches, wedges, circles and book tile. Red shale floor brick, measuring 8 1/4 x 4 x 1 3/8 inches and 8 x 3 7/8 x 1 3/8 inches or a fireclay tile 12 x 6 x 1 1/2 inches are usually recommended for floor construction.

Hard burned red shale brick has been used by the basic steel and fabricated metal products industries in acid processing work. Single 8 x 3 3/4 x 2 1/4 inch and double 8 x 3 3/4 x 4 1/2 inch brick are preferred for most operating conditions.

Carbon brick are used in stainless steel pickling or whenever appreciable quantities of fluorides or hot concentrated alkalies are present. Single 8 x 3 3/4 x 2 1/4 inch brick is used, to a large extent for floor work.

Because of its light color and better insulation properties, fireclay brick is being used to a considerable extent by the chemical process industry. Sometimes when iron contamination must be kept to an absolute minimum, brick with no iron content is specified.

Design Procedure

Masonry linings are subject to varying temperature conditions that cause expansion and contraction, which in turn produce stresses and strains that can fracture and destroy the masonry unless it is properly designed. The strongest and most durable construction is obtained by using the largest form-fittings masonry units joined with the most resistant cement available for the anticipated chemical and physical conditions.

Brick linings should be self-supporting structures, separated from the rigid steel or concrete shell by an impervious membrane. Claims have been made concerning the adhesion of brick to rubber and plastic membranes, but any such adhesive force would tend to prevent independent movement of the brick and shell, and would encourage failure of the unit. It is absolutely essential that the impervious membrane be bonded to the rigid shell, but there should be as little adhesion as possible between the brickwork and the membrane. When this requisite is accepted, the need for adequate design for the brick lining becomes obvious.

The first considerations in the design of a brick lining are the corrosive conditions and the maximum operating temperature. This knowledge will enable a design engineer to select the proper chemical-resistant construction materials, and specify the required thickness of brickwork necessary to reduce the temperature of the impervious membrane to 150°F or less.

Considerable information on the design of masonry linings can be obtained by a study of Figures 22-1 and 22-2. Figure 22-1 shows a lined steel tank with two courses of brick with an expansion joint and wooden bumpers. The design of the steel shell and the selection of the type of organic lining and chemical-resistant mortar cement used to joint the brickwork should be based on information given in Chapters 8, 9, and 20.

Figure 22-2 shows a reinforced concrete shell lined with an asphaltic-type membrane and protected on the inside and outside by brick sheathings. It is customary to use asphaltic expansion joints or pads in the ends of the concrete tanks and also to use interlocking expansion joints for long tanks. The longitudinal walls of long tanks should be bowed and battered whenever possible.

Bowing places the brick under compression since a slight outward arching of the sides approaches a circular shape. By designing so that the width at the bottom is less than the width at the top (battering) the tendency for the brick to fall inward is minimized. Additional information can be obtained from the construction procedures described below.

Brick Lining Construction With a Sulfur-Base Cement

Whenever a sulfur base cement is used, the first step consists in pouring and spreading a thin film of sulfur-base cement with a straight-

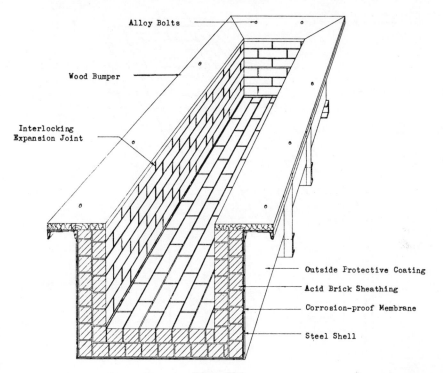

Alloy Bolts

Wood Bumper

Interlocking
Expansion Joint

Outside Protective Coating

Acid Brick Sheathing

Corrosion-proof Membrane

Steel Shell

Figure 22-1.

edged board over an impervious membrane on the floor of the tank. This will prevent the membrane from being damaged by falling brick, etc. If it is an asphaltic-lined concrete tank, the thin film of sulfur cement will also prevent the spacing chips from sinking into the membrane.

The floor itself is constructed by placing each brick on three preformed sulfur-base spacing chips, leaving 1/4-inch wide vertical joints open to the full depth of each brick. The first wall course should be started at the same time as the floor, and the brick should be laid from one end of the construction toward the other end. The joints should be poured full and additional pours should be made while the joints are still warm in order to compensate for initial shrinkage and to form homogeneous flush joints.

It is customary to leave a thin float coat of plasticized sulfur cement over the surface of the brick floor, although this may be removed if necessary. It is important always to pour molten sulfur cement at one point as long as it flows away readily. Another adjacent point is then selected and the step is repeated until the entire area has been poured. This technique minimizes the formation of air pockets.

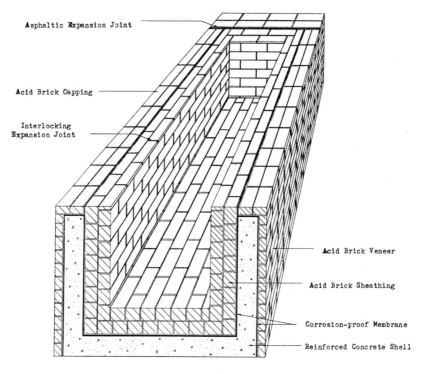

Asphaltic Expansion Joint

Acid Brick Capping

Interlocking
Expansion Joint

Acid Brick Veneer

Acid Brick Sheathing

Corrosion-proof Membrane

Reinforced Concrete Shell

Figure 22-2.

If a double course of brick is being used, the first course is set in the manner previously described. The second course is then placed on chips and the previous pouring step is repeated. The hot sulfur-base cement will fill the remainder of the joints in the first course and bond the two courses together. It is not necessary to secure completely full joints in the first course if two courses are used. However, no more than one course should be poured at any one time.

The construction of the vertical walls is continued by the setting of one entire course of brick on spacer chips. Spacer chips are also used to assure a 1/4 inch joint between the membrane and the brick lining and to secure 1/4 inch vertical joints between the brick surfaces throughout the walls.

The joints on the inside of the brick wall must be sealed by pasting strips of paper or cloth over the joints. Silicate of soda (water glass) is used as an adhesive. The adhesive should be brush applied as a thin coat to the paper or cloth and not to the brick. Only one course should be laid and poured at any one time. The paper should be cut into 6 inch widths, with pieces approximately 3 to 6 feet in length. The treated paper should be allowed to dry approximately

5 minutes after being applied to the brick before the hot sulfur-base cement is poured. After the tank is finished, the paper is easily removed with water.

When pouring sulfur-base cement, one should start at one corner of the tank and fill the joints to within 1/2 inch of the top, being careful not to spill the hot melt over the top surface of the brick. This precaution will minimize difficulties which might be encountered in laying the next course. As in the case of floor construction, the molten sulfur cement should be poured at one joint as long as possible. As soon as the molten cement stops flowing away, the process is repeated at another joint, and still another until the entire course is poured. This method of construction minimizes the formation of air pockets.

The construction is similar when a double course of brick is used, except that the forming paper is used only on the inner course. In this case it is essential that the line of joints be staggered throughout the wall and floor.

Details for single and double course linings using sulfur cement in steel tanks are shown in Figure 22-3.

Brick Lining Construction with a Chemical-Resistant Resin Mortar

A resin-base or a silicate cement mortar may be used as a bonding material throughout the masonry sheathing. These chemical-resistant cements, which are usually supplied as a powder and a liquid, are prepared on the job by adding the powder to the liquid in the proportions described by the manufacturer.

The bricks should be clean and dry and in cold weather should be heated to a temperature where they can still be held comfortably in the bare hand. The bricks are laid by buttering the contact surfaces with freshly mixed cement mortar to produce joints which are as thin as possible, usually 1/8 inch or less. Sometimes it is necessary to use wider joints in order to make up for irregularities in the brick. It is important to slide the buttered bricks in place and to avoid leaving any voids in either the bedjoint or in the joint between the brick. Any cement mortar that exudes may be removed with a trowel and reused while it is still in a workable stage.

Details for single and double course brick linings using resin mortar cements for concrete tanks are shown in Figure 22-4.

Modified Construction with Sulfur and Resin Cements

The coefficients of expansion of masonry linings, and the protected steel shell, vary considerably over the range of temperatures usually employed in the process industries. Rubber, plastic and other organic membrane linings are resistant to abrasion, but are deficient in their resistance to sharp objects. Therefore, it is essen-

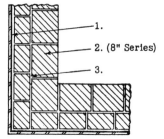

4" Standard Construction

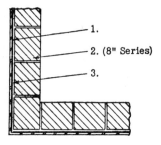

6-1/2" Standard Construction

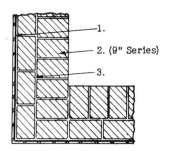

7-1/2" Standard Construction

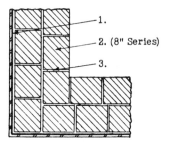

8" Standard Construction

Figure 22-3. Standard acid brick sheathing details for steel.
1. Corrosion-proof membrane
2. Acid brick (8 x 3¾ x 4½ in., 8 x 3¾ x 2¼ in., 9 x 4½ x 2½ in.)
3. ¼-in. sulfur cement joints

tial whenever possible, to prevent direct contact of infusible materials such as furan and phenolic cements with rubber-like membrane linings in rectangular vessels.

This inherent deficiency in rubber linings has been overcome in part through the use of modified dual construction in which a plasticized sulfur cement is used between the brick and the lining, and an infusible resin cement between the bricks. Such construction can be used at temperatures much higher than are possible with sulfur cements alone.

The labor cost for installing modified dual construction is usually less than that for a chemical-resistant mortar alone. The heat from the molten plasticized sulfur cement accelerates the set of the chemical-resistant mortar in the construction of the walls and permits the tanks to be placed in service somewhat sooner after completion of the construction work.

When modified dual construction is required, a thin film of plasticized sulfur cement should be poured and quickly spread with a

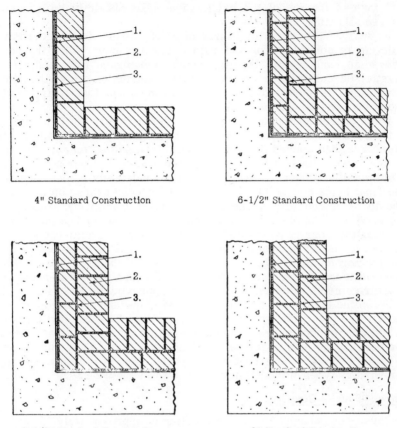

4" Standard Construction

6-1/2" Standard Construction

7-1/2" Standard Construction

8" Standard Construction

Figure 22-4. Standard acid brick sheathing details for concrete.
1. Corrosion-proof membrane
2. Acid brick (8 x 3¾ x 4½ in., 8 x 3¾ x 2¼ in., 9 x 4½ x 2½ in.)
3. 1/8-in. resin cement joints

straight edge over the chemical-resistant membrane on the bottom of the tank. This step is essential to prevent the membrane from being damaged by falling brick and to level the floor if the impervious membrane has lapped seams or other irregularities.

Acid-proof brick, laid on the floor of the tank, should be buttered on the sides and bottom with a chemical mortar and set in place, allowance being made for approximately 1/8 inch vertical and bedjoints. The exposed joints of the acid-proof brick in the wall should be buttered with a chemical resistant mortar and laid with a maximum allowance of 1/8 inch for the brick joint and 1/4 inch for the open backjoint. This backjoint between the brick lining and membrane should be poured with a plasticized sulfur cement to within

1/2 inch of the top of the brick. The walls should be built up one course at a time.

In dual construction the course of brick exposed to the corrosive solution is bonded throughout with a resin cement, while the back course in contact with the impervious membrane is joined with a plasticized sulfur-base cement. Dual construction offers the same advantages as modified dual construction except that it applies to more than one course of brick.

When dual construction is required, the first course of brick on the bottom of the tank is set on spacer ships to give 1/4-inch wide joints which are then poured full with a plasticized sulfur cement. The top of the first course of brick on the floor should be floor coated with molten sulfur cement in order to obtain a relatively smooth bed for the final brick course on the floor. The second course on the floor should be joined with a chemical-resistant mortar by setting the buttered brick in place to obtain joints approximately 1/8 inch wide.

After the floor is completed, the first course of acid-proof brick in the wall is set on spacer chips, leaving a 1/4 inch space between the membrane and the brick. The two sides of the brick that will be exposed to tank solution are then buttered with a chemical-resistant mortar cement, allowing an open joint approximately 1/4 inch wide between the inside and outside course of brick and a joint approximately 1/8 inch wide between vertical bricks. The exposed layer of brick, when bonded with a chemical-resistant mortar, acts as a form for pouring the plasticized sulfur in the backjoints. Only one course at a time should be constructed around the sides of the tank. Details for various types of dual lining are shown in Figure 22-5.

Three-Course Construction

Three-course brick linings, consisting of approximately 12 inches of brickwork, are used primarily for continuous strip steel pickle lines. The course of brick against the membrane is joined with a plasticized sulfur-base compound, and the two outer courses bonded throughout with a resin-base cement. This type of construction permits high temperature pickling and continual severe service.

Recommended Thickness for Masonry Sheathing in Rectangular Tanks

The following data on thickness of brick linings in rectangular vessels are approximate and make no allowance for specific processes and their behavior in the reaction vessel. It is advisable to contact engineers specializing in materials of corrosion-proof construction for more complete recommendations.

It is possible to reduce the masonry sheathing thickness in large rectangular vessels somewhat by battering or bowing the walls. When the walls of a supporting shell are battered, the masonry lining depends on the shell for some of its support, consequently, the brick lining can be reduced in thickness and the walls of the supporting must be strengthened to withstand the additional load. The bowing or arching of a brick lining places the brickwork under compression. A bowed wall exerts a side thrust on the end walls on expansion. When the end supporting walls resist this thrust, the arched masonry wall absorbs and transmits part of the pressure to its supporting walls, which should be designed sufficiently rigid to withstand this force. In tanks having perpendicular, straight walls, if the brick lining is not self-supporting, a force will be exerted against the ends of the tanks upon expansion. The ends of the tanks resist this thrust and the brick walls will be forced to move in the direction of least resistance. The result may be a collapsing of the tank wall in the center of the tank.

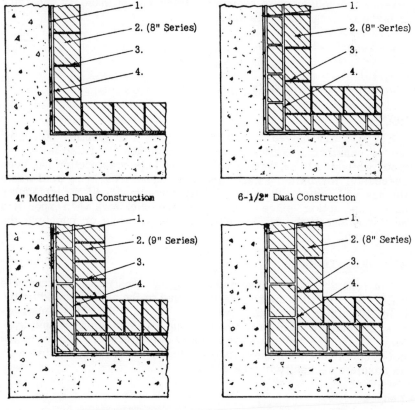

4" Modified Dual Construction

6-1/2" Dual Construction

7-1/2" Dual Construction

8" Dual Construction

Figure 22-5. Dual acid brick sheathing details for concrete.
1. Corrosion-proof membrane
2. Acid brick (8 x 3¾ x 4½ in., 8 x 3¾ x 2¼ in., 9 x 4½ x 2½ in.)
3. 1/8-in. resin cement joints
4. ¼-in. sulfur cement joints

Temperature less than 150°F   4 inches brick
          Tank walls 12 feet in length should not be over 10 feet in depth
          Tank walls 25 feet in length should not be over 5 feet in depth

Temperature 150 - 180°F   4 inches brick
          Tank walls 10 feet in length should not be over 10 feet in depth
          Tank walls 22 feet in length should not be over 5 feet in depth

Temperature 180 - 200°F   4 inches brick
          Tank walls 9 feet in length should not be over 10 feet in depth
          Tank walls 20 feet in length should not be over 5 feet in depth

Temperature 200 - 250°F   8 inches brick

Temperature 250 - 300°F   12 inches brick

Other methods used to reduce the thickness of masonry sheathing in large rectangular areas are:
1. Keyways
2. Alloy Steel Tie Rods
3. Ledges
4. Pilasters
5. Tapered Brick Walls

Keyways

Keyways are placed in the sidewalls of a supporting structure during construction. Header courses of brick are fitted into these slots while the brick wall is being laid. This construction has been successful for building walls and long tunnels carrying acid waste liquors and fumes. It is not usually recommended for rectangular tank construction, since expansion of the brickwork when exposed to heat may shear the header brick in the keyways or puncture the membrane.

Alloy Steel Tie Rods

Tie rods are usually inserted during the construction of concrete walls. An asphaltic membrane is applied to the wall followed by the brick sheathing, which is cemented to the tie rods. This construction is recommended only for building walls or fume exhaust systems where the brickwork is actually only a veneer. Tie rods are not recommended for use in tanks, since a continuous membrane is an absolute necessity in tank design.

Ledges

The masonry thickness in a deep unit may be reduced by the construction of a ledge in the reinforced concrete tank wall which divides the height of the wall in half. This construction has some merit in tank design if expansion joints are placed behind the brick walls at the ledge corners. An expansion joint allows the bottom half to move upward and sideways without cracking or spalling the ledge brick. There is, of course, the risk that the asphaltic lining at the ledge corners may be damaged if the brickwork moves excessively.

Pilasters

A European procedure for strengthening chemical-resistant masonry walls utilizes brick pilasters inside of tanks. This method has not been used to any extent in the United States. Since the pilasters would obstruct the flow in tanks, this type of construction would be suitable in vessels that require baffles.

Tapered Walls

The brick walls in a deep vessel can be tapered with the thickest part at the bottom. This method has been used primarily in towers, especially when ledges are required to support any grillwork.

Other design details such as capping and expansion joints are discussed below.

Capping

Capping is necessary in order to protect the exposed top of asphaltic-lined concrete shell or a rubber-lined steel tank from mechanical damage. An asphaltic-lined concrete shell should be capped with a brick veneer. A wooden bumper should in turn, protect the brick capping as illustrated. The top perimeter of a rubber lined steel tank may also be protected by means of a wooden bumper as shown previously in Figure 22-1.

Veneering

If it is above the ground, the outside of a concrete tank should be protected against spillage, splash and fumes by a single course of acid-proof brick veneering over a 1/4-inch asphaltic-type membrane as shown previously in Figure 22-2. When brick veneer is not practical, the outside concrete wall should be covered with a minimum of three coats of a chemical-resistant coating having a total thickness of not less than 5 mils.

Expansion Joints

Although chemically inert and structurally sound, a masonry sheathing in a rectangular tank may fail if expansion is not taken into consideration. It is necessary to compensate for this movement in the brick lining by the insertion of an expansion joint.

In sound design, expansion joints running transversely through the wall and floor sections are provided at intervals along the length of the tank. In this construction, unvulcanized rubber is embedded in the brickwork to effect a liquid-tight joint and yet permit expansion and contraction of the wall and floor within reasonable limits. The unvulcanized rubber, in itself, is not compressible, but is displaceable so that expansion of the wall or floor causes the rubber to exude at the open edges of the joint. The efficiency of the joint depends on the volume of rubber exuded.

To overcome the incompressibility of the unvulcanized rubber and the permeability of a compressible material, it has been found advantageous to use a combination of an uncompressible material such as unvulcanized rubber and a compressible cellular product such as sponge rubber.

A standard expansion joint consists of the following: (1) unvulcanized rubber, which is placed in front of the joint to provide a liquid-tight surface in contact with the corrosive solution. (2) Sponge rubber, placed directly in back of this unvulcanized rubber joint. This compressible material acts as a cushion and is readily displaced by the unvulcanized rubber which is extruded when the joint is put into compression by expansion of the brickwork. When contraction occurs, the elastic, unvulcanized rubber returns to its former position, thus maintaining a tight joint. The joints are staggered between courses of brick in order to make the expansion joint more efficient.

There is also a shearing action which takes place between courses of brick upon expansion or contraction. This condition is alleviated by installing shear pads between the courses of brick. Shear pads are also utilized to minimize the shearing action between the brick next to the membrane and those next to the solution.

In actual practice, the unvulcanized and sponge rubber, between adjacent brick and the unvulcanized rubber between adjacent courses of brick, consist of precut pieces cemented directly to the individual brick. The unvulcanized rubber between the rows of brick consists of one piece equal to the length of four bricks, since the expansion joint is usually laid up four courses at a time. Design details for expansion joints are given in Figure 22-6.

In providing relief against the thermal expansion stresses, it is essential that a sufficient number of joints be specified. The location and number of expansion joints recommended depends to a great extent on two factors: the over-all size of the unit and the maximum temperature to be encountered in actual service.

Generally speaking, in tanks where the maximum length does not exceed 12 feet, and the temperature does not exceed 150°F, no expansion joints or end pads are required. In tanks longer than 12 feet, where the maximum temperature ranges from 150°F to 180°F, it is general practice to utilize end pads when installing 4 inches of acid brick. Tanks longer than 15 feet are usually protected by 8 inches of acid-proof brick and, if the temperature is between 180 to 200°F, the joints should be located approximately 15 feet apart. In location of the expansion joint, the two outermost joints are usually

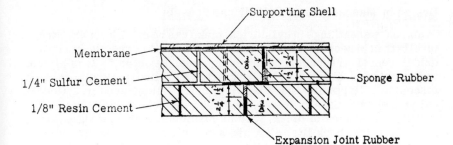

Section Thru Acid Brick Lining

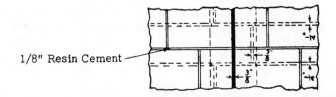

View Facing Lining

Figure 22-6. Interlocking expansion joint 8 inch dual sheathing.
Note: These construction details also apply to concrete shells.

placed 7 1/2 feet from the ends of the tanks, and the others are evenly spaced between these end joints.

The following data on expansion joints are approximate because not all of the factors are considered. A case history of a particular process unit may indicate that expansion joints may be eliminated.

Expansion Joint Requirements

Length of Tank (Ft)	Temp. (°F)	Remarks
0 - 12	0 - 150	No expansion provisions
10 - 15	150 - 180	4 in. (½ in. Expansion pads) 8 in. (one joint)
15 plus	180 - 200	Expansion joint every 15 ft (8 in.)
15 plus	200 - 220	Expansion joint every 12 ft (8 in.)
15 plus	220 plus	Expansion joint every 10 ft (8 in.)
40 plus	200 plus	Expansion joint 10 ft intervals (12 in.) plus 1 in. End pads

Design of Masonry-lined Cylindrical Vessels

Masonry sheathings in cylindrical tanks can be much thinner, struc-turally than in rectangular tanks. Brick installed correctly in a cylin-drical vessel are under compression and "keyed in." It is almost impossible for a brick lining, subjected to cylindrical compression forces, to collapse inward. Likewise, brick linings used in cylindri-cal vessels are usually less porous than in rectangular tanks.

Different shapes of brick, such as straights, arches, wedges, keys, necks, circles, book tile, etc., are available for forming cylindrical masonry sheathings. The walls of a cylindrical vessel may be con-structed of these various shapes. Photographs of the actual instal-lation of brick linings are presented in Figures 22-7, 22-8 and 22-9.

Stack Design

Stacks can be constructed of steel, reinforced concrete, brick or a combination of these materials. Stacks or chimneys which carry corrosive fumes to the atmosphere require special design.

When a corrosive atmosphere is present, it is usually best to con-struct a self-supporting brick chimney. When stacks or chimneys are braced, the corrosive atmosphere usually attacks the guy bands and bolts and eventually the guy wires.

There are three principal types of steel stacks. The first is a

Figure 22-7. Detailed view of construction of pickling tank masonry sheathing.

(Courtesy of Chemsteel Construction Co.)
Figure 22-8. Construction of a 165-ft continuous pickling line.

common straight stack, which is supported by guy wires. If operating under 160°F, this stack should be lined with a corrosion-resistant lining or coating having a minimum thickness of 60 mils. The outside should be protected with a minimum of 3 coats of a protective coating having a thickness of at least 5 mils. The guy bands and wires should also be coated.

The second type of stack has a bell-shaped base. The steel wall is of a sufficient thickness to eliminate the use of guy wires for support which makes it more suitable for corrosive fumes. It should be protected against corrosion in the manner described for the common stack.

The third type of stack is similar to the first two with the exception that this type operates at temperatures higher than 160°F. Thus, it is necessary to protect the plastic or rubber linings on the inside against thermal attack by means of a chemical-resistant masonry sheathing.

Steel stacks are usually built in courses of steel plate not over 72

Figure 22-9. Installation of a two-course brick lining using a sulfur cement in the back joints and a phenolic resin cement in the front joints. Tank to be used in chemical plant service.

inches high and so formed that each course telescopes into the bottom of the next succeeding course. The same thickness of steel plate should be used throughout the stack.

A self-supporting all-brick chimney should be constructed of special radial brick designed so that the finished brickwork has joints of uniform thickness throughout and a smooth surface to reduce the air friction. The interior of the chimney should be lined with an acid-proof brick sheathing joined with an acid-proof cement. A joint from 1/4 to 1 inch is allowed behind the acid-brick linings, and is filled with an asphaltic-type, hot-pour, chemical-resistant compound.

Design of Trenches

An open-type trench is preferred for the disposal of corrosive waste liquors in most industries. An open-type trench can be inspected quite easily and repaired, if necessary, with a minimum labor cost.

There are two basic types of open trenches, a rectangular brick trench (see Figure 22-10) and a rounded bottom trench constructed from half-round sections of vitrified clay pipe (see Figure 22-11). The rectangular trench is recommended most widely.

As shown in Figure 22-10, this construction consists of the concrete protected with a plasticized asphaltic membrane, followed by a masonry sheathing 4 inches thick on the side walls and 2 1/4 inches on the floor. The bricks are joined throughout with a chemical-resistant cement. It is standard practice to erect a few courses of brick in the walls before starting the floor.

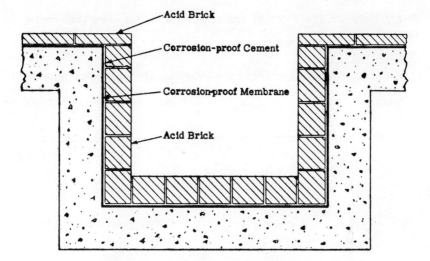

Figure 22-10. Trench gross section details.

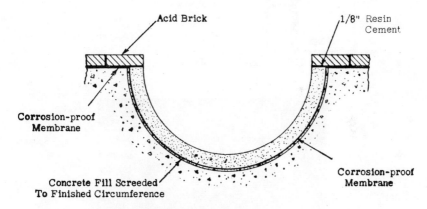

Figure 22-11. Half round vitrified clay pipe trench details.

Manholes, Sumps, Pits and Sewers

Manholes, sumps, etc., exposed to corrosive liquors must be lined with chemical-resistant linings. The interior of these structures, which are normally constructed of concrete, should be protected by an asphaltic triple-ply membrane. This in turn, is protected with a 4-inch thick acid-proof brick sheathing and joined throughout with a chemical-resistant cement.

In many manholes, the ceiling is constructed of liner plates measuring 9 x 18 x 1 1/4 inches and weighing approximately 14 pounds each. As shown in Figure 22-12, the plates are cast in the concrete, and the joints between the liner plates are filled with a chemical-resistant cement.

Estimating Data

Data for estimating quantities of various chemical-resistant mor-

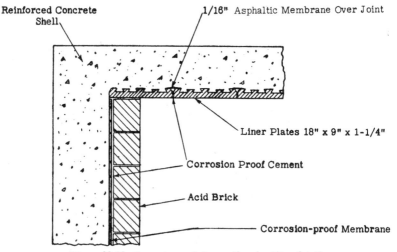

Figure 22-12. Concrete manhole – wall and ceiling detail.

Figure 22-13. Small tank lined with Saran rubber and acid brick joined with a furan cement.

tar cement for standard and dual construction are given in Tables 22-2 and 22-3. Additional information can be obtained from the references at the end of this chapter.

Typical brick-lined tanks used in various industries are shown in Figures 22-13, 22-14 and 22-15.

Figure 22-14. Interior of large concrete tank in an edible oil treatment plant. Asphalt lining, acid-proof brick, and furan cement.

TABLE 22-2. MATERIAL ESTIMATING TABLE PER SQUARE FOOT

One-Course Construction

Sheathing Thickness (In.)	Brick Size (In.)	Plasticized Sulfur Cement	Carbon-filled Furan or Phenolic Cement	Silicate Cement
2½	Singles 8 x 3¾ x 2¼	Cement: 6.5 lbs Brick: 4.37	Cement: 2.0 lbs Brick: 4.58	Cement: 3.2 lbs Brick: 4.58
4	Doubles 8 x 3¾ x 4½	Cement: 8.0 lbs Brick: 3.68	Cement: 2.4 lbs Brick: 3.84	Cement: 2.8 lbs Brick: 3.84
8	Doubles 8 x 3¾ x 4½	Cement: 16.0 lbs Brick: 7.36	Cement: 4.8 lbs Brick: 7.68	Cement: 6.4 lbs Brick: 7.68
2½	9 x 4½ x 2½	Cement: 6.4 lbs Brick: 3.28	Cement: 2.0 lbs Brick: 3.42	Cement: 2.6 lbs Brick: 3.42
4½	9 x 4½ x 2½	Cement: 11.0 lbs Brick: 5.67	Cement: 3.4 lbs Brick: 6.02	Cement: 4.5 lbs Brick: 6.02
9	9 x 4½ x 2½	Cement: 22.0 lbs Brick: 11.34	Cement: 6.7 lbs Brick: 12.04	Cement: 9.0 lbs Brick: 12.04

Note: Quantities in these tables are approximate and are presented only as a guide to the average user.

Figure 22-15. Concrete pickling tanks protected with asphalt membrane and brick sheathing using dual construction method.

TABLE 22-3. MATERIAL ESTIMATING TABLE PER SQUARE FOOT

Modified Dual Construction

Sheathing Thickness (In.)	Brick Size (In.)	Units	No. Brick	Plasticized Sulfur Cement (lbs)	No. Brick	Carbon-filled Furan Cement (lbs)	Silicate Cement (lbs)
			1/4-in. Joints		1/8-in. Joints		
4	8 x 3¾ x 4½	Walls		3.58	3.84	1.33	1.78
		Floor		3.58	3.84	2.38	3.18
4¾	8 x 3¾ x 4½	Walls		3.58	4.58	1.79	2.39
		Floor		3.58	4.58	2.84	3.79
4¾	9 x 4½ x 2½	Walls		3.58	6.02	2.30	3.07
		Floor		3.58	6.02	3.35	4.47
4¾	9 x 4½ x 3	Walls		3.58	5.05	2.01	2.68
		Floor		3.58	5.05	3.06	4.08
Dual Construction							
6½	8 x 3¾ x 2¼	Walls	4.37	10.08	3.84	1.33	1.78
	8 x 3¾ x 4½	Floor	4.37	6.50	3.84	2.38	3.18
8	8 x 3¾ x 4½	Walls	3.68	11.53	3.84	1.33	1.78
		Floor	3.68	7.95	3.84	2.38	3.18

Note: Quantities in these tables are approximate and are presented only as a guide to the average user.

One of the principal uses for chemical-resistant masonry is in the construction of chemical-resistant floors. Since this is essentially a separate subject, it has not been discussed with the construction of vessels, sumps, and pits but will be described in Chapter 23.

Suggested References

"Handbook of Brick Masonry Construction," John A. Mulligan, 1st Edition, McGraw Hill Book Co., New York, 1942.

"Brick and Tile Engineering Handbook of Design," Harry C. Plummer, Structural Clay Products Institute, 1950.

"Civil Engineering Handbook," Leonard Church Urquhart, 3rd Edition, McGraw Hill Book Co., New York, 1940.

"Plastics Meet the Acid Test," Raymond B. Seymour, Modern Plastics, August 1950.

"Plastic Materials of Construction," Raymond B. Seymour, Corrosion, May 1953.

23. CHEMICAL RESISTANT FLOORS

Modern chemical-resistant floors consist of brick or tile joined by chemical-resistant mortar cements. In spite of their importance, the joints account for a very small proportion of the entire structure.

As in the case of other masonry construction, described in Chapter 20, the sub-floor must be properly designed and protected by an impervious membrane. It is customary to use an asphaltic membrane under the brick or tile and to join the brick with a properly selected cement such as discussed in Chapter 9.

Design Considerations

In every floor design, proper attention must be given to the possibility of settling and seasonable variations in the ground water level, frost line, etc., as well as vibrations resulting from railroad or truck traffic or machinery within the building, and expected loads. In too many instances, failures resulting from improper design are attributed to construction or material failures. Industrial floors having a low factor of safety usually fail because of unexpected settling, vibrations, or heavy loads. For example, the fluctuations resulting from filling and emptying a 5,000-gallon tank within a building may be sufficient to cause structural failure of an under-designed floor.

Whether or not the floor surface over a properly designed sub-floor will be satisfactory depends to a large extent upon the service to be encountered. Many floors are subjected to the constant traffic of carts or trucks, some of which are equipped with improperly designed wheels which may ruin an otherwise satisfactory floor. Other floors are completely disintegrated by materials such as sugar, animal, vegetable or mineral oils, milk, beer, fruit juices, soda pop, detergents or ice cream. Sometimes floor construction that would not be acceptable for a residential lavatory is erroneously considered adequate for chemical process or textile plants. Many buildings fail because of inadequate attention to proper floor design.

Most floor failures can be attributed to a lack of knowledge of good design. The National Safety Council recommends that the floor and foundation should be designed to bear at least four times the anticipated stationary load and six times the anticipated maximum moving load placed on it, but many floors do not meet these specifications.

Any standard text on strength of material would serve as a guide for the design of the sub-floor but design information on industrial floor surfaces is not readily available. This chapter has been written in an attempt to overcome this deficiency.

A satisfactory floor surface must be free from nails, bolts, holes, splinters and other projections. It must be dry, low in heat conductivity, durable, and easily cleaned. In addition, it must be adequately resistant to the direct or indirect chemical action of any solid, liquid or gas to which it may be exposed.

Some industrial floors that have been considered satisfactory are earth, wood, metal, cement, wood or cement protected by mastics, cement admixtures, magnesite, terrazzo, linoleum, rubber and trowelled plastic cements or brick or tile joined with appropriate materials. The information in this chapter will be confined to the latter.

Regardless of what jointing material may be used with brick or tile, the sub-base must be designed to withstand all settlement, vibration and loads and all levels and slopes must be maintained as part of the sub-floor. It is difficult and uneconomical to correct mistakes on levels by adding varying amounts of mortar above the sub-floor.

Before application of an impervious membrane, the concrete sub-base must be given a wood float finish and all loose particles brushed from the surface. The contour of the brick floor will follow closely that of the sub-base since irregularities, such as low or high spots, will result in an irregular floor. The floor should be pitched about 1/4 inch per foot to all drains and gutters.

Impervious Membranes

Since the sub-floor is somewhat porous, it must first be protected by a waterproof membrane. If a properly selected heavy asphaltic membrane is used, the sub-base will be protected from both water and corrosive solutions.

In practically all cases, a primer coat should precede any membrane application. For best results, it is preferred to brush apply the primer. In all cases, the primer must be allowed to dry before subsequent coats are applied. Neither the primer nor membrane should be applied on green concrete.

One of the most satisfactory and most universally accepted corrosion-resistant membranes consists of an asphaltic-type primer followed by a hot-melt asphaltic composition. The latter is applied with a straight edge in several steps in order to obtain a 1/4 inch thickness. Since the product is resilient, thermoplastic, and tacky it cannot be used as a final surface. Even before application of the subsequent brick or tile, the asphaltic layer must be dusted with finely ground silica to prevent it from sticking to the bricklayers' feet.

A more serviceable and slightly more expensive corrosion-resistant membrane is obtained by reinforcing the membrane described above with woven "Fiberglas."

Types of Industrial Floors

Extra heavy-duty floors are composed of 3 3/4 inch thick brick joined with a properly selected cement. These are suitable for heavy trucking and have given excellent service in steel plants and heavy-equipment manufacturing plants. Heavy-duty floors are composed of 2 1/4 inch thick brick joined with properly selected cements and are suitable for moderate trucking. Such floors have been used for over ten years in chemical plants, textile plants and plating room floors. A cross section view of each type floor is shown in Figure 23-1.

Food plant floors which are of different type construction will be discussed subsequently. The application procedures for industrial brick floors are similar to those discussed for tank floors in Chapter 22.

Application of Sulfur Cements

When a sulfur cement is to be used, the acid-proof bricks are laid directly on the asphaltic membrane, leaving open joints 1/4 inch wide between the brick. Suitable containers for pouring the melted sulfur cement can be made from two-quart preserving cans, about 6 to 8 inches tall, with sides pinched to form a "V" pouring spout. This container should be handled with canvas gloves. It is recommended that about one dozen similar containers be available so that when the sulfur cement solidifies in the containers, they may be placed in the sulfur cement melting kettle and the accumulated materials recovered.

Pouring should be started by filling from 2 to 3 feet in length of open joint to within 1/4 inch of the top. This step should be repeated immediately so that the partly filled joints can be further filled to at least 1/16 inch above the surface of the tile.

The time interval between pours should be long enough to allow the original material to settle in the joint, and yet short enough to permit the second pour to become well bonded to the previously poured joints. A satisfactory bond cannot be obtained unless these precautions are observed.

Any excess material may be removed with a sharp edge chisel as soon as the sulfur cement solidifies, or it may be left to wear off under traffic. If a bed of cement is required, the brick should first be set in the prescribed manner on preformed sulfur chips before pouring the molten cement. When sulfur chips are used, attempts should be made to level the bricks, insofar as possible before pouring the hot cement.

Application of Resin-Base Mortar Cements

When a resin-base mortar cement is used to join the bricks, an asphaltic-type membrane is first applied to the concrete floor slab in the usual manner. All the metal drains, pipe, exposed concrete, etc., should then be coated with an asphaltic primer.

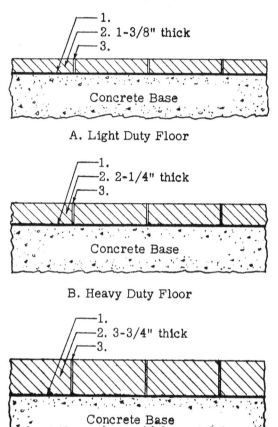

A. Light Duty Floor

B. Heavy Duty Floor

C. Extra Heavy Duty Floor

Figure 23-1. Industrial floor construction.
1. Chemical resistant membrane
2. Acid brick or tile
3. Chemical resistant cement

As pointed out in Chapter 9, most resin cements contain acid catalysts as hardening agents. If the cement is applied directly to a metal or concrete surface, the catalyst may be neutralized or weakened sufficiently to prevent the cement from settling.

Clean, dry brick should be laid by starting from one wall and working toward the opposite end. The contact vertical edges of the brick should be buttered and the brick set directly on the asphaltic membrane. At the same time, the brick should be squeezed together to obtain joints approximately 1/8 inch wide and any excess mortar which is forced out of the joint, should be removed with a trowel.

The width of the joint may vary from 1/16 to 3/16 inch to compensate for variations in the brick.

If the construction requires the use of a bed of resin cement over the membrane, a thin layer of mortar approximately 1/8 inch in thickness should be spread on top of the asphaltic layer before laying the brick. The contact vertical edges of the brick should be buttered with mortar and the brick bedded directly on the mortar. The brick should be tapped to the desired level and at the same time forced together to obtain approximately 1/8-inch joints. Any excess mortar which squeezes out of the joints should be removed with a trowel in the usual manner.

Material Requirements for Industrial Floors

The number of brick and the amount of chemical-resistant mortar cement required per square foot for various types of industrial floors are given in Table 23-1.

Food Plant Floors

The requirements for a modern food plant floor are:
1. A high degree of sanitation.

TABLE 23-1. TECHNICAL DATA FOR
INDUSTRIAL CHEMICAL-RESISTANT FLOORS

Type of Floor	Thickness of Brick (In.)	Size of Brick (In.)	Width of Vertical Joints (In.)	Number of Brick (per sq ft)	Resin-Based Cement (lbs/sq ft)	Sulfur-Based Cement (lbs/sq ft)
Light duty	1 1/2	12 x 6 x 1½	1/4	1.89	–	1.29
	1 1/2	12 x 6 x 1½	1/8	1.94	0.39	–
	1 3/8	8¼ x 4 x 1 3/8	1/4	4.00	–	1.70
	1 3/8	8¼ x 4 x 1 3/8	1/8	4.17	0.52	–
	1 1/8	8 x 3¾ x 1 1/8	1/4	4.37	–	1.46
	1 1/8	8 x 3¾ x 1 1/8	1/8	4.58	0.45	–
Heavy duty	2 1/4	8 x 3¾ x 2¼	1/4	4.37	–	2.92
	2 1/4	8 x 3¾ x 2¼	1/8	4.58	0.90	–
	2 1/2	9 x 4½ x 2½	1/4	3.28	–	2.79
	2 1/2	9 x 4½ x 2½	1/8	3.42	0.85	–
Extra	3 3/4	8 x 3¾ x 4½	1/4	3.68	–	4.37
heavy duty	3 3/4	8 x 3¾ x 4½	1/8	3.84	1.33	–

Asphaltic primer coverage is 0.01 gal/sq ft.
Asphaltic membrane a ¼ in. thickness is 1.5 lbs/sq ft.
The above figures are based on average practice.
Quantities may vary, depending upon individual conditions, at the job.
Excess waste and irregular brick require additional material.

1/4 in. bedjoint requires 3.58 lb sulfur-based cement per sq ft.
1/8 in. bedjoint requires 1.05 lb carbon-filled resin-based cement per sq ft.

2. Complete resistance to mild and food acids, grease, detergents and other liquids characteristic of the food industry.

3. Ability to withstand steam, sterilization and damage from impact by cans, cases and bottles.

4. Attractive appearance and freedom from odors.

5. Long service life.

As will be evident from the subsequent description, these requirements are met by modern quarry tile floors in which both the bed and vertical joints consist of a chemical-resistant resin cement. Other types of floors previously tolerated before the development of modern food plant floors are no longer acceptable to conscientious food plant owners or health authorities.

This construction usually makes use of the 1/2 or 3/4 x 6 x 6 inch quarry tile to produce an attractive permanent dairy floor. However, brick pavers may be used.

As in the case of the industrial floor, it is essential that a minimum temperature of 60°F be provided and that the concrete subbase be given a wood float or troweled finish. Since the tile floor will follow closely that of the sub-base, few if any, irregularities should be present and the floor should be pitched about 1/4 inch per foot to all drains and gutters. It is important that the waterproof membrane in the floor slab be extended up the vertical walls and other protrusions to a height above the final finished floor level and that provisions be made for one course of vertical tile around the entire area.

In this construction, freshly prepared resin-cement mortar is troweled to approximately 1/8 inch on the smooth clean floor slab. Tiles having the upper side coated with paraffin wax are then embedded in the resin while it is still in workable state. All grooves in the bottom of the tile must be completely filled with the bed cement mortar.

Tile may be pressed or beaten down to secure a satisfactory level surface. The width of the joint must be at least 1/4 inch. Any bed-joint resin exuding in the vertical joints will not interfere with the set of the black furan vertical joint cement.

After the tiles are set rigidly, a thin furan mortar is prepared and used to fill the joints. Provided air is not present in the mortar, essentially flush joints will then be secured when it hardens. With 1 3/8 inch thick tile, it is preferable to strike the joints with a wet trowel and to point up any that have settled due to escape of entrapped air. Modifications of this technique may work but are not recommended.

Approximately 24 hours after the joints have become thoroughly hard, the floor is steamed to remove paraffin and excess furan cement from the tile surfaces. This is usually about 48 hours after the installation with the temperature range held between 60 to 85°F. Figures 23-2 to 23-6 illustrate the various steps in the construction of a food plant floor.

Figure 23-2. Installation of a food plant brick floor. Troweling of special resin cement setting bed.

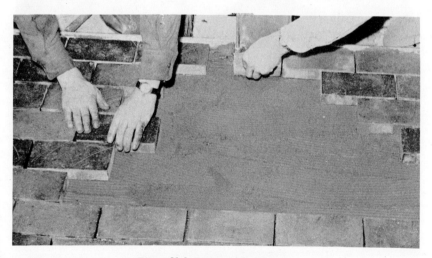

Figure 23-3. Setting of floor brick.

Material Requirements for Food Plant Floors

The number of tile and the amount of furan resin mortar cement required per square foot for different sized tile are given in Table 23-2.

TABLE 23-2. TECHNICAL DATA FOR
FOOD PLANT FLOORS

Type of Tile	Number Time (per sq ft)	Bed Cement (lbs/sq ft)	Grout Cement (lbs/sq ft)
6 x 6 x ½ in. quarry tile	3.7	1.12	0.44
6 x 6 x ¾ in. deep-grooved quarry tile	3.7	1.60	0.66
6 x 6 x ¾ in. shallow-grooved quarry tile	3.7	1.12	0.66
8¼ x 4 x 1 3/8 in. matt bottom floor tile	4.0	1.12	1.10

Note: Quantities will vary depending upon individual conditions at the job. Deep-grooved bottom tile will require approximately 30 per cent additional chemical bed cement. "Deep groove" tile are tile with bottom grooves exceeding 3/32 inch in depth.

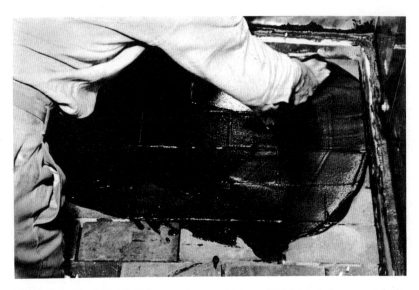

Figure 23-4. Grouting of fluid furan resin cement into vertical joints between waxed tile.

Repair of Existing Tile Floors

Unfortunately, too few food plant owners are aware of industrial acid-proof or furan food plant floors. Consequently, they learn about the inadequacies of tile floors joined with portland cement only after the floor starts to disintegrate. When this occurs, there is no fool-proof solution but temporary protection can be secured.

Figure 23-5. Cleaning completed floor to remove wax and excess resin cement.

Repair of portland cement joined tile floor usually consists in cutting out the vertical joints to a minimum depth of 1/2 inch. All loose portland cement and food residue must be removed from the open joints. This is usually accomplished by washing with 10 per cent hydrochloric acid followed by alternate washes with water and 10 per cent trisodium phosphate. The open joint, before being pointed, must be dry and free from acid, alkali or other residues.

The surface of the tile is usually protected from becoming coated with the repair cement by adhering paper over the area under repair. The paper can then be removed from the joints by passing a blow torch over the entire surface. In this manner, the paper over the open joints is removed by burning but the tile top surface remains protected.

A freshly-mixed, somewhat fluid chemical-resistant resin cement mortar is then poured in the joints. The chemical-resistant resin cement mortar joints will harden in 4 to 6 hours at 70° F. Longer times are required for hardening at lower temperatures.

Figure 23-6. Chemical resistant floor in a margarine plant.

After the joints have become hard, the surface paper may be removed by steaming.

Additional information on modern industrial floor construction can be secured from the references at the end of the chapter.

Suggested References

"Plastics Meet the Acid Test," Raymond B. Seymour, <u>Modern Plastics</u>, Aug. 1950.

"Plastic Materials of Construction," Raymond B. Seymour, <u>Corrosion</u>, May 1953.

"Plastics Equipment Reference Sheet No. 16—Furane Cement," Raymond B. Seymour and Robert H. Steiner, <u>Chem. Eng. Prog.</u>, Dec. 1952.

"Furane Cements," Raymond B. Seymour and Robert H. Steiner, <u>Chem. Eng.</u>, Dec. 1951.

"Maintenance of Industrial Floors," Raymond B. Seymour, <u>Southern Power and Industry</u>, May and June 1951.

"Floor Repair Procedures Improved," Raymond B. Seymour, <u>Southern Power and Industry</u>, May 1952.

"Plant Floors That Can 'Take It,'" Raymond B. Seymour, <u>Food Engineering</u>, Sept. 1952.

"The Material Safety Council," Safety Practice Pamphlet 11, 1954.

SECTION V
PLASTICS SELECTION
GUIDE

24. SELECTION OF PLASTICS FOR THE SOLUTION OF CORROSION PROBLEMS

After studying the previous chapters, the reader might conclude that many different plastics can be utilized satisfactorily for the manufacture of all coatings, linings, cements, castings, impregnants, pipe and molded fittings. Some of the resulting indecision may be reduced by consulting the charts in the chapters, but most design engineers will prefer more definite recommendations. Some useful information on suitable materials for specific industrial applications is outlined below.

Storage

Concentrated sulfuric acid may be stored satisfactorily in unlined steel vessels. Sulfuric acid in concentrations up to 50 per cent should be stored in rubber-lined tanks. Sheet linings of neoprene and plasticized polyvinyl chloride are satisfactory but natural rubber is usually preferred because of many years of successful experience. Plasticized polyvinyl chloride sheet linings have been used successfully for concentrations in excess of 50 per cent.

In spite of a surface hardening effect, natural rubber-lined tanks are also preferred for the storage of hydrochloric acid. Plasticized polyvinyl chloride sheet lining may also be used, but neoprene is usually considered too permeable to hydrochloric acid to permit the storage of this acid except in dilute concentrations.

Phosphoric acid in all concentrations may be stored in rubber-lined equipment. Tests should be made to ascertain that there is no discoloration with any specific commercial rubber lining. Plasticized polyvinyl chloride and sheet neoprene may also be used.

Water and salt water may be stored in tanks with protective coatings. In such cases, surface preparation and application are generally more important than the selection of materials because of the wide choice of products that are resistant to these liquids. Vinyl, neoprene, chlorinated rubber and baked phenolic coatings have all given satisfactory service when properly applied.

Solutions of sodium hydroxide up to 70 per cent and at temperatures up to 240°F have been stored satisfactorily in steel tanks coated with liquid neoprene. The purpose of the coating is primarily to prevent metallic contamination of the product.

Tank Cars--Tank Trucks

Whenever its chemical resistance is suitable, natural rubber is preferred for lining tank cars and trailer trucks because of the years of experience. Natural rubber linings have given satisfactory service with phosphoric and hydrochloric acid in all concentrations and with sulfuric acid up to 50 per cent concentration. Neoprene linings are preferred for transportation of hot caustic solutions.

Vinyl coatings have been used successfully for coating the interiors of tank car and trailers transporting wine and other mildly corrosive liquids. Short-term experience indicates that reinforced polyester tanks are also suitable for the transportation of milk, wine, oil and gasoline.

Protection of Buildings, Equipment and Tank Exteriors

Because of years of usage, vinyl-base coatings are usually preferred for the protection of tank exteriors, overhead structures and building sidings. Neoprene is preferred where abrasion is a factor and where light colors are not required. Chlorinated rubber is essentially interchangeable with vinyl coatings in most recommendations but in spite of many years of availability has not been used as extensively as vinyls.

The exteriors of outdoor equipment are often protected by high pressure-sprayed asphaltic-type mastics. Cork-filled mastics can be used to insulate tanks and chemical equipment.

Flooring

Even in the presence of mild corrosion, brick or tile floors joined with chemical-resistant cements are recommended. In addition to the chemical process industries, such floors are required in dairies, breweries, soft drink bottling works, meat packing plants, tanneries and many other types of plants.

Waste Lines

Vitrified clay pipe joined with a suitable chemical-resistant material is preferred for most waste lines. Hot-poured plastic materials are generally suitable for cold solvent-free wastes but furan-sulfur cement combination joints are required as jointing materials for most industrial waste lines.

Exhaust and Piping Systems

As the result of almost twenty years successful European experience and because of the advantages of using homogeneous chemical-resistant construction, unplasticized polyvinyl chloride should be considered for hoods, ducts, fans and low-pressure piping. Polyethylene pipe should be considered where flexible chemical-resistant pipe or tubing is required.

Paper Mill Applications

As shown in Figure 24-1, modern sulfite digesters are lined with tile in which the course in contact with the process liquor is joined with a furan cement. Carbon brick have been used to some extent for the sulfate process. In most cases, portland cement joints are satisfactory for this service.

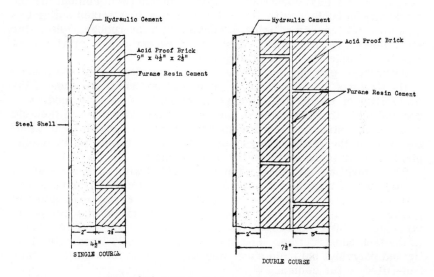

Figure 24-1. Sulfite pulping vessel cross sections.

In spite of a moderate amount of attack, carbon-filled phenolic cements have been used for many years for joining brick in chlorine bleaching towers. Bleach-resistant cements have given satisfactory service when used to join brick and tile in chlorine dioxide bleaching units.

Chlorinated rubber-base coatings have been used successfully for coating exteriors of various equipment in the paper industry. Vinyl coatings and liquid neoprene coatings are also satisfactory. It is standard practice to coat the exteriors of reaction vessels in many paper plants with high pressure sprayed asphaltic mastics.

On the basis of approximately two years of service, it may be concluded that styrene copolymer rubber resin blend pipe is suitable for transporting many cold liquors in paper mills. Rigid polyvinyl chloride pipe, hoods and exhaust systems are preferred for chlorine and chlorine dioxide service.

Steel Pickling

Plastic materials of construction have been used successfully for batch and continuous pickling processes for over twenty years. Continuous pickling units for carbon steel are essentially a series of tanks holding 20 per cent sulfuric acid at temperatures as high as 230°F. These tanks are followed by water rinse tanks.

Standard construction consists of a steel shell protected with a natural rubber sheet lining which in turn is protected by an acid-proof brick sheathing with at least 8 inches of brick work. Standard design utilizes dual construction with a furan-resin cement for the brickwork in contact with the solution and a plasticized sulfur cement for the course of brick in contact with the rubber. The water rinse tanks are of similar construction except that a maximum of 8 inches of brick is usually adequate.

Batch-type pickling units are usually operated at temperatures in the order of 190°F with 10 per cent sulfuric acid. Because of the possibility of mechanical damage from rolls of wire or bundles of rod and plate that are lowered, pickled and then lifted out of the acid solution, construction similar to continuous pickling lines is used. Because of the lower temperature, the brick sheathing in batch-pickling units is seldom greater than 8 inches.

Batch-pickling units are often constructed with a concrete shell. In this case, a triple layer asphaltic lining protected by brick joined with furan-resin cement is satisfactory. Since stainless steel is pickled with mixtures of hydrofluoric and nitric acid at temperatures up to 150°F, carbon brick must be used in place of acid brick in the tank construction. The steel shell is usually lined with plasticized polyvinyl chloride sheet and the brick is joined with a carbon-filled sulfur cement.

Floor construction in the steel industry is usually of the extra-heavy duty type consisting of a plasticized sulfur cement joined brick over an asphaltic membrane. Overhead structures, tank exteriors and siding are usually protected by vinyl coatings.

Masonry fume exhaust systems consisting of brick joined with furan cements are used in conjunction with continuous pickling lines in modern mills. Trenches are lined with single-layer or triple-seal asphalt membrane and protected with brick and furan resin cements. Waste lines are usually vitrified clay pipe joined with a combination of furan and plasticized sulfur cement.

Textile Industry

The modern textile mill is related to the chemical process industry. Hence, floors in wet processing areas should be joined with furan cements and walls, and equipment should be coated with vinyl coatings. A styrene copolymer coating containing a mildewproofing agent is often used for walls and ceilings in textile mills.

Nylon plants require rubber-lined equipment protected by brick joined with furan cements and brick floors joined with the same product. Floors in rayon plants also consist of brick joined with furan cements. Trenches in rayon plants are usually of standard construction, consisting of triple-layer asphalt membrane protected by brick joined with a furan resin cement.

Rayon fume stacks and plenum chambers usually consist of brick joined with a furan-resin cement over a triple-layer asphalt membrane. Type I and Type II unplasticized polyvinyl chloride hood and exhaust systems are now standard in many modern rayon plants. Because of its freedom from attack, unplasticized polyvinyl chloride is also being used for the fabrication of many of the units in the spinning process.

Food Industry

Walls, ceilings and equipment in bakeries, breweries, dairies, canning plants, etc., have been coated successfully with chlorinated rubber or vinyl-base paints. The standard floor in food plants consists of tile laid in a polyester resin base cement with vertical joints of furan resin cement. Electroplating tanks are usually lined with natural rubber but plasticized polyvinyl chloride is used when oxidizing agents are present. Brick sheathing joined with furan cement is standard for tanks operating at temperatures above 150° F.

Electroplating

Asbestos-phenolic or asbestos-furan cast tanks have also been used successfully for the electroplating industry. Reinforced polyester tanks and steel tanks with prefabricated polyethylene insert liners have also been used for low temperature plating operations.

Vinyl plastisol coated plating racks have given very good service in a wide variety of plating processes. Some plating barrels have been constructed from welded polymethyl methacrylate sheet but unplasticized polyvinyl chloride is being used more and more for this application where transparency is not required.

Floors in plating plants usually consist of brick joined with a furan cement laid on an asphaltic membrane. Unplasticized polyvinyl chloride hoods and exhaust systems and fans have given good service both in Europe and in the United States and should replace previously used vinyl coated metal structures to a large extent.

Inorganic Chemicals

The use of silicate cements as joints for brickwork in various towers for sulfuric acid manufacture has been standard for many years. Silicate cements are also used for joining brick in manufacturing processes for nitric and chromic acid.

Much of the equipment in the salt process for the manufacture of hydrochloric acid is phenolic-asbestos construction or brick joined with silicate cement. Alum has been produced successfully in asphalt-lined vessels protected by brick joined with silicate cements.

Petrochemical Processes

Reaction vessels in the petrochemical industry have been lined with lead and protected by brick joined with furan cements. Fiberglas-furan membranes have been used where lead has not been satisfactory. A coating consisting of alternate layers of chlorinated rubber and vinyl paint has given good service. Epoxy coatings have also shown considerable promise for the protection of equipment against splash and fumes in the presence of acids and solvents.

Miscellaneous

Vinyl, chlorinated rubber or neoprene coatings may be used successfully for protection against splash and fumes in almost all industries. Likewise, furan cement joined tile laid on asphalt membrane is usually suitable for standard industrial floors. Unplasticized polyvinyl chloride is possibly the most universal structure for fume exhaust systems.

It is hoped that the data in Tables 24-1, 24-2 and 24-3 will help simplify material choice. In many cases, where several materials might be used interchangeably, the selection should be made on a basis of experience. It should be emphasized, that these recommendations are not to be considered as a condemnation of any other product nor as a substitute for experience or consultation with those having expert knowledge of plastics and their application in the chemical process industry.

In Table 24-1, many materials of construction have been rated on the basis of practical consideration and chemical resistance. Since the ten items under consideration are rated from 1 to 10, the perfect material would obviously have a total rating of 100. While the perfect material does not exist, these data may be used to help select materials based on the highest rating for the type of service intended.

The first, second and third choice of plastics for general industrial application in the chemical process industry are given in Table 24-2. The empirical selections are based on economics and practical application considerations for typical commercial products. The numbers refer to the listing given after Table 24-3.

More specific information on plastics application for the chemical process industry may be obtained from Table 24-3 in which the most suitable plastic has been selected empirically for a wide variety of services. Again, it must be remembered that in many cases, two or more materials might be rated almost equally on the basis of present day experience.

TABLE 24-1. PRACTICAL INDICES FOR CHEMICAL-RESISTANT PLASTICS

| | Practical Considerations | | | | | | Chemical Resistance | | | | | | Total Index |
	Cost	Sp. Gr.	Structural Strength	Resistance to Physical Damage	Resistance to Temperature	Total Practical Index	Solvents	Salts	Alkalies	Acids	Oxidation	Total Chemical Resistance	
Plasticized sulfur	10	6	2	2	5	25	2	10	1	10	3	26	51
Polyethylene	7	9	3	10	1	30	5	10	10	10	7	42	72
Polyisobutylene	7	9	1	10	1	28	2	10	10	10	5	37	65
Asphalt	10	9	1	3	1	24	1	10	7	10	1	29	53
Coal Tar	10	9	1	3	1	24	1	10	10	10	1	32	56
Coumarone-indene	10	9	1	4	1	25	1	10	10	10	2	33	58
Polystyrene	7	9	6	3	3	28	3	10	10	10	3	36	64
High-impact styrene	7	8	6	6	3	30	3	10	7	9	3	32	62
Styrene-acrylonitrile	7	8	6	4	3	28	4	10	6	9	3	32	60
Polymethyl methacrylate	4	8	6	7	3	28	4	10	7	9	3	33	61
Type II unplasticized polyvinyl chlorida	5	8	6	8	3	30	5	10	10	10	7	42	72
Type I unplasticized polyvinyl chloride	5	8	7	4	3	27	6	10	10	10	9	45	72
Plasticized polyvinyl chloride	6	8	4	10	3	31	4	10	9	10	5	38	69
Vinyl chloride acetate copolymer	6	8	5	6	3	28	3	10	7	9	4	33	61
Polyvinyl butyral	3	9	4	7	3	26	3	8	6	6	1	24	50
Saran	5	7	7	7	4	30	5	10	7	10	6	38	68
Saran rubber	6	7	4	8	3	28	3	9	3	9	4	28	56
Polytetrafluoroethylene	1	6	2	6	9	24	10	10	10	10	10	50	74
Silicone	1	7	3	7	9	27	3	5	4	3	1	16	43

TABLE 24-1 (Continued).

	Practical Considerations						Chemical Resistance						
	Cost	Sp. Gr.	Structural Strength	Resistance to Physical Damage	Resistance to Temperature	Total Practical Index	Solvents	Salts	Alkalies	Acids	Oxidation	Total Chemical Resistance	Total Index
Nylon	3	8	10	7	6	34	7	10	7	3	1	28	62
Natural rubber	7	9	4	10	4	34	2	10	10	10	1	33	67
Butyl rubber	7	9	4	10	3	33	2	10	10	10	6	38	71
Chlorosulfonated polyethylene	3	8	4	10	4	29	3	10	10	10	6	39	68
Chlorinated rubber	6	7	3	3	3	22	2	10	10	10	4	36	58
Styrene rubber	7	9	4	10	4	34	2	9	10	10	1	32	66
Neoprene	6	8	4	10	5	33	3	9	10	9	1	32	65
Reinforced polyesters	6	8	10	8	6	38	6	10	3	7	5	31	69
Phenolic resin cements	8	7	5	6	8	34	9	10	3	10	3	35	69
Epoxy resin cements	6	7	5	7	6	31	6	10	7	9	1	33	64
Furan resin cements	8	7	5	6	8	34	10	10	10	10	1	41	75
Cellulose acetate butyrate	4	8	4	7	3	26	3	7	2	2	1	15	41
Polyvinyl acetate	8	8	3	7	3	29	2	2	2	2	1	9	38
Redwood	10	10	9	7	7	43	7	7	7	4	1	26	69
Oil-base paint	9	9	1	2	3	24	2	5	1	1	1	10	34
Aluminum	7	5	9	6	10	37	10	8	1	2	3	24	61
Steel	9	1	10	6	10	36	10	2	5	1	2	20	56
Stainless steel 316	1	1	10	6	10	28	10	9	7	4	8	38	66
Pyrex	7	6	5	1	10	29	10	10	2	9	10	41	70
Cement-asbestos board	8	6	4	6	9	33	9	8	5	2	1	25	58
Acid brick	10	4	3	2	10	29	10	9	3	9	10	41	70

TABLE 24-2. MATERIALS OF CONSTRUCTION
RECOMMENDED FOR SPECIFIC APPLICATIONS
IN THE CHEMICAL PROCESS INDUSTRY

Application	First Choice	Second Choice	Third Choice
Coatings for splash and fume service			
Steel	28	25	20
Concrete	23	24	25
Industrial atmospheres	28	24	25
Acids and solvents	25	28	24
Linings for immersion service up to 150°F			
Steel	5	22	25
Concrete	9	–	–
Non-oxidizing corrosives	5	22	25
Oxidizing corrosives	22	–	–
Solvents and acids	16	–	–
Cement for joining brick in tanks, stacks and floors			
Acids - salts	16	17	18
Oxidizing acids 250°F	19	–	–
Acid - alkali - solvent	16	–	–
Bleaching agents	21	17	–
Joints for vitrified clay pipe			
Cold solvent - free waste	9	8	18
Acid - solvent waste	16-18	21-9	20-18
Hoods and exhaust systems			
Non-oxidizing acids	11	10	13
Oxidizing acids	11	13	14
Low pressure piping			
Water (cold)	13	3	15
Salt water - oil	3	10	11
Acids	11	10	13
Oxidizing acids	11	13	6
Acids - solvents	6	26	27
Acids - alkalies - solvents	6	27	1
Acids – temperatures above 250°F	6	1	–

Conclusion

It is recognized that few readers will assimilate all the information outlined in the preceding chapters and the suggested references. Nevertheless, it is hoped that the corrosion engineer will become sufficiently familiar with the arrangement of subject matter to permit the use of this book as a ready reference.

As shown in Table 24-4, the entire plastics industry is new but it is already producing at the rate of 5 million pounds per day. The application of these materials to the solution of corrosion problems is even more recent and the growth of this phase of the plastics industry is at least as rapid as that of the industry as a whole.

Obviously, new information on the successful application of plas-

TABLE 24-3. PREFERRED CHEMICAL RESISTANT PLASTIC
FOR SPECIFIC APPLICATIONS

	Coatings for Splash and Fume Service			Linings for Immersion Service			Cement for Joining Brick and Tile			Structural Plastics for Hoods and Exhaust Systems			Piping		
	C	W	H	C	W	H	C	W	H	C	W	H	C	W	H
Acids:															
Acetic, 10%	28	20	20	4	4	16	16	16	16	11	11	12	11	11	27
Acetic, glacial	–	–	–	4	16	16	16	16	16	11	27	27	27	27	27
Benzene, sulfonic, 10%	28	28	20	22	22	22	18	16	16	11	11	12	13	11	26
Benzoic, satd.	28	28	25	22	22	22	18	16	16	11	11	12	13	11	26
Boric, 10%	28	28	25	22	22	22	18	16	16	11	11	12	13	11	26
Butyric, 100%	20	–	–	4	16	16	16	16	16	11	27	27	27	27	6
Chloroacetic, 10%	20	20	–	4	4	16	18	16	16	11	11	27	11	27	27
Chromic, 10%	28	28	20	22	22	22	18	18	19	11	11	6	11	11	6
Chromic, 50%	28	–	–	22	–	–	19	19	19	11	11	6	6	6	6
Citric, 25%	24	24	25	22	22	22	18	16	16	11	11	12	11	11	26
Fatty Acids (C$_6$ and up)	28	20	20	22	16	16	16	16	16	11	11	27	11	27	27
Fluosilicic, 40%	28	28	25	5	5	16	16	16	16	11	11	6	11	11	1
Formic, 90%	28	20	–	4	16	16	16	16	16	11	27	27	11	1	1
Hydrobromic, 40%	28	28	20	22	22	22	18	17	17	11	11	27	11	11	1
Hydrochloric, 37%	28	28	20	5	5	–	18	16	16	11	11	27	11	11	1
Hydrocyanic, 25%	24	24	20	22	22	22	18	16	16	11	11	12	15	15	26
Hydrofluoric, 40%	28	28	20	5	5	–	16	16	16	11	11	6	11	11	1
Hypochlorous, 10%	24	24	–	4	4	4	21	21	19	11	11	6	11	11	6
Lactic, 25%	28	28	25	25	25	25	18	16	16	11	11	12	15	15	26
Maleic, 25%	24	25	25	5	5	5	16	16	16	11	26	26	15	15	26
Nitric, 5%	28	28	–	22	22	22	18	19	19	11	11	6	11	11	6
Nitric, 20%	28	–	–	22	–	–	18	19	19	11	11	6	11	11	6
Nitric, 40%	–	–	–	–	–	–	19	19	19	11	11	6	11	6	6
Oleic, 100%	20	20	20	25	25	25	16	16	16	11	27	27	11	1	1
Oxalic, 10%	24	25	25	22	22	22	18	16	16	11	11	26	11	11	26
Perchloric, 40%	28	28	–	22	22	22	18	16	16	11	11	26	11	11	26
Phosphoric, 85%	25	25	25	22	22	22	18	16	16	11	11	26	11	11	1
Picric, 10% in ethanol	24	23	–	16	16	16	16	16	16	12	12	12	15	1	1
Stearic, 100%	20	20	20	25	25	25	16	16	16	11	11	12	11	1	1
Sulfuric, 50%	25	25	–	5	5	–	18	16	16	11	11	12	11	11	1
Sulfuric, 70%	28	–	–	4	–	–	16	17	19	11	11	6	11	11	1
Sulfuric, 93%	–	–	–	–	–	–	19	19	19	11	1	6	11	1	6
Oleum	–	–	–	–	–	–	19	19	19	6	6	6	6	6	6
Mixed acids, 28% HNO$_3$ 55% H$_2$SO$_4$	6	–	–	–	–	–	19	19	19	11	11	6	11	6	6
Alkalies:															
Ammonium hydroxide	28	25	25	25	25	25	16	16	16	11	11	27	11	11	1
Calcium hydroxide	25	25	25	25	25	25	16	16	16	11	11	27	11	11	1
Potassium hydroxide	25	25	25	25	25	25	16	16	16	11	11	27	11	11	1
Sodium hydroxide	25	25	25	25	25	25	16	16	16	11	11	27	11	11	1

TABLE 24-3 (Continued).

	Coatings for Splash and Fume Service			Linings for Immersion Service			Cement for Joining Brick and Tile			Structural Plastics for Hoods and Exhaust Systems			Piping		
	C	W	H	C	W	H	C	W	H	C	W	H	C	W	H
Acid Salts:															
Alum	28	28	25	5	5	–	18	16	16	11	11	12	11	11	26
Ammonium chloride, nitrate, sulfate	28	28	25	22	22	–	18	16	16	11	11	12	11	11	26
Copper chloride, nitrate, sulfate	28	28	20	22	22	–	16	16	16	11	11	12	11	11	26
Ferric chloride, nitrate, sulfate	28	20	20	22	22	–	16	16	16	11	11	27	11	11	27
Nickel chloride, nitrate, sulfate	28	28	25	22	22	–	16	16	16	11	11	12	11	11	26
Stannic chloride	28	20	20	22	22	22	16	16	16	11	11	27	11	11	27
Zinc chloride, nitrate, sulfate	28	28	20	22	22	–	16	16	16	11	11	12	11	11	26
Alkaline Salts:															
Barium sulfide	28	25	25	22	25	–	16	16	16	11	11	27	11	11	1
Sodium bicarbonate	28	25	25	22	25	–	16	16	16	11	11	27	11	11	1
Sodium carbonate	28	25	25	22	25	–	16	16	16	11	11	27	11	11	1
Sodium sulfide	28	25	25	22	25	–	16	16	16	11	11	27	11	11	1
Trisodium phosphate	28	25	25	22	25	–	16	16	16	11	11	27	11	11	1
Neutral Salts:															
Calcium chloride	24	24	20	5	5	–	18	16	16	11	11	12	11	11	26
Calcium sulfate	24	24	20	5	5	–	18	16	16	11	11	12	11	11	26
Magnesium chloride, nitrate, sulfate	24	24	20	5	5	–	18	16	16	11	11	12	11	11	26
Potassium chloride, nitrate, sulfate	24	24	20	5	5	–	18	16	16	11	11	12	11	11	26
Sodium chloride, nitrate, sulfate	28	28	20	5	5	–	18	16	16	11	11	12	11	11	26
Gases:															
Chlorine, dry	24	24	–	22	22	22	21	19	19	11	11	6	11	11	1
Chlorine, wet	24	24	–	22	–	–	21	19	19	11	11	6	11	11	6
Sulfur dioxide, dry	28	25	25	22	22	–	16	16	16	11	11	12	11	11	27
Sulfur dioxide, wet	28	25	25	22	22	–	16	16	16	11	11	12	11	11	27
Organic Materials:															
Acetone	–	–	–	4	16	16	16	16	16	6	6	6	1	1	6
Alcohol, methyl, ethyl	28	20	25	5	5	5	16	16	16	11	11	27	11	11	1
Aniline	–	–	–	–	–	–	–	–	–	11	6	6	1	1	1
Benzene	20	20	–	16	16	16	16	16	16	27	27	27	1	1	1
Carbon tetrachloride	20	20	–	16	16	16	16	16	16	11	26	26	27	27	27
Chloroform	20	20	–	16	16	16	16	16	16	11	26	26	27	27	27
Ethyl acetate	20	–	–	16	16	16	16	16	16	11	6	6	1	1	6
Ethylene chloride	20	–	–	16	16	16	16	16	16	27	27	27	27	27	27

TABLE 24-3 (Continued).

	Coatings for Splash and Fume Service			Linings for Immersion Service			Cement for Joining Brick and Tile			Structural Plastics for Hoods and Exhaust Systems			Piping		
	C	W	H	C	W	H	C	W	H	C	W	H	C	W	H
Organic Materials (Continued):															
Formaldehyde, 37%	25	25	25	25	25	25	18	16	16	11	11	12	11	11	1
Phenol, 5%	20	20	–	16	16	16	16	16	16	11	27	27	11	27	27
Refinery crudes	14	14	–	16	16	16	16	16	16	11	11	27	3	26	26
Trichloroethylene	20	–	–	16	16	16	16	16	16	6	–	–	1	1	6
Papermill Applications:															
Kraft liquor	24	25	25	5	5	5	16	16	16	11	11	27	11	11	1
Black liquor	24	25	25	5	5	5	16	16	16	11	11	27	11	11	1
Green liquor	24	25	25	5	5	5	16	16	16	11	11	27	11	11	1
White liquor	24	25	25	5	5	5	16	16	16	11	11	27	11	11	1
Sulfite liquor	24	25	25	5	5	5	16	16	16	11	11	27	11	11	1
Chlorite bleach	28	24	–	22	22	–	21	–	–	11	11	6	11	11	6
Alum	28	28	25	5	5	–	16	16	16	11	11	12	11	11	26
Chlorine dioxide, acid solution	24	24	–	22	22	22	21	21	21	11	11	12	11	11	6
Chlorine dioxide, alkaline to pH 11	24	24	–	22	22	22	21	21	21	11	11	6	11	11	6
Photographic Industry:															
Developers	28	28	25	22	22	–	16	16	16	11	11	26	11	11	1
General use	28	28	25	22	22	–	16	16	16	11	11	26	11	11	1
Silver nitrate	28	28	–	22	22	–	16	16	16	11	11	26	11	11	1
Fertilizer Industry:															
General use	24	25	25	5	5	–	16	16	16	11	11	26	11	11	27
Steel Industry:															
Sulfuric acid pickling	28	28	20	5	5	–	16	16	16	11	11	26	11	11	1
Hydrochloric acid pickling	28	28	20	5	5	5	16	16	16	11	11	26	11	11	1
H_2SO_3–HNO_3 acid pickling	28	–	–	22	22	–	18	18	19	11	11	6	11	6	6
Textile Industry:															
General use	23	23	20	5	5	–	16	16	16	11	11	26	11	11	1
Hypochlorite bleach	28	24	–	22	22	–	21	–	–	11	11	6	11	11	6
Food Industry:															
General use	28	28	20	5	5	–	16	16	16	11	11	1	15	15	1
Breweries	28	28	20	–	–	–	16	16	16	11	11	27	15	15	1
Dairies	28	28	20	–	–	–	16	16	16	11	11	27	15	15	1
Miscellaneous Industries:															
Plating	28	28	20	22	22	–	16	16	16	11	11	27	11	11	1
Petroleum	14	14	–	–	–	–	16	16	16	11	11	26	3	26	26
Tanning	28	28	20	22	22	–	16	16	16	11	11	–	11	11	27
Oil and Soap	24	20	20	–	–	–	16	16	16	11	27	27	11	27	27
Water and Sewer	9	23	25	9	–	–	16	16	16	11	11	27	13	11	27

TABLE 24-3 (Continued).

Ratings: C — Cold 70°F
               W — Warm 140°F
               H — Hot 212°F

1. Impervious graphite
2. Urea resin
3. Cellulose acetate butyrate
4. Hard rubber
5. Vulcanized rubber
6. Polyfluorocarbon
7. Polymethyl methacrylate
8. Coal tar pitch
9. Asphalt
10. Unplasticized polyvinyl chloride Type II
11. Unplasticized polyvinyl chloride Type I
12. Polyester glass laminate
13. Polyethylene
14. Saran

15. Styrene copolymer rubber resin blend
16. Furan cement
17. Phenolic cement
18. Sulfur cement
19. Silicate cement
20. Epoxy resin
21. Polyester cement
22. Plasticized polyvinyl chloride
23. Styrene butadiene copolymer
24. Chlorinated rubber
25. Neoprene
26. Phenolic asbestos
27. Furan asbestos
28. Plasticized vinyl chloride acetate copolymer

TABLE 24-4. ANNUAL PRODUCTION OF PLASTICS IN THE UNITED STATES

(Millions of Pounds)

	1950	1951	1952	1953
Coumarone-indene and related products	143	177	166	206
Polystyrene and related products (includes unsaturated polyesters)	355	394	425	508
Polyvinyl chloride and related products	426	476	420	516
Alkyd resins and related products	402	440	431	419
Cellulose plastics	130	117	98	129
Urea and melamine plastics	219	237	228	257
Phenolic and related plastics	451	473	393	465
Miscellaneous plastics (polyethylene, acrylates, silicones, nylon, epoxy, etc.)	125	171	201	271
Total	2,251	2,385	2,362	2,771
Rubber, natural and synthetic	2,400	2,300	2,400	2,550

tics by corrosion engineers is being recorded continuously. Hence, while this book will give considerable background information, it is essential that the corrosion engineer keep abreast of new developments as recorded in the trade literature under plastics materials of construction.

410   PLASTICS SELECTION GUIDE

Suggested References

"Chemical Engineering Plant Design," 3rd Edition, Frank C. Vilbrandt, McGraw-Hill Publishing Co., New York, 1949.

"Chemical Process Industries," R. Norris Shreve, McGraw-Hill Publishing Co., New York, 1945.

"Materials of Construction for Chemical Process Industry," James A. Lee, McGraw-Hill Publishing Co., New York, 1950.

"Plastics in the Plating Shop," V. Evans, British Plastics, 162, April 1950.

"Plastics Meet the Acid Test," Raymond B. Seymour, Modern Plastics, Aug. 1950.

"Plastic Materials of Construction," Raymond B. Seymour, Corrosion, May 1953.

"Fight Corrosion with Plastics," Raymond B. Seymour and E. A. Erich, Petroleum Processing, Aug. 1951.

"Practical Indices for Chemical Resistant Plastics," Raymond B. Seymour, SPE Journal, Jan. 1954.

"References on Plastics for the Corrosion Engineer," Raymond B. Seymour, Corrosion, June 1953.

"Maintenance of Industrial Floors," Raymond B. Seymour, Southern Power and Industry, May and June 1951.

"Plant Floors That Can 'Take It'," Raymond B. Seymour, Food Engineering, Sept. 1952.

"Solving Corrosion Problems in the Textile Industry," Raymond B. Seymour, and W. L. Worth, Jr., Am. Dyestuff Reptr., Oct. 1949.

"Construction Materials in the Paper Industry," Raymond B. Seymour, Tappi, 35, 3, 153A (1952).

"Solving Corrosion Problems in the Paper Industry With Plastics," Raymond B. Seymour and G. P. Gabriel, Paper Mill News, Aug. 1953.

"Latest Developments in Use of Plastic Materials of Construction," Raymond B. Seymour and Martin H. Smith, Paper Trade Journal, Dec. 1953.

"Corrosion Handbook," H. H. Uhlig, John Wiley & Sons, Inc., New York, 1948.

"16th Biennial Materials of Construction Report," Chem. Eng., 172-234, November 1954.

"Neoprene," Raymond B. Seymour, Materials & Methods, 40, 6, 93 (Dec. 1954).

"Plastics," Raymond B. Seymour, Ind. Eng. Chem., 46, 2135 (Oct. 1954).

Results of Survey No. 1, Committee T-5D, NACE, Corrosion, 10, 11, 9-10 (1954).

"Synthetic Resins and Polymers and Chemical Resistant Coatings," Raymond B. Seymour, in "Organic Finishing Handbook," pp. 36 and 199, 1954.

AUTHOR INDEX

SUBJECT INDEX